Everyday Mathematics®

The University of Chicago School Mathematics Project

Teacher's Reference Manual

Early Childhood

D1295076

Wright Group

The McGraw·Hill Companies

The University of Chicago School Mathematics Project (UCSMP)

Max Bell, Director, UCSMP Elementary Materials Component; Director, *Everyday Mathematics* First Edition
James McBride, Director, *Everyday Mathematics* Second Edition
Andy Isaacs, Director, *Everyday Mathematics* Third Edition
Amy Dillard, Associate Director, *Everyday Mathematics* Third Edition

Authors

Max Bell	James Flanders	Deborah Arron Leslie*
Jean Bell	Dorothy Freedman*	James McBride
John Bretzlauf	Robert Hartfield	Kathleen Pitvorec
Amy Dillard	Andy Isaacs	Peter Saecker
		*Third Edition only

Technical Art

Diana Barrie

Editorial Assistant

Patrick Carroll

Contributors

Ann E. Audrain, David W. Beer, Margaret Krulee, Barbara Smart

Photo Credits

© Alamy, cover *bottom left;* © Getty Images, cover *bottom right, top right,* p. iv *left;* Sharon Hoogstraten, back *left,* cover *top left;* © Jupiter Images, cover *top center;* © Photospin, p. 6; © Punchstock, p. 1; With permission of Bob Thaves, p. 109; all other photographs by Phil Martin and Jack Demuth

www.WrightGroup.com

Send all inquiries to:
Wright Group/McGraw-Hill
P.O. Box 812960
Chicago, IL 60681

ISBN 0-07-604510-2

7 8 9 MAZ 12 11 10 09 08 07

The *McGraw-Hill* Companies

Table of Contents

13 Reference Frames   108

14 Estimation, Mental Arithmetic, and Number Sense   115

15 Patterns, Sequences, Functions, and Algebra   128

16 Problem Solving   141

Glossary   153

Introduction

i How to Use this Book

This *Everyday Mathematics Teacher's Reference Manual*™ has three main parts: a seven-chapter Management Guide, nine chapters discussing Mathematical Strands and Threads, and a Glossary. The Management Guide includes suggestions on implementing the *Everyday Mathematics*® program in early childhood classrooms; ideas for organizing the curriculum, the children, and the program materials; and descriptions of important program features for Pre-Kindergarten and Kindergarten. The Mathematical Strands and Threads chapters contain reliable information on the mathematics in the curriculum. *Strands* are the familiar topics of mathematics such as numeration and geometry; *threads* are ways of thinking about mathematics that cross the strands, such as problem solving and estimation. These chapters are followed by a detailed Glossary of mathematical and special terms used in *Everyday Mathematics*.

In order to familiarize yourself with the program's features and routines, you may find it helpful to read all seven chapters of the Management Guide before you begin teaching with *Everyday Mathematics*. This reading will also help you decide on organizational strategies for your classroom. Then, as the school year progresses, you may want to refer to some sections again in order to gain further insights.

The nine Mathematical Strands and Threads chapters do not have to be read in their entirety or in any particular order. The topics presented in each chapter are summarized in a table of contents at the beginning of the chapter. You can skim the chapter, consult its table of contents for a specific topic, or read it straight through.

Every effort has been made to make this manual easy to use. The authors hope you find it worthwhile and invite your suggestions on how it could be improved.

ii The *Everyday Mathematics* Program

Everyday Mathematics is a comprehensive Pre-Kindergarten through sixth-grade mathematics curriculum embracing many of the traditional goals of school mathematics as well as two ambitious goals for the 21st century:

- To substantially raise expectations regarding the amount and range of mathematics that children can learn;
- To support teachers and children with the materials necessary to enable the children to meet these higher expectations.

Philosophy

Children need a mathematics curriculum that is rigorous and balanced and that:

- Emphasizes conceptual understanding while building a mastery of basic skills;
- Explores a broad mathematics spectrum, not just basic arithmetic;
- Is based on how children learn and what they're interested in while preparing them for their future mathematical needs.

An ever-increasing demand for mathematics competence and problem-solving agility both in and out of school requires us to continue to change both the mathematics we teach and how we teach it. Beginning in Pre-Kindergarten, *Everyday Mathematics* makes these changes by introducing children to these six major mathematical content domains: number sense, algebra, measurement, geometry, data analysis, and probability. The program helps children build and maintain basic skills, including automatic fact recall, while helping you use everyday, real-world problems and situations to nurture their higher-order and critical-thinking skills.

Everyday Mathematics differs from traditional, textbook-centered instruction in a number of ways.

- It is consistent with how children actually learn mathematics as it builds understanding over a period of time, first through informal exposure and then through more formal and directed instruction. Because learning proceeds from the known to the unknown, new learning needs to be connected to, and built upon, an existing knowledge base.
- Mathematical content is taught in a repeated fashion, beginning with concrete experiences. Children using *Everyday Mathematics* are expected to master a variety of mathematical skills and concepts, but not the first time they are encountered. It is a mistake to proceed too quickly from the concrete to the abstract or to isolate concepts and skills from one another or from problem contexts. Children also need to "double back" by revisiting topics, concepts, and skills, and then relating them to each other in new and different ways.
- Pacing is important. Children learn best when new topics are presented briskly and in an interesting way. Most children will

not master a new topic the first time it is presented, so *Everyday Mathematics* allows children to revisit content in varied contexts, integrating new learning with previous knowledge and experiences. When newly learned concepts and skills are periodically reviewed, practiced, and applied in a wide variety of contexts, they are better retained.

It is important to note how the differences between *Everyday Mathematics* and other programs may affect your day-to-day planning and teaching. Daily routines and games are a necessary part of the program, not optional extensions. Routines and games are designed to build conceptual understanding and ensure mastery of basic skills in authentic and interesting contexts. *Everyday Mathematics* also differs from other programs in that it is designed for the teacher. Rather than being centered on a student textbook, it offers materials that provide children with a rich variety of experiences across mathematical content strands and threads.

Because language, communication, social interaction, tools, and manipulatives all play important roles in helping children acquire skills, *Everyday Mathematics* employs cooperative-learning activities, Explorations, and Projects. The program gives guidance on how to set up your classroom to accommodate group work and on how to help children work together without direct supervision.

For more information, see Chapter 4: Organizing Children.

Through a comprehensive approach to differentiating instruction, *Everyday Mathematics* provides a variety of ways to help children and teachers manage different learning backgrounds, styles, and pacing needs. Advice on how to adjust activities for children with different needs is integrated throughout the *Teacher's Guide to Activities*™.

For more information, see Chapter 5: Differentiating Instruction.

In *Everyday Mathematics,* assessment is closely linked with instruction. While some formal assessment is necessary, a balanced approach including less formal, ongoing methods provides a more complete picture of each child's progress. A number of assessment tools are built into the *Everyday Mathematics* program to help you get feedback about your children's instructional needs and information you can use to report on their progress.

For more information, see Chapter 6: Managing Assessment and the *Assessment Handbook*.

In summary, *Everyday Mathematics* is committed to establishing world-class mathematics standards for our nation's schools. The program assumes that virtually all children are capable of a much greater understanding of and proficiency in mathematics than has been traditionally expected; so it provides the features and materials you need to help them meet those higher expectations.

iii Program Highlights

Highlights of the *Everyday Mathematics* program include:

- *Problem solving in everyday situations* Research and experience show that children who are unable to solve problems presented in purely symbolic form often have little trouble solving them when they are presented in everyday contexts.

- *Developing readiness through hands-on activities* In *Pre-Kindergarten* and *Kindergarten Everyday Mathematics,* most activities are concrete and hands-on. As children move through later grades, *Everyday Mathematics* offers many suggestions for Explorations and Projects on which children work together. These activities pave the way for the introduction of new mathematical ideas.

- *Establishing links between past experiences and explorations of new concepts* Ideas that have been explored with concrete materials or pictorial representations are revisited through oral descriptions and symbolic representations. Children learn to shift comfortably among various representations and to select models that are most appropriate for given situations.

- *Sharing ideas through discussion* Children gain important insights about mathematics by building on each others' discoveries—one idea leads to another or to refinements of a child's own understanding. Discussion promotes good listening habits and fosters a receptive attitude to the ideas of classmates. Because verbalization often clarifies concepts, talking about mathematics is an important part of thinking about mathematics.

- *Cooperative learning through partner and small-group activities* Children discover that working together is usually more enjoyable and stimulating than working independently. Moreover, as children learn to work as a team, cooperation replaces competition and the less-skilled among them benefit by drawing support from the more-skilled.

- *Practice through games* Children need frequent practice to master a skill. Unfortunately, drills become monotonous and lose effectiveness over time. Games, however, relieve the tedium of rote repetition, reduce the need for worksheets, and offer an almost unlimited source of problem material because, in most cases, numbers are generated randomly.

- *Ongoing review throughout the year* It is rare that children master something new the first time they encounter it. For this reason, repeated exposure to key ideas presented in slightly different contexts is built into the *Everyday Mathematics* program.

- *Daily routines* The program suggests routines that children can perform on a regular basis. Tasks such as keeping the daily schedule, class calendar, weather and temperature records, and attendance chart are learning experiences in themselves. Other regular classroom tasks help children develop a sense of order, initiative, and responsibility while reinforcing numerous mathematical concepts.

- *Informal assessment* In addition to independent review exercises, *Everyday Mathematics* provides many suggestions for small-group activities to help you assess children's progress. Through your interactions with small groups of children, you obtain a clearer understanding of individual strengths and weaknesses.

- *Home-and-school partnership* Optimal learning occurs if it involves the child, the teacher, and people at home. The *Home Connection Handbook*™ offers many suggestions for this. Family Letters help inform parents and guardians about the *Everyday Mathematics* program. Parents or other caregivers are invited to participate in their child's mathematics experiences through Home Links and *Mathematics at Home* books.

iv Mathematical Content

Pre-Kindergarten through *Third Grade Everyday Mathematics* is organized into the following content strands:

- Number and Numeration
- Operations and Computation
- Data and Chance
- Geometry
- Measurement and Reference Frames
- Patterns, Functions, and Algebra

Woven throughout the content strands are three important mathematical threads:

- Estimation, Mental Arithmetic, and Number Sense
- Problem Solving
- Algorithms

Special emphasis is placed on:

- Establishing links between new and past experiences through activities with concrete materials, pictures, oral statements, and symbolic mathematical statements. For example, children might act out a problem or talk about it to get a feel for what is happening. Or they might draw simple pictures or diagrams, or do some mental arithmetic, which eventually leads them to write a number model.
- Discussing and sharing ideas. *Can you tell us how you do that? Why do you think so? Does everyone agree?*
- Using and comparing equivalent expressions. *What other ways can we say or write . . .?*
- Expressing quantities and measurements in context by including labels or units. *Five what?*
- Learning about the reversibility of most things: put in, take out; add, subtract; take apart, put together; go away, come back; expand, shrink; spend money, earn money; positive, negative; and so on.
- Using calculators as tools for counting, displaying numbers, developing concepts and skills, and solving problems—especially real-life problems in which numbers are not always "nice."

By becoming a part of everyday work and play, the lessons, exercises, and concepts in *Everyday Mathematics* gradually shape children's ways of thinking about mathematics and foster the development of their mathematical intuition and understanding.

Management Guide

Everyday Mathematics is an effective program for teaching mathematics in a variety of early childhood classrooms because it is based on some fundamental ideas that can be implemented in a wide range of situations. *Pre-Kindergarten* and *Kindergarten Everyday Mathematics* are based on research about how young children learn, and they have been field tested in a variety of early childhood classrooms.

This Management Guide explains some important elements of the *Everyday Mathematics* curriculum and provides suggestions for using the program's features and materials, especially in the context of early childhood classrooms. It also provides suggestions for using mathematical tools, organizing children for instruction, reaching all children, assessing progress, and communicating with families.

Contents

1 Mathematics in the Early Childhood Classroom: The *Everyday Mathematics* Viewpoint

We read exciting and informative stories, even great works of literature, to young children. We spontaneously communicate with them at their level of spoken and receptive language. It does not occur to us that we should limit our verbal interactions with young children because of their limited ability to use symbolic, written language. Yet with mathematics, all too often we treat learning as an entirely symbolic process. We fail to recognize and build upon children's rich and ever-expanding store of mathematical understanding and knowledge.

Pre-Kindergarten and *Kindergarten Everyday Mathematics* remedy this situation, placing mathematics learning right in the midst of children's varied, enjoyable, and accessible world where it rightfully belongs. These programs are based on a philosophy, developed through research, about how young children learn mathematics. This research has shown that for most young children, it is appropriate to substantially expand their range of mathematics experiences and ideas. In addition to this expansion, *Everyday Mathematics* seeks to increase the time children spend on mathematics learning by integrating mathematics into other subject areas and by infusing mathematics into both the ongoing daily routines of the classroom and those odd bits of time that occur during every school day. This section discusses some issues that are central to teaching and learning mathematics in early childhood classrooms, such as the importance of play in the learning of young children, the use of classroom learning centers, and the particulars of half-day (or other part-time) programs and full-day programs.

> **NOTE:** Chapter 2: Managing the Curriculum, which begins on page 12, also includes important information about integrating mathematics into the early childhood classroom through specific elements and components of the *Everyday Mathematics* curriculum.

1.1 The Importance of Play and Playfulness

Play is the natural work of young children. Ideally, children may not make a distinction between their play and work and thus bring the same energy and attention to both. *Everyday Mathematics* endorses this view of children as playful learners. The Pre-Kindergarten and Kindergarten programs are designed to relate to children's interest in the world around them and to engage them in meaningful ways as they interact with materials, their environment, and each other. One important goal of the *Everyday Mathematics* curriculum is to help teachers and children recognize and build upon the mathematics opportunities that are embedded in children's everyday experiences, including their play in all areas of the classroom and outdoors. The activities in the Pre-Kindergarten and Kindergarten programs can be conducted in a variety of groupings and settings. Regardless of the specifics of implementation, though, most are best approached in the playful, exploratory manner that is the natural learning style of young children.

▶ 1.2 Mathematics around the Classroom

Young children spontaneously explore mathematics all the time as they interact with materials, with each other, and with their surroundings. They count and sort, notice and describe shapes and patterns, estimate and compare sizes, and wonder about the numerals they see all around them. These mathematical observations, concepts, and skills are important tools that children use as they explore and make sense of their world.

Children learn a great deal from their self-chosen interests and activities. It is important to be aware of the mathematics that is going on all around as children work and play at school and to set up your classroom environment to promote their natural mathematics explorations. By recognizing what children are already doing with mathematics, you will be better equipped to respond to their spontaneous mathematical activities in ways that foster continued exploration and learning.

Even as you use the activities in the Pre-Kindergarten and Kindergarten programs, be mindful of the valuable opportunities for "unplanned" mathematics practice, application, and learning that emerge from children's ongoing work and play in the early childhood classroom every day. The "Mathematics All Around" sections in the Pre-Kindergarten *Teacher's Guide to Activities* and in *Resources for the Kindergarten Classroom*™ describe common examples of children's self-initiated mathematical endeavors in various areas of the early childhood classroom. This information is intended to help you recognize opportunities for observing and encouraging children's natural explorations of mathematics during the school day.

▶ 1.3 Encouraging Problem Solving: Sharing Strategies and Solutions

NOTE: See Chapter 16: Problem Solving for a detailed explanation of the *Everyday Mathematics* approach to problem solving and mathematical modeling.

In *Everyday Mathematics,* problem solving is much more than solving word problems. Children solve a wide range of problems in every strand of the *Everyday Mathematics* curriculum. For young children, problems that emerge from everyday situations—sharing snacks equally, gaining or losing supplies, timing turns on the swings, and so on—are abundant and meaningful. Some problems require children to apply their current mathematical knowledge; others stretch children's skills and understanding. Problems for which children have no method of solution immediately at hand are often the most productive. Children are encouraged to solve all problems in many different ways. Sharing and comparing solution methods is an important part of *Everyday Mathematics.*

NOTE: For more information, see "Exploring Mathematics through Talking and Writing" by Whitin and Whitin (2000). A full reference is on page 152.

Research indicates that children develop a variety of problem-solving strategies if they are given the opportunity to share their ideas with their peers. If this sharing takes place in an open, receptive environment, children will learn that inventing creative, innovative ways of solving problems is acceptable in mathematics. The practice of gathering together to share solutions after individual or group problem solving continues throughout *Everyday Mathematics.*

Number stories offer an excellent context for developing habits of sharing ideas. Children learn a great deal from explaining their own strategies and solutions for number stories and from listening to those of others. In order for this exchange to be meaningful and instructive, work to establish a classroom environment in which:

- Children feel comfortable taking risks;
- Children feel comfortable asking questions;
- Children recognize that mistakes are inevitable and are an important part of learning;
- Children are encouraged to change their minds and revise their ideas based on the input of others;
- Children are free to use a variety of strategies, including fingers, pictures, counters, or other concrete materials, to solve problems. Children develop a better understanding of various mathematical processes when asked to think and strategize rather than when they are merely asked to repeat the steps of a standard procedure or written algorithm.

With practice, children will become comfortable sharing their strategies and be able to talk about them freely and fluently, listen to one another attentively, and revise their own strategies and adopt new ones based on the discussions.

1.4 Flexible Implementation of the Curriculum

An important part of the philosophy behind *Everyday Mathematics* is that teachers are best equipped to make decisions about their children and classrooms. Because early childhood classrooms are so varied, the Pre-Kindergarten *Teacher's Guide to Activities* and Kindergarten *Teacher's Guide to Activities* suggest various options for implementing the activities, including a variety of grouping possibilities and multiple suggestions for applying and extending the activities. Be sure to review the introductory section of the *Teacher's Guide to Activities* for your level. There you will find specific information about the format and components of the Pre-Kindergarten or Kindergarten activities. You will also find advice about how to make use of each of these components and how to use the guide as a whole.

1.5 Multiple Exposures and Spaced Practice

Everyday Mathematics is structured so that after initial introduction or exposure to topics, children revisit concepts and skills multiple times, often over the course of several years, as they develop proficiency and understanding. Often, children are introduced to topics earlier than in other programs, with the recognition that their understanding will develop over time. Children's comprehension of mathematics is deeper and more lasting as result of these recurrent experiences. This approach also allows children to learn at a more individualized pace, because they have many opportunities to work on a particular mathematical concept or skill. In *Pre-Kindergarten* and *Kindergarten Everyday Mathematics,* the same mathematical topics are the focus of numerous activities. This gives children opportunities to work with these concepts and skills many times, in many different ways. The Ongoing Daily Routines (see page 12), games (see page 12), *Minute Math* (see page 14), and Resource Books (see page 14) are also ways that "distributed practice" is embedded in the curriculum.

▶ 1.6 Using Centers in the Classroom

Many early childhood classrooms have specific areas, or centers, for exploration, study, and play. This organization of classroom space allows individuals or small groups to access different materials, to follow up on something introduced to the whole class, and to interact with materials that have not yet been formally presented to the group. Children need these opportunities to explore and become familiar with materials. It can also be revealing to observe which materials children select on their own and how they use them.

At any one time, the Math Center might contain pattern blocks, scales, measuring tools, selected games, calculators, manipulatives for counting, or other mathematics materials. Encourage children to use these math tools whenever they need them. For example, they may want to measure a block building, play store, write a phone number, or weigh a seashell. It is through this kind of integration of mathematics with everyday classroom life that children develop a true understanding of the usefulness of mathematics. The activities in the *Teacher's Guide to Activities* for each level also often suggest ways to extend mathematics into other learning centers, such as the writing or art center, the science center, the block area, or the Dramatic Play center. The Home Links and *Mathematics at Home*™ books help extend mathematics into children's lives outside of the classroom in natural and playful ways.

▶ 1.7 Half-Day and Full-Day Programs

Pre-Kindergarten and *Kindergarten Everyday Mathematics* are rich and complete programs; both include more activity suggestions than most teachers in half or full-day programs can implement in a given school year. Consider the suggestions listed below as you plan and construct a solid half-day or full-day mathematics program.

For Pre-Kindergarten:

- **Ongoing Daily Routines** These are essential in both half- and full-day programs. See Section 2.1: Ongoing Daily Routines in this manual and the Ongoing Daily Routines section of the Pre-Kindergarten *Teacher's Guide to Activities* for more information on daily routines.
- **Mathematics around the Classroom** Half- and full-day teachers should read all of the "Mathematics All Around" descriptions in the Pre-Kindergarten *Teacher's Guide to Activities* to help them recognize how to make the most of the mathematics that is embedded in all areas of the classroom.

> **NOTE:** See the beginning of the *Teacher's Guide to Activities* for your level for a more detailed explanation about the components described in this section.

- **Mathematics Activities** Half- and full-day teachers should choose from the activities in the Pre-Kindergarten *Teacher's Guide to Activities* to meet the needs and interests of their classrooms. Full-day teachers will probably be able to use more activities than half-day teachers over the course of the year. All teachers should use the core activities from each mathematical topic area as well as a variety of other activities that interest them.
- **Pre-Kindergarten *Minute Math*®** Half- and full-day teachers should use *Minute Math* activities during transition times and other spare moments in the day. See Section 2.4: *Minute Math* for a description of this component.
- ***Resources for the Pre-Kindergarten Classroom*** Half- and full-day teachers can use the optional suggestions for thematic activities, children's literature, songs and chants, and commercial games to integrate mathematics into their program as they see fit. See Section 2.7: Resource Books for Pre-Kindergarten and Kindergarten Classrooms for a description of this component.

For Kindergarten:

- **Daily Routines** These are essential in both half- and full-day programs. See Section 2.1: Ongoing Daily Routines in this manual and the Ongoing Daily Routines section of the Kindergarten *Teacher's Guide to Activities* for more information on daily routines.
- **Core Activities** Half- and full-day teachers should use both activities in Part A of each numbered activity in the Kindergarten *Teacher's Guide to Activities*. The main activity is described first and in the most detail. The revisit activity brings back an earlier activity for continued practice, a different approach, or perhaps a more advanced variation.
- **Teaching Options** These optional activities in Part B of each numbered activity in the Kindergarten *Teacher's Guide to Activities* suggest ways to extend and apply the mathematics content from the main activity into other areas of the classroom or parts of the school day. Full-day teachers will be able to use more of these Teaching Options than half-day teachers, but half-day teachers will also undoubtedly find many of these ideas useful for integrating mathematics throughout their school day.
- **Kindergarten *Minute Math*** Half- and full-day teachers should use *Minute Math* activities during transition times and other spare moments in the day. See Section 2.4: *Minute Math* for a description of this component.
- ***Resources for the Kindergarten Classroom*** Half- and full-day teachers should use the optional suggestions for thematic activities, children's literature, songs and chants, and commercial games to integrate mathematics into their program as they see fit. See Section 2.7: Resource Books for Pre-Kindergarten and Kindergarten Classrooms for a description of this component.

NOTE: Half-day and full-day teachers can complete all of the core activities during the school year if they do the core activities from three or four numbered activity pages each week.

NOTE: See Chapter 5: Differentiating Instruction for suggestions about how the Teaching Options activities in Part B can be used to support differentiation in the classroom.

2 Managing the Curriculum

Perhaps the single greatest difference between *Everyday Mathematics* and other curricula is that *Everyday Mathematics* is written for you, the teacher, rather than focused on a student textbook. Student materials are supplements to facilitate your use of the program. This section discusses features of the curriculum and describes materials that support its instruction. The items described on the following pages begin in Pre-Kindergarten or Kindergarten and are maintained across grade levels in the *Everyday Mathematics* curriculum. Several other recurring program elements are initiated in *First Grade Everyday Mathematics*.

▶ ### 2.1 Ongoing Daily Routines

The Ongoing Daily Routines are a cornerstone of the *Everyday Mathematics* curriculum. They should be initiated at the beginning of the school year and sustained throughout the year. The Ongoing Daily Routines are designed to integrate mathematics in a natural and interesting way into the daily life of your classroom. As the year progresses, you will discover many ways to embed mathematics learning in the context of these daily routines; they will greatly add to the richness of children's mathematics experiences as you continue to build upon them. These routines make teaching easier too—it's like putting a complex machine into operation at the beginning of the year and then seeing it sustained by children's initiative and energy as much as by your own!

▶ ### 2.2 Games

Games are an integral part of *Everyday Mathematics*. They allow children to discover ideas and to develop an understanding of mathematics at their own pace. They provide opportunities for the playful practice of mathematics skills and are a far more effective learning experience than tedious drills and worksheets are. Games also put children in a position to learn from and teach one another as they play.

Children use games for different purposes. Some children may want or need to play a particular game over and over again to reinforce a concept, build speed or confidence, or simply enjoy themselves. The games included in the program provide excellent tools for individualizing instruction while continuing to emphasize cooperative group work. Numbers or concepts can usually be varied within a game to make it easier or more difficult or to emphasize different skills. For example, children can play *Top-It* and most of the other card games with larger or smaller numbers in the card deck to adjust the level of difficulty. You can add a recording aspect to *Number Gymnastics* to emphasize numeral writing. Children can play *Monster Squeeze* with higher numbers with or without a number line.

NOTE: The Pre-Kindergarten *Teacher's Guide to Activities* and the Kindergarten *Teacher's Guide to Activities* detail the routines for each grade level.

Competition

Because many teachers are justifiably concerned about the competitive aspect associated with most games, many games in *Pre-Kindergarten* and *Kindergarten Everyday Mathematics* de-emphasize competition by not including designations of winners and losers. For example, instructions for *Top-It* specify that play ends when children have used up all the cards. Even in games where children do complete play by accumulating points, it is not necessary to label the person who has the most points the winner. You can teach a useful lesson in probability by flipping a coin (before or after playing) to decide whether the person with the fewest points or the most points "wins." You can also encourage children to keep a record of their own scores before putting the game away or playing again. Some *Everyday Mathematics* games emphasize cooperation by setting a shared goal as the outcome.

The early childhood years are important for shaping children's attitudes toward game playing. Ideally, young children will *play to see what happens, not to see who wins*. In talking with children about games, focus on what occurred during the game. *Was it fun? Interesting? Easy? Difficult? Long? Short?* Teachers have also suggested several other ways to de-emphasize competition as you make games a part of your mathematics program. For example, you might involve children in discussing why you do not want to have winners and losers in games, even though that may happen when they play games in other places. Through such a discussion, children may highlight reasons such as *We should help each other play and learn, Losing sometimes makes people feel sad,* and *Games should be fun and interesting to everyone.*

Some of the games in *Pre-Kindergarten* and *Kindergarten Everyday Mathematics* will be unfamiliar to children's families. Consider the benefits of signing out games for home use: Children practice mathematics skills at home, families learn about the program, children learn to be responsible for materials, and children can teach their families—an empowering experience for the children. You can follow a procedure similar to the one used by a library. Put materials for games in a large envelope or plastic bag along with an instruction sheet. You might also include a sheet for children and families to write comments about the game, perhaps arranging for families to read one another's comments. Sometimes families suggest interesting game variations in those comments. Establish a policy about when games should be returned. A short borrowing period increases the chances of return without loss of materials. One night is generally sufficient.

▶ 2.3 Home Links

Home Links suggest activities for family members and children to do together. Home Links are suggested to complement the content of many activities in the *Teacher's Guide to Activities*. You can find Home Link masters in the *Math Masters*™ book for your level.

> **NOTE:** Young children, especially Pre-Kindergartners, are only beginning to understand and accept the rule-bound nature of games. So, although many games are intended to be played in pairs or small groups, children may still need considerable support as they play together. Children will enjoy adapting the games to play by themselves, too!

2.4 *Minute Math*

Minute Math is an important teacher resource that consists of brief verbal interactions that provide support for the multiple-exposure, spaced-practice, and problem-solving emphases of *Everyday Mathematics*. These activities are flexible, require no advance preparation or props, and can be accomplished in a few moments anytime during the day. Children especially love the number stories if you use their own names and interests in telling them. (One class referred to the book as the "joke book.") Besides providing a variety of counting activities and number stories, *Minute Math* provides reinforcement and review and gives children valuable opportunities to think and talk about mathematics.

2.5 Museums

Everyday Mathematics encourages the development of classroom museums using a table, group of desks, or bulletin board where related items can be collected, categorized, and labeled. For example, Kindergarten children create 100 Collections for display in a 100th Day Museum to celebrate the 100th day of school. (See Project 5, page 268 in the Kindergarten *Teacher's Guide to Activities* for detailed information.) Pre-Kindergarten and Kindergarten children can also make a Shapes Museum to collect, group, and display examples of 2-dimensional and 3-dimensional shapes. You might think of other topics for which you can create classroom museums, such as patterns, symmetry, or various uses of numbers.

2.6 Projects

Projects begin in *Kindergarten Everyday Mathematics*. The Projects cover a wide range of mathematics activities and concepts and integrate well with other subject areas. They are designed to allow you to explore a topic or activity in depth for several days or over a longer period, guided by class interest. You will find a Project at the end of each of the eight sections in the Kindergarten *Teacher's Guide to Activities*.

2.7 Resource Books for Pre-Kindergarten and Kindergarten Classrooms

Resources for the Pre-Kindergarten Classroom and *Resources for the Kindergarten Classroom* are collections of materials and resources that you can use to supplement the activities in each level's *Teacher's Guide to Activities*. These books provide suggestions for additional ways to reinforce, enrich, and extend children's mathematics experiences, with an emphasis on integrating mathematics into all aspects of the classroom. Each book contains suggestions for optional mathematics activities that can be used as part of common early childhood themes; literature, software, and commercial games lists; mathematics-related songs, poems, chants, and fingerplays; and Family Letters and other suggestions for communicating with families at home. The resource books reflect the *Everyday Mathematics* philosophy that young children should have many opportunities to explore mathematical concepts through play, informal interactions with adults and other children, and exposure to a variety of materials and manipulatives in a range of contexts.

3 Managing Tools

The following sections focus on tools that are used often in *Pre-Kindergarten* and *Kindergarten Everyday Mathematics*. More information about these and other tools can be found in some of the Mathematical Strands and Threads chapters, which link specific tools to the teaching, learning, and application of particular mathematical topics.

▶ 3.1 Electronic Tools

Electronic tools for mathematics education include calculators, computers, and computer peripherals such as probes, videodiscs, and CDs. Access to electronic tools is varied, and *Everyday Mathematics* is very conservative in its assumptions about which tools are available to every child. In fact, 4-function calculators are sufficient in Kindergarten through Grade 3, and scientific calculators are sufficient in Grades 4 through 6. Some links to Internet sites are included in the materials for older grades, but none are required for any activities or lessons.

3.1.1 Calculators

In the more than a quarter-century since electronic calculators have become widely available, many researchers have studied their effects on how children learn. The preponderance of evidence from these studies suggests that the proper use of calculators can enhance children's understanding and mastery of arithmetic, promote good number sense, and improve problem-solving skills and attitudes toward mathematics.

Three summaries of this research are:

- "Research on Calculators in Mathematics Education" by Ray Hembree and Donald J. Dessart;
- "A Meta-Analysis of Outcomes from the Use of Calculators in Mathematics Education" by Brian A. Smith;
- "A Meta-Analysis of the Effects of Calculators on Students' Achievement and Attitude Levels in Precollege Mathematics Classes" by Aimee J. Ellington.

The Smith and Ellington studies also conclude that calculator usage does not hinder the development of paper-and-pencil skills. Ellington recommends that calculators be used by children in Kindergarten through Grade 2 for experimenting with arithmetic concepts in problem-solving contexts.

Both teacher experience and educational research show that most children develop good judgment about when to use and when not to use calculators. Throughout the grades, *Everyday Mathematics* supports children's need to learn how to decide when it is appropriate

NOTE: Encourage children to respect and care for mathematical tools just as doctors, carpenters, and others respect and take care of the tools they use.

NOTE: For complete references to these studies and information on other calculator research, see "Resources on Calculators" on pages 17 and 18.

to solve an arithmetic problem by estimating or calculating mentally, by using paper and pencil, or by using a calculator. The evidence indicates that children who use calculators are able to choose appropriately.

Calculators also allow children to solve interesting, everyday problems requiring computations that might otherwise be too difficult for them to perform, including problems that arise outside of mathematics class. There is no evidence to suggest that this will cause children to become dependent on calculators or make them unable to solve problems mentally or with paper and pencil. Before the availability of inexpensive calculators, the elementary school mathematics curriculum was designed primarily so that children would become skilled at carrying out paper-and-pencil algorithms. Thus, there was little time left for children to learn to think mathematically and solve problems. Calculators enable children to think about the problems themselves, rather than focus on carrying out algorithms without mistakes.

How the Authors Used Calculators when Writing *Everyday Mathematics*

In the second edition of *Everyday Mathematics,* one calculator was chosen as representative of all calculators for Kindergarten through Grade 3 materials and another for Grades 4 through 6. This choice allowed the authors to give examples of specific key sequences for a variety of calculations. However, having just one representative calculator led authors to explain features that were available only on the chosen machine and not on most other available calculators. To present a more balanced view, the third edition features key sequences for *two* widely available calculators.

By choosing two calculators, the authors have been able to define a "generic" calculator to support *Everyday Mathematics.* Only those functions that are on *both* calculators, and so likely to be on any other comparable calculator, are considered to be generic tools for problem solving.

For Kindergarten through Grade 3, the authors used TI-108 and Casio SL-450 4-function calculators. Both calculators offer the same functions. However, not all keys for common functions are the same on both machines, so *Everyday Mathematics* presents key sequences for both. Because of this, you should be able to find the help you need to use any 4-function calculator. It probably will not matter for Kindergarten children, but it may be useful for you to know that both the TI-108 and Casio SL-450 are nonalgebraic calculators, which means that they do the operations in the order in which they are entered, rather than according to the algebraic order of operations.

Calculator Basics and Key Sequences

Children begin using calculators in *Kindergarten Everyday Mathematics* to display numbers, to count, and to perform addition and subtraction. Whenever an operation that can be performed on a calculator is introduced, *Everyday Mathematics* includes an activity that introduces new calculator key(s). It is recommended that you draw the new key(s) on the board or on an overhead transparency.

NOTE: Neither the TI-108 nor the Casio SL-450 is required to use *Everyday Mathematics*. Any 4-function calculator will suffice.

Calculator A: the TI-108

Calculator B: the Casio SL-450

The order in which keys are pressed to perform a calculation is called a *key sequence*. In *Everyday Mathematics* key sequences, function keys such as [+] and [−] are written with square brackets or shown as pictures of actual keys. Numbers, including decimals, are not. For example, a key sequence to calculate 12 − 3 + 5 is 12 [−] 3 [+] 5 [=]. The authors recommend that you use the square-bracket notation and encourage children to follow it when they are asked to write key sequences. Encouraging children to "discover" an appropriate key sequence is a suitable activity at any grade level and fits well into the *Everyday Mathematics* philosophy.

It's advisable to try calculator activities ahead of time using the same model calculator the children use so that you will be familiar with all symbols and key sequences involved. Use your owner's manual to answer questions not addressed in the *Teacher's Guide to Activities*.

Resources on Calculators

Campbell, P. F., and Stewart, E. L. (1993). "Calculators and Computers." In Jensen, R. (Ed.) *Research Ideas for the Classroom: Early Childhood Mathematics*. New York: Macmillan.

Demana, F., and Leitzel, J. (1988). "Establishing Fundamental Concepts Through Numerical Problem Solving." In Coxford, A. F., and Shulte, A. P. (Eds.) *The Ideas of Algebra, K–12: 1988 Yearbook*. Reston, VA: National Council of Teachers of Mathematics.

Groves, S., and Kaye, S. (1998). "Calculators in Primary Mathematics: Exploring Numbers before Teaching Algorithms." In Morrow, L. J. (Ed.) *The Teaching and Learning of Algorithms in School Mathematics*. Reston, VA: National Council of Teachers of Mathematics.

Ellington, A. J. (2003). "A Meta-Analysis of the Effects of Calculators on Children's Achievement and Attitude Levels in Precollege Mathematics Classes." *Journal for Research in Mathematics Education 34(5):* pp. 433–463.

Hembree, R., and Dessart, D. J. (1992). "Research on Calculators in Mathematics Education." In Fey, J. T., and Hirsch, C. R. (Eds.) *Calculators in Mathematics Education: 1992 Yearbook*. Reston, VA: National Council of Teachers of Mathematics.

National Council of Teachers of Mathematics. (2005). *Position Statement: Calculators, Computation, and Common Sense*. Reston, VA: Author. Retrieved from www.nctm.org/about/position_statements/computation.htm

National Council of Teachers of Mathematics. (2003). *Position Statement: The Use of Technology in the Learning and Teaching of Mathematics*. Reston, VA: Author. Retrieved from www.nctm.org/about/position_statements/position_statement_13.htm

National Council of Teachers of Mathematics. (1998). *Position Statement: Calculators and the Education of Youth*. Reston, VA: Author. Retrieved from www.nctm.org/about/position_statements/position_statement_01.htm

management guide

Smith, B. A. (1997). "A Meta-Analysis of Outcomes from the Use of Calculators in Mathematics Education." *Dissertation Abstracts International 58:787A.*

Waits, B. K., and Demana, F. (2000). "Calculators in Mathematics Teaching and Learning: Past, Present, and Future." In Burke, M. J., and Curcio, F. R. (Eds.) *Learning Mathematics for a New Century: 2000 Yearbook.* Reston, VA: National Council of Teachers of Mathematics.

3.1.2 Computers and the Internet

Because computer access and availability vary widely across the United States, computer-based activities are currently not integrated into the core curriculum of *Pre-Kindergarten* through *Third Grade Everyday Mathematics.*

Many existing software programs can be used with *Everyday Mathematics.* Some of these software programs are designed as instructional tools that can be used by teachers to model, demonstrate, or explain mathematical concepts. Children can use other software for concept development, practice, enrichment, motivation, and exploration.

As the Internet has become more widely available to the public and to schools, *Everyday Mathematics* has incorporated it into the program in a modest way. This section lists Web sites that seem destined to survive over the years and that supplement activities in a substantive way. At this writing, these include the Web sites listed in the table below.

Mathematics Web Sites: Cross-Grade Resources	
Organization	**Web Site**
UCSMP *Everyday Mathematics* Center	everydaymath.uchicago.edu
Eisenhower National Clearinghouse	www.enc.org
National Council of Teachers of Mathematics (NCTM)	www.nctm.org
The Math Forum	mathforum.org
Shell Centre	www.nottingham.ac.uk/education/shell

▶ 3.2 Topical Tools

There is a variety of conceptual devices, manipulatives, and other tools that children use to help them understand *Everyday Mathematics* topics. This section summarizes them and discusses some management strategies. More information on each tool is located in the appropriate Mathematical Strands and Threads chapter.

3.2.1 Numeration and Computation Tools

Counting Manipulatives

It is often suggested in the Pre-Kindergarten and Kindergarten activities that children use "counters" to represent numbers, perform simple addition and subtraction problems, model number stories, divide collections in half, and concretely work through or model other mathematical problems and situations. These counters can be everyday objects, such as pennies, buttons, or paper clips. They can also be commercial products, such as counting bears or counting chips. Commercial counters often incorporate varied colors or sizes that make them useful for other tasks, such as sorting.

Straws or craft sticks that can be easily bundled into groups of 10 and 100 are useful for representing larger numbers and for thinking and learning about place value concepts. In later grades, base-10 blocks are also an important manipulative.

Regardless of which types of counters you use, young children should have ready access to concrete materials such as those described above when exploring number, counting, and mathematical operations. Using these materials is not "cheating," but rather a legitimate strategy that helps children develop strong number sense over time. Fingers are another highly valuable counting manipulative!

Number Grids, Scrolls, and Lines

A *number grid* consists of rows of boxes, usually ten in each row, containing consecutive integers.

Number grids have many wonderful features that can help children with pattern recognition and place value. However, their original use in *Everyday Mathematics* was simply to solve the problem of number lines being unmanageably long. Number lines can be cumbersome even when stretched along a classroom

									0
1	2	3	4	5	6	7	8	9	10
11	12	13	14	15	16	17	18	19	20
21	22	23	24	25	26	27	28	29	30
31	32	33	34	35	36	37	38	39	40
41	42	43	44	45	46	47	48	49	50
51	52	53	54	55	56	57	58	59	60
61	62	63	64	65	66	67	68	69	70
71	72	73	74	75	76	77	78	79	80
81	82	83	84	85	86	87	88	89	90
91	92	93	94	95	96	97	98	99	100
101	102	103	104	105	106	107	108	109	110

wall, and it is nearly impossible to print them in children's books without breaking them into chunks. Number grids may be considered number lines that fit nicely on a page or a classroom poster.

Number scrolls are number grids that children fill in to extend forward (positively) into the hundreds or thousands or backward (negatively) into negative numbers. Children can make scrolls by attaching new grids to existing ones and rolling the result like a scroll.

Children use *number lines*—lines that show numbers in sequence at regularly spaced intervals—when counting and skip counting, performing measuring activities, and adding and subtracting. In Kindergarten, children build a "Growing Number Line" as they track the number of days they have been in school.

For more information, see Section 8.6.2: Number Grids, Scrolls, and Lines.

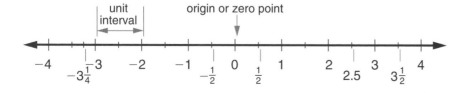

Slates

Slates provide convenient and inexpensive surfaces on which children can write their mathematical work. They provide an excellent way for everyone to answer a question quietly and simultaneously, and they help you see at a glance which children may need extra help. They also save paper. Children may use plastic write-on/wipe-off slates with dry-erase markers or small, individual chalkboards. Establish a regular routine for the distribution and pickup of slates in your classroom. Have children get into the habit of cleaning their slates at the end of each activity. Children can use a sock to wipe the slates and to store the chalk or marker. Encourage children to use their slates to practice number writing during free time. If slates are unavailable, you might simply have children fold a piece of paper into fourths, giving them eight cells in which to write answers. The classroom chalkboard also provides a good place to work with individuals, small groups, or the whole class.

NOTE: Establish a routine for using slates that provides all children with sufficient time to think before seeing everyone else's responses. To help prevent confusion, you might want to use a procedure with 1-word cues, such as Listen, Think, Write, Show, and Erase.

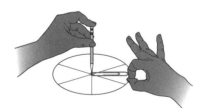

3.2.2 Data and Chance Tools

In *Pre-Kindergarten* and *Kindergarten Everyday Mathematics,* children use dice and spinners to generate random outcomes for games. Many games call for teachers to make special dice or spinners, such as dice marked with + and − symbols or spinners with specified numerals.

You can use plastic or wooden cubes or blank dice to make customized dice. Directions for marking the cubes or blank dice are included in the applicable activity descriptions in the *Teacher's Guide to Activities.*

Spinners can be made with a pencil and paper clip as shown in the margin. Use either a large (about 2-inch) or standard (about 1-inch) paper clip for the part that spins. The larger size is preferred because it spins more easily. Make a mark as a pointer at one end of the paper clip using a permanent felt-tip pen. Spinning mats may be drawn on cardstock or paper. Sometimes a mat is supplied as a master. If you make your own mat, start with a circle or square big enough to accommodate the paper clip. Mark the center of the circle, choose the number and sizes of the regions, and then measure and draw the appropriate angles. For example, six equal-sized regions would each measure $60°$ ($360° \div 6$). You can use various shapes for the spinner, and the regions do not have to be the same size.

Children are encouraged to think about the probability, or chance, of getting various outcomes when they work with dice and spinners.

3.2.3 Geometry Tools

There are many objects that can be used to explore geometric ideas, ranging from objects found around the house, such as shoe boxes or marbles, to elaborate kits sold by curriculum supply companies. Some simple tools that are readily available and relatively easy to manage are highlighted on the next page.

Pattern-Block Template

Pattern-Block Templates are useful for exploring patterns and plane figures and for recording children's work with pattern blocks. Children also use their Pattern-Block Templates to draw circles and other shapes. Children may need support when using the templates, especially in placing them so the shapes are positioned on the paper in the way the children intend. Offer as much support as needed until children become proficient. For some young children, it may be easier to simply trace around pattern block shapes, especially if someone holds the shape still for them.

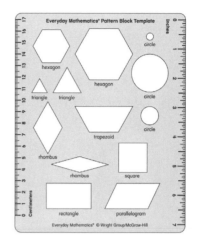

Pattern Blocks and Geometric Solids

Pattern blocks help children learn the names and features of geometric objects. They also are useful for exploring patterns. In Kindergarten and first grade, children identify categories of shapes and colors of pattern blocks. Children are also encouraged to find different ways of categorizing blocks on their own, that is, to create multiple perspectives of a given set of blocks. This ability to think about the same things in different ways is important for many problem-solving activities. Science educators also identify classification as one of the most important processes of science.

If building blocks are available in your classroom, children learn a great deal about 2- and 3-dimensional shapes and about spatial relationships as they explore and build with the blocks. Many Pre-Kindergarten and Kindergarten activities include suggestions that make use of building blocks to enhance children's learning of particular topics.

Straws and Twist-Ties and Marshmallows and Toothpicks

Constructing 2- and 3-dimensional objects with straws and twist-ties or with marshmallows and toothpicks is a popular activity beginning in *Kindergarten Everyday Mathematics*. Children learn a great deal about the properties of shapes when they work to construct shapes from raw materials. Because of their developing fine motor skills, young children may initially need help working with these materials. Marshmallows and toothpicks are typically a bit easier for them to manage than are straws and twist-ties.

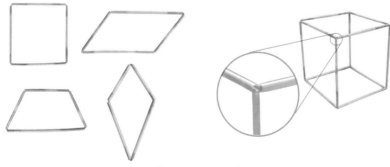

Straw constructions

3.2.4 Measuring Tools

Children in *Pre-Kindergarten* through *Third Grade Everyday Mathematics* use a wide variety of informal and formal tools for measuring.

Nonstandard Measuring Tools and Units

Children begin to explore measurement using different measurement units (their own feet, arms, and hands; blocks; connecting cubes; links; and other items) to help build an awareness of the need for standard units of measure. As they measure with these nonstandard tools, children can also begin to learn about proper measuring techniques, such as lining up the end of the measuring "tool" (body part, block, or other manipulative) with the object being measured.

For more information, see Section 12.10.2: Rulers and Tape Measures.

Rulers and Tape Measures

Children are formally introduced to standard units of measurement about midway through the Kindergarten year, and rulers and tape measures are among the first tools they use. If the children use retractable tape measures, teach and enforce the "2-inch, 5-centimeter no-zap rule": Do not "zap" the tape measure until no more than 2 inches or 5 centimeters show. This will extend the life of these tools, as well as make your own life quieter and easier.

Scales and Balances

A scale is another historically old measuring tool. *Scales* are used to measure how heavy things are according to a standard weight. Different scales are used for different purposes, both in everyday life and in *Everyday Mathematics*.

For more information, see Section 12.10.3: Scales and Balances.

In Pre-Kindergarten and Kindergarten, children weigh and then order objects by weight using pan balances and bathroom scales. Children begin by comparing weights with their own hands and then with pan balances. In first grade, pan balances are used to introduce the symbols for relations such as <, >, and =.

4 Organizing Children

Each main activity in *Pre-Kindergarten* and *Kindergarten Everyday Mathematics* includes one or more of the following grouping suggestions: Whole Group, Small Group, Partners, or Center. These varied options make the programs flexible enough to work well in a variety of early childhood classrooms. To make best use of the range of activities in the program, a classroom setup that allows for whole-group, small-group, partner, and center-based activities, as well as smooth transitions from one type of activity to another, is desirable. Also plan to spend time helping children learn how to work productively in each of these contexts.

It is expected that you will make grouping decisions based on your own situation, but is important to realize that a pervasive element of the program is a belief in the value of cooperative learning. The following sections outline hints for managing your classroom to facilitate cooperative group work and also to make use of the technique of group responses.

4.1 Cooperative Groupings

Cooperative learning helps children by:

- Improving attitudes toward learning and academic achievement;
- Improving social skills and time spent on task;
- Helping develop speaking, listening, and writing skills;
- Creating an atmosphere for sharing ideas and problem-solving strategies that they may not have discovered on their own;
- Preparing them for real-life situations in which people often share responsibilities with others and need to cooperate and work together toward common goals.

Learning becomes a dynamic process during group activities, when interaction among group members encourages an inquisitive spirit and introduces new avenues for exploration, while instilling a spirit of teamwork. Use careful thought and planning when assigning children to groups. Different activities and different classes require different types of groups, and even good activities can fail if groups are poorly formed. So, consider group size (four is often a good number for small groups), heterogeneity (often a mixed-ability group is best, but sometimes it is not), and individual personalities when grouping children for particular activities.

Resources for Cooperative Learning

Artzt, A. F., and Newman, C. M. (1997). *How to Use Cooperative Learning in the Mathematics Class (Second Edition)*. Reston, VA: National Council of Teachers of Mathematics.

Adrini, B., and Kagan, S. (1992). *Cooperative Learning and Mathematics*. San Juan Capistrano, CA: Kagan Cooperative Learning.

Johnson, D. W., and Johnson, R. T. (1991). *Learning Mathematics and Cooperative Learning*. Edina, MN: Interaction Book Company.

Johnson, D. W., Johnson, R. T., and Holubec, E. J. (1994). *The Nuts and Bolts of Cooperative Learning*. Edina, MN: Interaction Book Company.

Kagan, S. (1992). *Cooperative Learning*. San Juan Capistrano, CA: Kagan Cooperative Learning.

Shulman, J. H., Lotan, R. A., and Whitcomb, J. A. (Eds.) (1998). *Groupwork in Diverse Classrooms: A Casebook for Educators*. New York: Teachers College Press.

4.2 Group Responses

Just as choral readings have proved to be beneficial for beginning readers, a group-response approach (in which more than one child participates at the same time) can be useful for topics such as plain and fancy counting, calculator counting, and a variety of problem-solving situations. Many *Minute Math* activities can be done with group responses. Slate activities also involve group responses.

See page 14 for a discussion of *Minute Math*. See page 20 for a discussion of slates.

Group-response activities allow all children to participate at their own levels without being put on the spot. More-skilled children will have the opportunity to lead while others hear them and are thereby strengthened in the concepts in which they are weak. Keep group-response activities brief and playful. If you have children work in small groups or sit around tables, you can focus on one group at a time, even if the whole class is responding. This will help you identify children who may need extra help.

5 Differentiating Instruction

"Differentiation is a philosophy that enables teachers to plan strategically in order to reach the needs of the diverse learners in classrooms today." (Gregory, 2003, p. 27)

A differentiated classroom is a rich learning environment that provides children with multiple avenues for acquiring content, making sense of ideas, developing skills, and demonstrating what they know. In this sense, differentiated instruction is synonymous with good teaching. Many experienced teachers differentiate instruction intuitively, making continual adjustments to meet the varying needs of individual children. By adapting instruction, teachers provide all children opportunities to engage in lesson content and learn.

Though children may follow different routes to success, and may acquire concepts and skills at different times, the philosophy of *Everyday Mathematics* is that all children should be expected to achieve high standards in their mathematics education—reaching the Grade-Level Goals in *Everyday Mathematics* and the benchmarks established in district and state standards and frameworks. *Everyday Mathematics* is an ideal curriculum for differentiating instruction for a variety of reasons. The *Everyday Mathematics* program:

- Begins with an appreciation of the mathematical sensibilities that children bring with them to the classroom and connects to children's prior interests and experiences;
- Incorporates predictable routines that help engage children in mathematics and regular practice in a variety of contexts;
- Provides many opportunities throughout the year for children to acquire, process, and express mathematical concepts in concrete, pictorial, and symbolic ways;
- Extends children's thinking about mathematical ideas through questioning that leads children to deepen their understanding of concepts;
- Incorporates and validates a variety of strategies;
- Emphasizes the process of problem solving as well as finding solutions;
- Provides suggestions for enhancing or supporting children's learning;
- Encourages collaborative and cooperative groupings in addition to individual and whole-class work;

- Facilitates the development and use of mathematical language and promotes academic discourse;
- Provides teachers with information about the learning trajectories or paths associated with Grade-Level Goals;
- Highlights opportunities for teachers to assess children in multiple ways over time;
- Suggests how children can demonstrate what they know in a variety of ways;
- Encourages children to reflect on their own strengths and weaknesses.

In addition to the fundamental elements of the program mentioned above, this edition of *Everyday Mathematics* includes extended support for recognizing and individualizing the program for children with a range of learning needs. The activities in the *Teacher's Guide to Activities* for both Kindergarten and Pre-Kindergarten include specific information about modifying content and/or instruction to meet the needs of particular children, including the following features:

- Suggestions for highlighting terminology that might be particularly confusing to English-language learners.
- Teaching Options and Extensions that can be used to help with differentiation as well as to help you bring mathematics into all areas of the classroom and parts of the school day. In Kindergarten, select activities in the Teaching Options section are labeled as "Readiness," "Enrichment," "ELL Support," and "Extra Practice." These labels serve to identify activities that are particularly useful for helping children with different needs access or extend the content of the main activity.
- Adjusting the Activity suggestions that provide ideas for making particular activities better match children's needs and proficiencies.

Resources on Differentiation

Baxter, J., Woodward, J., and Olson, D. (2001). "Effects of Reform-Based Mathematics Instruction on Low Achievers in Five Third-Grade Classrooms." *The Elementary School Journal 101(5):* pp. 529–547.

Garnett, K. (2004). "Math Learning Disabilities." Reprint from the *Division for Learning Disabilities Journal of the Council for Exceptional Children.* (November 1998). Retrieved from www.ldonline.org/ld_indepth/math_skills/garnett.html

Gregory, G. (2003). *Differentiated Instructional Strategies in Practice.* Thousand Oaks, CA: Corwin Press.

Johnson, D. (2000). *Teaching Mathematics to Gifted Children in a Mixed-Ability Classroom.* Arlington, VA: ERIC Clearinghouse on Disabilities and Gifted Education.

Lock, R. (1996). "Adapting Mathematics Instruction in the General Education Classroom for Children with Mathematics Disabilities." Reprint from the *LD Forum: Council for Learning Disabilities* (Winter 1996). Retrieved from: www.ldonline.org/ld_indepth/ math_skills/ adapt_cld.html

Tomlinson, C. (1999). *The Differentiated Classroom.* Alexandria, VA: Association for Supervision and Curriculum Development.

Usiskin, Z. (1994). "Individual Differences in the Teaching and Learning of Mathematics." *UCSMP Newsletter 14 (Winter 1994).* Chicago: University of Chicago School Mathematics Project.

Villa, R., and Thousand, J. (1995). *Creating an Inclusive School.* Alexandria, VA: Association for Supervision and Curriculum Development.

Woodward, J., and Baxter, J. (1997). "The Effects of Reform-Based Mathematics Instruction on Low Achieving Children in Inclusive Settings." *Exceptional Children 63(3):* pp. 373–388.

6 Managing Assessment

From the beginning, the philosophy of *Everyday Mathematics* regarding assessment has been clear. From the *Assessment Handbook:*

> Too often, school assessment tends to provide only scattered snapshots of student achievement rather than continuous records of growth. In *Everyday Mathematics,* assessment is like a motion picture, revealing the development of each child's mathematical understanding over time while also giving the teacher useful feedback about the instructional needs of both individual children and the class as a whole.

For assessment to be useful to teachers, children, parents, and others, the *Everyday Mathematics* authors believe that . . .

- teachers need to have a variety of assessment tools and techniques from which to choose so that children can demonstrate what they know in a variety of ways and teachers can have reliable information from multiple sources.
- children should be included in the assessment process. Self assessment and reflection are skills that children will develop over time if encouraged.
- assessment and instruction should be closely aligned. Assessment should assist teachers in making instructional decisions concerning both individual children and the whole class.
- assessment should focus on all important outcomes, not simply on outcomes that are easy to measure.
- a good assessment program makes instruction easier.
- the best assessment plans are those developed by teachers working collaboratively within their own schools and districts.

The authors of *Pre-Kindergarten* and *Kindergarten Everyday Mathematics* continue to believe that *ongoing assessment* is the most productive and informative way to assess young children's mathematics development. This type of assessment, combined with nonthreatening and informal *periodic assessment,* gives teachers a tremendous amount of information about children's understanding and progress in mathematics.

For more information, see the Assessment Handbook.

ASSESSMENT HANDBOOK

Everyday Mathematics

The University of Chicago School Mathematics Project

In addition to the assessment features from previous editions, the third edition of *Kindergarten Everyday Mathematics* provides teachers with extensive new support in managing these assessment goals. This support includes:

- Clearly articulated *grade-level goals* for the program organized by mathematics strands across all grades. Specific opportunities for assessment are identified throughout the activities and are linked to grade-level goals.
- *Ongoing assessment notes* to highlight activity-based opportunities for monitoring children's progress. Specifically, these notes point out activities in which you can:
  - *Recognize student achievement* by collecting assessment data to monitor children's progress with respect to grade-level goals. These data come from a variety of sources, such as responses during an activity or *My First Math Book* pages.
  - *Inform instruction* through tips that help you be on the lookout for children's mistakes or misconceptions and highlight their successful solution strategies. Suggestions are given on how to evaluate children's performance and how to adapt your instruction to meet individual needs when appropriate.
- Improved support for *ongoing learning and practice* of mathematics skills through "revisit" activities, games, and Home Links.
- More ideas for using "everyday kid-watching" to assess children's development of mathematical contexts and skills. These suggestions are included in the *Kindergarten Assessment Handbook*.
- A summary of periodic and ongoing assessment opportunities (including "everyday kid-watching") for each *grade-level goal*. The summary tables for the goals in each strand are included in the *Kindergarten Assessment Handbook*.

Resources on Assessment

Black, P., and Dylan, W. (1998). "Assessment and Classroom Learning." *Assessment in Education 5(1):* pp. 7–74.

Black, P., and Dylan, W. (1998). "Inside the Black Box: Raising Standards Through Classroom Assessment." *Phi Delta Kappan 80(2):* pp. 139–149.

Bush, W. S. (Ed.) (2001). *Mathematics Assessment: Cases and Discussion Questions for Grades K–5.* Reston, VA.: National Council of Teachers of Mathematics.

Glanfield, F., Stenmark, J. K., and Bush, W. S. (Eds.) (2003). *Mathematics Assessment: A Practical Handbook for Grades K–2.* Reston, VA: National Council of Teachers of Mathematics.

Kloosterman, P., and Lester, F. K., Jr. (Eds.) (2004). *Results and Interpretations of the 1990 through 2000 Mathematics Assessments of the National Assessment of Educational Progress.* Reston, VA: National Council of Teachers of Mathematics.

Kuhn, G. (1994). *Mathematics Assessment: What Works in the Classroom.* San Francisco: Jossey-Bass Publishers.

Mathematical Science Education Board/National Research Council. (1993a). *Measuring Up: Prototypes for Mathematics Assessment.* Washington, DC: National Academy Press.

Mathematical Sciences Education Board/National Research Council. (1993b). *Measuring What Counts: A Conceptual Guide for Mathematics Assessment.* Washington, DC: National Academy Press.

National Assessment Governing Board. (2004). *Mathematics Framework for the 2005 National Assessment of Educational Progress.* Washington, DC: U.S. Department of Education. Retrieved from www.nagb.org/pubs/m_framework_05.html

National Council of Teachers of Mathematics. (2000). *Position Statement: High-Stakes Testing.* Reston, VA: Author. Retrieved from www.nctm.org/about/position_statements/highstakes.htm

National Council of Teachers of Mathematics. (2000). *Principles and Standards for School Mathematics.* Reston, VA: Author.

National Council of Teachers of Mathematics. (1995). *Assessment Standards for School Mathematics.* Reston, VA: Author.

Shepard, L. A. (1995). "Using Assessment to Improve Learning." *Educational Leadership 52(5):* pp. 38–43.

Stenmark, J. K., and Bush, W. S. (Eds.) (2001). *Mathematics Assessment: A Practical Handbook for Grades 3–5.* Reston, VA: National Council of Teachers of Mathematics.

Stiggens, R. J. (1997). *Student-Centered Classroom Assessment.* Englewood Cliffs, NJ: Prentice-Hall.

Webb, N. L., and Coxford, A. F. (Eds.) (1993). *Assessment in the Mathematics Classroom: 1993 Yearbook.* Reston, VA.: National Council of Teachers of Mathematics.

7 Providing for Home-and-School Communication

Discussion, experimentation, and play are at the heart of *Everyday Mathematics* in early childhood classrooms. Family members who have been accustomed to conventional mathematics programs may think that because children are not bringing home daily or weekly arithmetic sheets, they are not learning or doing mathematics. The Home Links, *Mathematics at Home* books, and Family Letters and newsletter suggestions described below reassure them that this is not the case.

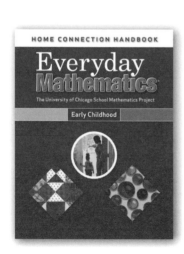

You received a *Home Connection Handbook* in your *Classroom Resource Package* that contains articles, explanatory material about the *Everyday Mathematics* philosophy and program, and suggestions for parents regarding how to become involved in their children's mathematics education. Much of the information in the *Home Connection Handbook* can be copied and sent to families to provide information about and promote involvement in the *Everyday Mathematics* curriculum.

7.1 Home Links

 Home Links activities serve two main purposes: They *promote follow-up* to classroom activities and *involve parents or guardians* in their children's mathematics education.

Home Links activities also:

- Encourage children to take initiative and responsibility;
- Reinforce newly learned skills and concepts;
- Relate what is learned in school to the children's lives outside of school, tying mathematics to their everyday world;
- Serve as informal assessment tools.

Home Links instruct children to complete activities with someone at home—a parent, guardian, older sibling, or other adult. Each Home Link includes a Family Note at the top that gives background information to an adult at home about the mathematics content in the Home Link activity.

7.2 *Mathematics at Home* Books

Mathematics at Home books are included as part of *Pre-Kindergarten* and *Kindergarten Everyday Mathematics*. These books highlight and suggest informal mathematics activities that children can do outside of school, such as sorting silverware or laundry, counting steps in their house, or finding varied mathematics opportunities on family trips or in the grocery store. These books offer another way to communicate with families about the philosophy of the *Everyday Mathematics* program and to help children see and capitalize on the mathematics in their everyday environment.

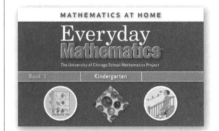

7.3 Family Letters and Ideas for Newsletters

You will find some Family Letters in *Resources for the Pre-Kindergarten Classroom* and *Resources for the Kindergarten Classroom*. Send home the introductory Family Letter at the beginning of the year, followed by the other letters as indicated in the resource book for your level.

The resource books also feature many short, parent-friendly descriptions about the mathematics you will do in class. You can incorporate these suggestions into your newsletters or other home/school communication.

Number and Counting

Contents

Children already know a great deal of mathematics when they begin school. They are fluent in the practical geometry of everyday life; they enjoy patterns of sound, shape, and movement; they can reason a little. But probably their most important mathematical skill is counting. Counting provides a foundation for understanding our number system and the basic operations of arithmetic. Arithmetic operations with counting numbers lead, in turn, to other kinds of numbers such as positive rational numbers (fractions and decimals) and negative numbers, and eventually to algebra and higher mathematics.

Numbers and counting are integral to most of the topics in this book. This chapter addresses noncomputational aspects of numbers, including number systems and uses of numbers. Numbers are also discussed at length in Chapter 9: Operations and Number Models; Chapter 14: Estimation, Mental Arithmetic, and Number Sense; and Chapter 15: Patterns, Sequences, Functions, and Algebra.

▶ 8.1 Number Uses

If you're looking for one phrase to capture the overall philosophy of *Everyday Mathematics,* it might be "Numbers All Around." In Pre-Kindergarten and Kindergarten, children explore their surroundings in search of numbers. In first grade, children create a "Numbers All Around Museum" and collect numbers about themselves. In second grade, children collect numbers about their worlds and curate another Numbers All Around Museum. Similar lessons using numbers and mathematics from children's everyday experiences continue through *Sixth Grade Everyday Mathematics.*

The numbers that surround us in today's world are not all the same. Some are counts, some are measures, and others are used for identification. The developers of *Everyday Mathematics* have identified five basic categories, or *use classes,* that cover 90% of number uses:

- Counts
- Measures
- Locations
- Ratio comparisons
- Codes

Counts and *measures* are straightforward: 6 eggs, 3 pounds, and so on. *Locations* are a bit trickier: 9:05 A.M. expresses a location in time; 72°C is a location on a temperature scale; pairs of numbers such as 42°N, 87°W mark a location on Earth's surface.

A *ratio comparison* is a number such as *3 times as much* or $\frac{1}{2}$ *as many.* Ratio comparisons are less common in primary grade mathematics than are counts and measures, but they become increasingly important in later grades.

Codes are numbers used as identification tags, which often also include letters. Codes are used for credit cards, Social Security numbers, phone numbers, and so on. Often a code has several parts. For example, in the zip code 60637:

    6   refers to Illinois, Missouri, Nebraska, or Kansas.

    06 refers to Chicago.

    37 refers to the neighborhood in Chicago that includes the University of Chicago.

Children are also interested in the way ancient people used numbers. In *Second Grade Everyday Mathematics,* they explore the Roman numeral system in which letters used alone and in combination to represent numbers are a sort of code when compared to our decimal system. Roman numerals are still found on clocks, building cornerstones, preliminary pages in books, and copyright dates in some movies.

For more information on numbers as measures and locations, see Chapter 12: Measurement and Chapter 13: Reference Frames.

Roman Numerals					
I	= 1	XX	= 20 (2 tens)	CC	= 200
II	= 2	XXX	= 30 (3 tens)	CCC	= 300
III	= 3	XL	= 40 (50 less 10)	CD	= 400
IV	= 4	L	= 50	D	= 500
V	= 5	LX	= 60 (50 plus 10)	CM	= 900
VI	= 6	LXX	= 70 (50 plus 20)	M	= 1,000
VII	= 7	LXXX	= 80 (50 plus 30)	$\overline{X}$	= 10,000
VIII	= 8	XC	= 90 (100 less 10)	$\overline{C}$	= 100,000
IX	= 9	C	= 100	∞	= 100,000,000
X	= 10				or infinity

▶ 8.2 Whole Numbers

Thousands of years ago people managed without numbers or with only the numbers 1, 2, 3, ... Eventually, however, these numbers were found to be inadequate for certain purposes, and other number systems were invented. The inventions of these new number systems were motivated either by the everyday needs of people or mathematical needs, or by both. In this and the following sections, we discuss various number systems, including whole numbers and positive and negative rational numbers.

The first numbers people used were for counting: 1, 2, 3, 4, ... These numbers were the beginning of mathematics. Zero was invented both to express "none" as a count and to make writing numbers easier. The numbers 0, 1, 2, 3, 4, . . . are known as the *whole numbers*.

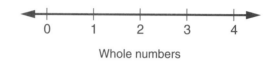

Whole numbers

8.2.1 Numeration and Place Value

Today, people everywhere write whole numbers in the same way. The system of numeration we all use was invented in India more than a thousand years ago and came to Western Europe via the Middle East and North Africa. This highly efficient system, known as *Hindu-Arabic numeration,* has contributed significantly to the tremendous advances in mathematics and science in the past 500 years.

Hindu-Arabic numeration uses 10 digits to represent whole numbers, called *base-ten numeration*. The digits are placed according to one basic rule: The value of a digit is 10 times the place to its right. Thus the 2 in 72 is worth just 2, but the 2 in 27 is worth 10 times as much, or 20; and the 2 in 275 is worth another 10 times as much, or 200. The system is called a *place-value* system because the value of a digit depends on its place in the number.

Mastering Hindu-Arabic numeration is a major goal of primary grade *Everyday Mathematics*. The process begins in Pre-Kindergarten and continues in Kindergarten when children count up to and beyond 100 by both 1s and by 10s and observe what happens to the written numbers as the count passes landmarks like 100. Kindergarteners also work with number lines and number grids that include numbers beyond 100. At this stage, many children have little or no understanding of the place-value structure of numbers—writing the number 57 may be as much as like spelling as mathematics—but these activities at least provide children a familiarity with 2- and 3-digit numbers that they can build on in later grades. In Kindergarten, children learn that the term *digits* refers to the 10 symbols, 0 through 9. They discuss and explore how these symbols can be used to write all numbers. Becoming familiar with the concept of digits lays important groundwork for understanding place value. As part of their initial investigations of place value, Kindergarteners also group objects by tens and make exchanges of ones and tens in a variety of activities and games.

In first grade, children group objects by 10s and 100s and make exchanges across places. For example, they may trade 3 tens for 2 tens and 10 ones. First graders extend their counting beyond 1,000, including counts by 1s, 10s, and 100s, and continue to work with number lines and number grids. They also begin exploring ideas of place value and make connections between written numbers and manipulatives like base-10 blocks. First graders also do many activities that highlight the idea that numbers have equivalent names; for example, $100 = 10$ tens. Realizing that numbers have equivalent forms is essential for understanding written procedures for whole-number computation and is an important building block for algebra.

Through all of this number work in Pre-Kindergarten through Grade 3, children use a variety of manipulatives, such as base-10 blocks, counters, craft sticks, coins, straws, number lines, digit cards, Ten Frames, and dominoes. Particular attention is paid to helping children make connections among various representations of numbers, including symbols, words, pictures, manipulatives, and real objects.

8.2.2 Plain and Fancy Counting

Research shows that very young children, as well as certain animals, have rudimentary nonverbal counting abilities. These counting foundations appear to be hard-wired into our being. Building on these fundamental nonverbal capabilities, verbal counting is one of the most useful ways to introduce young children to many important mathematical concepts. Just as one needs to be familiar with the progression of notes in a musical scale before one can play a piece of written music, children need a secure grasp of counting before they can understand the decimal number system and develop arithmetic competence. Throughout *Everyday Mathematics,* you are encouraged to incorporate many varied and playful rote-counting and rational-counting activities into your lesson plans.

Rote Counting

Children first learn to count aloud by reciting a string of number words by rote, without understanding the significance behind what they are saying. At first, they make mistakes like *one, two, three, six, nine, eleven, threeteen, . . .,* although they often make the same mistakes every time. Eventually, they learn to recite the number sequence correctly to 10, 20, or beyond, but generally without full numerical understanding, especially for higher numbers.

Rote, oral counting is important for learning about our number system. As children count, they hear, and then later see, the order and number-word patterns of the decimal system. Counting past the barrier of 100 gives young children a sense of the repetitive nature and the comprehensibility of our number system. Types of rote counting include the following:

- Counting on from numbers other than 0 or 1. This is the foundation for later activities with addition and subtraction. It is also an efficient way to rote count to higher numbers.

- Counting backward from a number. This may be difficult at first, but will become easier with practice and familiarity. It, too, helps children develop number sense and can be useful for understanding subtraction.

 **perspective**

Place value is presented more formally in second grade. Children rename 2- and 3-digit numbers in various ways and investigate place value to 10,000s. Much of this work is integrated with learning how to add and subtract multidigit numbers, because most computational algorithms depend heavily on place value. One of the main reasons Hindu-Arabic numeration has been so widely accepted is that it makes computation so much easier. (Imagine multiplying with Roman numerals!) By third grade, children begin to extend their understanding of place value to numbers up to a million and to decimals.

- Skip counting by 2s, 5s, 10s, and so on, from 0 at first and then later from other numbers. Skip counting reveals some of the patterns in our number system. It is also an efficient way to count and lays the foundation for multiplication. As they count by 2s (2, 4, 6, 8, . . .), children see and sense the even-number pattern.

All these types of counting help children develop the skills and understandings that are used to solve problems. Counting on, for example, is a good way for Kindergarten or first-grade children to solve simple addition problems.

A variation on any of the above rote-counting activities is called *interrupted oral counting*. This includes having one group of children count so far, stopping them, and then having another group continue. A more advanced version of interrupted counting is having children stop in the middle of a counting activity such as counting backward or skip counting by 2s and then giving them a new starting number from which they continue with the same activity.

There are many ways to add variety to rote-counting activities. For example: *Count and do "noodle knocks" (knock on head with knuckles); count and nod your head, tap your foot, tap your knee, tap your stomach,* and so on; *count in whispers;* and *count in shouts.* You might also intersperse more vigorous counts using, for example, jumping jacks or touches. Whatever you do, keep oral-counting sessions active, short, and lively.

Rational Counting (Counting Things)

Reciting number words by rote is just the beginning. Children also need to learn to count collections of objects correctly. This involves coordinating the spoken number words with pointing to or touching the objects being counted. Children must also avoid skipping objects or counting some twice, and they must come to realize that the order in which objects are counted makes no difference. Such meaningful counting is called *rational counting* and is achieved only after a great deal of practice.

Pre-Kindergarten and Kindergarten children need to have many experiences counting things of various sizes, shapes, and arrangements. Through such experiences, children become increasingly adept at counting. They also develop their number sense and understanding of quantity—the "four-ness" of four, for example. As you work with young children to help them develop their rational-counting skills, consider the following:

- Children need to learn to match one-to-one (one number name to one object) so that when given a specific number of objects to count, they end up with the same number each time.
- By counting 1, 2, 3, 4, 5, . . ., children are not simply matching names to objects, but they are figuring out the number of objects in a whole group. (*Five* is not the name of the last object counted; *five* is the number of members in the group.)

- It is easier to count accurately and to avoid counting some objects more than once if the objects are arranged in a line or in rows rather than in irregular positions, or if objects are moved or marked as they are counted.

- Once children have mastered verbal counts by 5s and 10s, they can group and count large collections by those numbers quickly and more accurately.

8.2.3 Ordinal Numbers

The counting numbers tell how many; for example, 5 apples, 3 books, or 2 birds. A different kind of number, called an *ordinal number,* tells the order of objects in a sequence, such as first, second, third, and so on.

Ordinal numbers are not as simple as they seem. Suppose you have an apple, a pear, a peach, a banana, and a plum. Counting these pieces of fruit is easy; there are 5 of them. But assigning ordinals is not so easy. The apple is listed first, but it could easily be listed third or fifth. Indeed, the apple might be first in alphabetical order and fifth in weight. Also, 5 refers to the entire collection of fruit, but *fifth* refers to only the last piece in a sequential ordering of the five fruits. Fortunately, children can learn to use ordinal numbers without having to bother about these rather abstract issues.

- Ask children, for example: *Who is first in line? Who is third from the end? Who is third from the beginning? What number is that person from the end? Who is eighth in line?*

- Identify children by their place in line; then ask them to perform some sort of action. For example, have the third child in line and the seventh child in line change places. Ask, *Is the fourth child in line still the same one?*

Ordinal number exercises

8.3 Rational Numbers: Fractions, Decimals, and Percents

The whole numbers are adequate for counting, but measurement requires numbers between the whole numbers. A pencil, for example, might be more than 5 inches long but less than 6 inches long. The *measure numbers,* or *positive rational numbers,* fill this need. The positive rational numbers include fractions, terminating or repeating decimals, and the numbers {1, 2, 3, . . .}. The efficient and convenient notations we have today for fractions and decimals evolved later, but the numbers themselves were invented thousands of years ago.

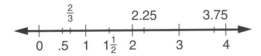

Zero and some positive rational numbers

The importance of alternate notations for numbers is emphasized throughout *Everyday Mathematics.* All three notations for rational numbers—fractions, decimals, and percents—can help children see connections between rational numbers and whole numbers. Fractions build on ideas of equal sharing and whole-number operations, decimals extend the whole-number place-value system, and percents connect to the important ideas of ratio and proportion. The payoff for repeated, early, and informal experiences with decimals, fractions, and percents

NOTE: The term *rational number* may be confusing. Rational numbers are no more "reasonable" than other numbers. Rational numbers are called *rational* because they can be written as *ratios* of integers. Every positive rational number can be expressed as a ratio or fraction in which the numerator is a whole number and the denominator is a nonzero whole number. For example, the rational number 7.5 can be expressed as the ratio $\frac{75}{10}$.

NOTE: Fractions may also be difficult for children simply because their symbols are more complicated than those of whole numbers.

Early attention to fractions, decimals, and percents prepares students for learning about operations with numbers in these notations in Grades 4 through 6.

comes later in the *Everyday Mathematics* program, when seeing relationships among the numbers allows children to use mental computation and estimation with a high degree of sophistication. For example, knowing that 10% is equal to $\frac{1}{10}$ or 0.1 makes the problem *How much is 10% of a $30 cab ride?* easy to solve mentally by taking $\frac{1}{10}$ or 0.1 of $30 to get $3.

Fractions are confusing to many people, perhaps because the procedures for adding, subtracting, multiplying, and dividing them seem arbitrary and unpredictable. For example, it is likely that few people really understand the "invert and multiply" rule for division by a fraction. It may be that these mysterious fraction manipulations, often taught without real-life problems or concrete embodiments to give them meaning, are what have convinced so many adults that mathematics is impossible to understand and that getting "correct" results is more a matter of good luck than good comprehension.

One reason many people experience difficulties with fractions may be that many school programs avoid fractions for several years while children work exclusively with whole numbers. When children are finally introduced to fractions, many find them confusing because the results often run counter to what they expect from having dealt only with whole numbers. For example, unlike whole numbers, fractions are generally harder to add than to multiply; a product may be smaller than its factors; a quotient may be larger than the number being divided; and "repeated addition" has little meaning in the multiplication of two fractions.

So, while much of the content of traditional mathematics programs for the primary grades is concerned with whole numbers, including place-value notation, addition, subtraction, and multiplication, *Everyday Mathematics* extends traditional work with these numbers by introducing children to:

- Negative numbers, with temperatures and number lines, and the concept of *half,* in Kindergarten;
- Fractions, with measures and "part of" situations, and decimals, mainly with notation, in first grade;
- More fractions such as "1 tenth of . . ." in second grade.

Children can better understand these new numbers when they are presented as part of everyday experiences. For example, even before the authors began to develop *Everyday Mathematics*, they found, through interviews with 5- and 6-year-olds, that young children respond quickly and accurately when asked for "half of" something, probably as a result of sharing things equally with siblings and friends. Building on these observations, the primary grade program includes negative numbers, fractions, decimals, and percents. These are used mainly to convey information, without becoming involved in arithmetic operations.

8.4 Positive and Negative Numbers

The invention of negative numbers was prompted by both practical and mathematical considerations. From a mathematical point of view, negative numbers are needed:

- To make subtraction *closed*. When negative numbers are allowed, there is an answer to every subtraction problem, including differences such as $3 - 10$.
- To complete the number line. With negative numbers, the number line can extend below zero.
- To give every number an *additive inverse*. The sum of a number and its additive inverse is zero. The additive inverse of a positive number is negative.

In the everyday world, negative numbers answer the need for specifying locations in reference frames in relation to a *zero point* (starting point) and for naming measures that extend in both directions from the zero point.

Beginning in Kindergarten, children use positive and negative numbers to locate points in reference to a zero point, for example, on a temperature scale, and to represent the result of a change situation, such as using -3 to mean a loss of 3 pounds. Other situations in which positive and negative numbers are used are given in the table below.

Situation	Negative	Zero	Positive
bank account	withdrawal	no change	deposit
time	before	now	after
games	behind	tied	ahead
business	loss	break even	profit
elevation	below sea level	sea level	above sea level

Such situations are useful in helping children understand that negatives are opposites of positives. Positives and negatives come in pairs, and familiarity with negatives can be improved by comparing them with their positive opposites.

> **NOTE:** The *integers* are the whole numbers {0, 1, 2, 3, . . .} and their opposites {0, −1, −2, −3, . . . }. Note that zero is its own opposite. Zero is neither positive nor negative.

References and Resources for Number and Counting

Gratten-Guinness, I. (1997). *The Norton History of the Mathematical Sciences*. New York: W. W. Norton.

Kline, M. (1977). *Mathematical Thought from Ancient to Modern Times*. New York: Oxford University Press.

Menninger, K. A. (1992). *Number Words and Number Symbols: A Cultural History of Numbers*. New York: Dover.

8.5 Numeric Relations

In mathematics, a *relation* tells how one thing compares to another. This section discusses numeric relations, that is, relations between numbers and expressions. The most common numeric relations are equality ($=$) and inequality ($<$ and $>$), but there are others.

For more information, see Section 11.6: Geometric Relations.

chapter 8

Even preschool children have some idea of "more" and "less." They may be deceived by appearances but, under the right conditions, they can judge bigger/smaller, shorter/taller, heavier/lighter, and so on. This capacity for judging more/less is the basis for understanding numeric relations.

As children begin to count or measure objects, they learn to write symbols for relations between the counts or measures of different objects. The following table shows the most common symbols for expressing numeric relations. In Kindergarten, children learn about the = symbol in contexts that illuminate its meaning, such as in number stories and with a pan balance.

Symbols for Numeric Relations		
Symbol	**Read it as**	**Examples**
=	"equals" "is equal to" "is the same as"	$3 = \frac{6}{2}$ 3.0 seconds = 3 seconds $\frac{1}{2} = 50\%$
>	"is greater than"	12 > 4 1.23 > 1.2 6,000 ft > 1 mi
<	"is less than"	8 million < 12 million 0.1 < 1.1 $\frac{5}{2} < 4$
≥	"is greater than or equal to"	attendance ≥ 250 people 2 + 2 ≥ 4 area ≥ 2 acres
≤	"is less than or equal to"	2 + 2 ≤ 4 fee ≤ \$25 time ≤ 2 hours
≠	"does not equal" "is not equal to" "is not the same as"	10 ≠ 100 $\frac{10}{120} \neq \frac{1}{2}$ 85% ≠ 85

8.5.1 Equality

Although the concept of equality seems straightforward, children who have been through several years of schooling often have difficulty using the = symbol. Research studies show that many older children reject such number sentences as 5 = 5 (they say there is no problem), 4 = 2 + 2 (they say that the answer is on the wrong side), and 4 + 3 = 5 + 2 (they say there are two problems, but no answers).

The origin of these errors seems clear. Children in school usually see number sentences written only with a problem on the left-hand side of the equal sign and the answer on the right-hand side: 5 + 7 = 12. So, deliberately write 12 = 5 + 7 as often as 5 + 7 = 12, and encourage children to say *means the same as* or *looks different, but is really the same as* when reading the equal symbol.

In large part, arithmetic consists of simply replacing numbers or expressions with equivalent (equal) numbers or expressions. You can

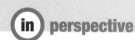

in perspective

Children begin to use the other relation symbols in this table in *First Grade Everyday Mathematics*.

NOTE: Some computer programming languages use "<>" for "not equal."

NOTE: The French mathematician Henri Poincar (1865–1912) once remarked, "Mathematics is the art of giving the same name to different things." For example, mathematicians give the name "polygon" to many different shapes, including squares, triangles, and pentagons.

For more information about equivalent names for numbers and name-collection boxes, see Section 8.6.3: Name-Collection Boxes.

chapter 8

replace $7 + 8$ with 15, or substitute 27 for $459 \div 17$. When it suits you, you can use $\frac{1}{2}$ in place of $\frac{1}{3} + \frac{1}{6}$ and vice versa. Number sense and arithmetic skill consist largely of being aware of the many possibilities for equivalent names for numbers and being able to use them flexibly.

8.6 Number and Counting Tools and Techniques

Children in *Everyday Mathematics* use a variety of manipulatives including base-10 blocks, counters, coins, craft sticks, straws, number lines, Ten Frames, digit cards, name-collection boxes, and dominoes. Some of the more important tools are discussed in the following sections.

8.6.1 Base-10 Blocks

In *Everyday Mathematics,* children use base-10 blocks starting in first grade. They build structures and count cubes to check estimates of height or length. They also make exchanges to investigate place value. Base-10 blocks are used for some games as well.

A variety of names are used for base-10 blocks. The following names are used in *Everyday Mathematics*: *cube* for the smaller 1-cm cube, *long* for the block consisting of ten 1-cm cubes (1×10), *flat* for the block consisting of one hundred 1-cm cubes (10×10), and *big cube* for the larger cube consisting of one thousand 1-cm cubes ($10 \times 10 \times 10$).

First graders may also use base-10 blocks to solve number models. For example, to solve the number model $41 - 18 = n$, children might match two sets of base-10 blocks one to one and then count the unmatched blocks; or they might count out 41 blocks, remove 18, and count the blocks left. The blocks also may be used on pan balances instead of weights to represent number sentences.

The shorthand shown below is handy for drawing quick pictures of base-10 blocks. Such pictures are often more convenient to use than are the actual blocks, especially the larger blocks, and can be useful for explaining and recording solutions.

Base-10-Block Shorthand		
Name	**Block**	**Shorthand**
cube		▪
long	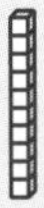	│
flat	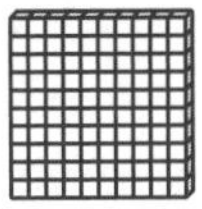	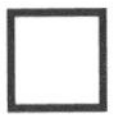 ▢
big cube	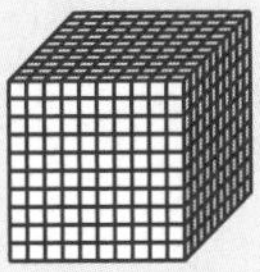	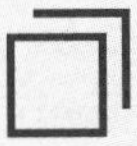 ◰

chapter 8

8.6.2 Number Grids, Scrolls, and Lines

Grid is short for *gridiron,* an old English word for a framework of metal bars or wires used to grill meat or fish. Generally, a grid is any set of equally spaced parallel lines, squares, or rectangles used to help establish locations of objects.

In *Everyday Mathematics,* children use many types of grids, including number grids, coordinate grids, grids for estimating area, and grids for interpreting maps. The tick marks on a number line form perhaps the most primitive grid structure. Lattices and arrays are organizations of objects into gridlike formations, a common example of which is a calendar.

Number Grids

A *number grid* consists of rows of boxes, usually ten in each row, containing consecutive integers. Children are introduced to number grids in *Kindergarten Everyday Mathematics.*

									0
1	2	3	4	5	6	7	8	9	10
11	12	13	14	15	16	17	18	19	20
21	22	23	24	25	26	27	28	29	30
31	32	33	34	35	36	37	38	39	40
41	42	43	44	45	46	47	48	49	50
51	52	53	54	55	56	57	58	59	60
61	62	63	64	65	66	67	68	69	70
71	72	73	74	75	76	77	78	79	80
81	82	83	84	85	86	87	88	89	90
91	92	93	94	95	96	97	98	99	100
101	102	103	104	105	106	107	108	109	110

A number grid

Number grids have many wonderful features that can help children with pattern recognition and place value. However, their original use in *Everyday Mathematics* was simply to solve the problem of number lines being unmanageably long. Number lines can be cumbersome even when stretched along a classroom wall, and it is nearly impossible to print them in children's books without breaking them into chunks. Number grids may be considered number lines that fit nicely on a page or a classroom poster.

A number grid lends itself to many activities that reinforce understanding of numeration and place value. For example, by exploring the patterns in rows and columns, children discover that any number on the number grid is:

- *1 more* than the number to its left;
- *1 less* than the number to its right;
- *10 more* than the number above it;
- *10 less* than the number below it.

In other words, as you move from left to right, the ones digit increases by 1 and the tens digit is the same. As you move down, the tens digit increases by 1 and the ones digit is the same.

Number grids can be used to explore number patterns. For example, children can color boxes as they count by 2s. If they start at zero and count by 2s, they will color the even numbers as shown below; if they start at 1, they will color the odd numbers. If they count by 5s, starting at zero, they will color numbers with 0 or 5 in the ones place.

									0
1	2	3	4	5	6	7	8	9	10
11	12	13	14	15	16	17	18	19	20
21	22	23	24	25	26	27	28	29	30
31	32	33	34	35	36	37	38	39	40
41	42	43	44	45	46	47	48	49	50
51	52	53	54	55	56	57	58	59	60
61	62	63	64	65	66	67	68	69	70
71	72	73	74	75	76	77	78	79	80
81	82	83	84	85	86	87	88	89	90
91	92	93	94	95	96	97	98	99	100
101	102	103	104	105	106	107	108	109	110

For older children, number grids are also useful for addition and subtraction. For example, to find the difference 84 − 37, you can:

- Count the number of tens from 37 to 77 (*4 tens*) and then count the number of ones from 77 to 84 (*7 ones*) as shown on the next page. So 84 − 37 is 4 tens plus 7 ones, or 47. This difference corresponds to the *distance* between the points 37 and 84 on a number line.

perspective

In the primary grades, *Everyday Mathematics* includes many counting activities that use number grids, for example, counting by 10s starting at 17 and counting backward by 10s starting at 84. Children also solve puzzles based on the number grid. These puzzles are pieces of a number grid in which some, but not all, of the numbers are missing. Number-grid puzzles are used through third grade, mostly for numbers in the hundreds and thousands.

A number-grid puzzle

perspective

Identifying number patterns in grids can help children understand divisibility rules, prime numbers, and factoring in later grades.

chapter 8

									0
1	2	3	4	5	6	7	8	9	10
11	12	13	14	15	16	17	18	19	20
21	22	23	24	25	26	27	28	29	30
31	32	33	34	35	36	37	38	39	40
41	42	43	44	45	46	47	48	49	50
51	52	53	54	55	56	57	58	59	60
61	62	63	64	65	66	67	68	69	70
71	72	73	74	75	76	77	78	79	80
81	82	83	84	85	86	87	88	89	90
91	92	93	94	95	96	97	98	99	100
101	102	103	104	105	106	107	108	109	110

One way to find 84 − 37

- Start at 84 and count back to 37, noting as before how many numbers have been counted.
- Count back 37 from 84 by tens and ones: 74, 64, 54, 53, 52, 51, 50, 49, 48, 47.

Addition problems can also be solved on the number grid using similar methods. Clearly, the number grid simplifies "double counting," or counting the number of numbers counted, that is required in many addition and subtraction procedures.

From the time they are introduced, children see that number grids can be extended to negative numbers. This is especially useful as a tool for finding differences or to illustrate, for example, that −17 is less than −6.

−19	−18	−17	−16	−15	−14	−13	−12	−11	−10
−9	−8	−7	−6	−5	−4	−3	−2	−1	0
1	2	3	4	5	6	7	8	9	10
11	12	13	14	15	16	17	18	19	20

A grid extended to −19

Number Scrolls

Number scrolls are extended number grids. You can make them by adding single sheets of 100 numbers to existing sheets, either forward (positively) or backward (negatively). Among other things, scrolls give children the chance to experience the ongoing repetitive patterns of our base-ten number system beyond 100—*101, 102, 103*, . . .—so that they do not continue, as children often do, with *200, 300, 400,* . . .. Teachers have found that many children get excited when they discover these patterns and realize that they are capable of writing bigger and bigger numbers based on their discoveries. Meanwhile, they are practicing their handwriting as well as their counting skills.

Number Lines

A *number line* is a line on which points are indicated by *tick marks* that are usually at regularly spaced intervals from a starting point called the *origin,* the *zero point,* or simply "0." Numbers are associated with the tick marks, and the interval from 0 to 1 on the line is called the *unit interval.*

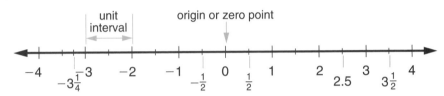

Like any line, a number line extends without end in both directions. Any drawing of a number line is a model of just part of the line. Where you place the zero point is arbitrary, and how you space the numbers depends on the situation you wish to illustrate. You might, for example, mark every other unit-interval point and label by 2s as in Figure 1 below; or you may mark every half-interval point and label by halves as in Figure 2.

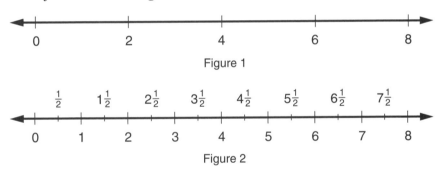

Figure 1

Figure 2

<in> perspective

In *First* through *Sixth Grade Everyday Mathematics,* children are often asked to solve incomplete-number-line problems that help them understand these concepts.

An ordinary ruler uses part of a number line for measuring length, with inch unit intervals, centimeter unit intervals, or other unit intervals. A ruler based on the number line in Figure 3, for example, can be used for measuring distances in inches and halves of inches.

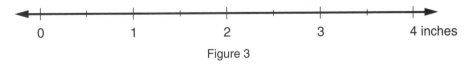

Figure 3

For more information, see Section 12.3: Length.

The number line in Figure 3 has tick marks at all unit and half-unit intervals. You may recognize the similarities between the scale on this line and the one on a U.S. customary foot ruler. This line has fewer fraction-of-unit intervals marked than most rulers. In contrast, foot-rulers are usually marked every sixteenth of an inch.

chapter 8

You can assign any scale to a number line. For example, a unit interval on a map scale might represent one mile on the map. Such a line would not be used to measure distances directly in the real world but instead to convert distances on the map into actual distances.

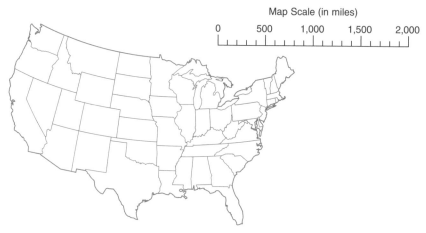

A number line always has a zero point, even when it doesn't show. On the number line in Figure 4, the zero point is understood to be off to the left. Sometimes you see a broken-line symbol as in the number line in Figure 5. This symbol indicates that a piece of the line between 0 and 330 has been omitted. The symbol, or another similar to it, is often used in technical drawings to show important details while still indicating that something is missing.

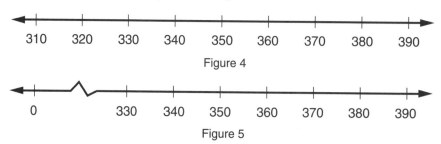

Figure 4

Figure 5

Beginning in *Kindergarten Everyday Mathematics,* children use number lines for counting and skip counting. They also create a Growing Number Line on the classroom wall by adding a new number every day. Children also use number lines on thermometers and on linear measuring tools. Number lines in coordinate graphing systems are introduced in third grade.

8.6.3 Name-Collection Boxes

Name-collection boxes give children the opportunity to experience the idea that numbers can be expressed in many different ways. In first through third grade, a *name-collection box* is a box with a label identifying the number whose names are collected in the box. For example, the box shown in the margin is a 16-box, a name-collection box for the number 16. Kindergarteners also make name collections as they explore equivalent names for numbers.

Names can include sums, differences, products, quotients, the results of combining several operations, words in English or other languages, tally marks, arrays, and Roman numerals.

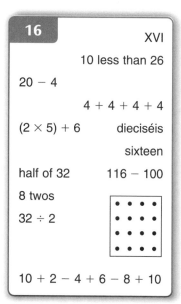

A 16-box

NOTE: Number lines can also have nonlinear scales, meaning the distances between the numbers are not proportional to the differences between the numbers. For example, radio dials are based on logarithmic scales, one type of nonlinear scale. Nonlinear scales do not have unit intervals.

Operations and Number Models

Contents

For many adults, elementary school mathematics consisted of little more than learning to add, subtract, multiply, and divide whole numbers, fractions, and decimals. Unfortunately, this is still the experience of many children today. The authors of *Everyday Mathematics* hope that your acquaintance with our texts and your reading of this manual convince you that elementary school mathematics needs to be far more than arithmetic with the four basic operations.

Nevertheless, the importance of arithmetic in mathematics as well as in everyday life cannot be denied. *Everyday Mathematics* combines activities that focus on understanding the basic operations with activities that apply arithmetic in geometry, data exploration, measurement, and other contexts. This ensures that children receive ample practice with arithmetic skills and that they will be better able to use those skills to solve problems. Children in *Everyday Mathematics* see many uses of all the operations from the beginning of the program and build upon these uses year after year. Rather than having multiplication and division delayed until third grade or later, they see these operations as well as addition and subtraction in first and second grades. Even in Kindergarten, children are exposed to the concept of multiplication through simple arrays and to the concept of division through equal sharing.

In *Pre-Kindergarten* and *Kindergarten Everyday Mathematics,* the emphasis is on using operations to solve concrete problems that arise from children's daily lives in the classroom. For example, *How many juice cups do we need since Jose and Yuri are absent? How many chairs do we need if 2 visitors sit at the little table with us? How can we share the snacks equally? Are there enough snacks for second helpings for everyone?*

Many adults who associate school mathematics with arithmetic also tend to think that an arithmetic operation is what you "do" to get the answer. For example, to these adults division means carrying out the traditional long-division algorithm. In *Everyday Mathematics,* how one "does" an operation is referred to as "applying an algorithm" or "carrying out a computation." Although *Everyday Mathematics* recognizes the importance of knowing algorithms and introduces a variety of algorithms for each operation beginning in Grade 2, it also provides the activities that children need in order to understand the meaning behind each operation. These types of activities are the focus in Pre-Kindergarten and Kindergarten, but they also continue throughout the program. Choosing the proper algorithm and interpreting the result correctly depends on understanding the operation itself. Ultimately, children need to both understand the meanings of the operations and become proficient at carrying out algorithms to become successful problem solvers.

This chapter begins with discussions about number stories, arithmetic symbols, number expressions and sentences, and number models. It then turns to specific approaches to solving number stories using situation diagrams for the four basic arithmetic operations.

▶ 9.1 Number Stories

In *Everyday Mathematics,* children's earliest experiences with operations are based on making up and acting out their own number stories. This approach puts children in charge of their learning and capitalizes on activities they love: stories and play acting. Number stories provide a natural bridge from spoken language to mathematical symbolic language. Using pictures to record and solve number stories is an important intermediate step for many children. Over time and through many experiences, children are encouraged to move from modeling number stories with their own bodies or counters, or with both, to representing them with pictures. They then use numbers and symbols to represent number stories with number models and number sentences, which are described in the next section. Through their early experiences with number stories, children also begin to develop a solid understanding of the meanings of addition and subtraction and of the reversible relationship between these two operations. This helps them to develop a wider range of strategies for solving problems now and later.

▶ 9.2 Number Sentences and Number Models

In *Everyday Mathematics,* number models are used to represent situations and to summarize relationships among quantities in problems. The early years of the program emphasize concrete, verbal (usually oral), and pictorial models. However, written number models are also gradually introduced in this meaningful context as a quick and efficient way to record or represent the stories. Symbols for operations such as $+$, $-$, and $\times$ and for relations such as $=$, $>$, and $<$ are introduced informally in the context of writing number models to match number stories. Blank response lines for unknown numbers are also informally introduced this way. In Kindergarten, the focus is on the $+$, $-$, and $=$ symbols. In later grades, more symbols are introduced and children take on greater responsibility for writing the number models.

Writing number models is in some ways similar to writing English sentences. Written English and written mathematics both have rules and conventions about grammar, syntax, punctuation, and usage. These rules clarify thinking and make communication easier. So before looking at a formal definition of number model, the authors discuss the arithmetic symbols themselves and how they are used in number sentences and numerical expressions.

For information about managing children's use of number models, see Section 9.2.3: Teaching with Number Sentences and Number Models.

9.2.1 Arithmetic Symbols

Many people feel that mathematics has too many symbols. Symbols, however, are vitally important to the subject. They make the language of mathematics more concise and, ultimately, easier to communicate and understand. Symbols can increase mathematical power by relieving the mind of unnecessary work and leaving it free to focus on problem solving.

Writers of school mathematics programs face a dilemma. On one hand, an efficient set of symbols is needed so that activities may progress smoothly in a classroom. But symbols, especially if they are introduced too early, may pose an unnecessary obstacle to the understanding of a concept. With this in mind, the authors of *Everyday Mathematics* have been careful to avoid the premature introduction of symbols, and mathematical vocabulary in general. Symbols are introduced only when they help children communicate more efficiently.

The curriculum must introduce both the symbols needed for classroom activities and the symbols required for real-world general knowledge. Symbols for classroom activities can be introduced on an *ad hoc* basis and could be restricted to a small and efficient set. But the need for children to understand mathematics within a broader social context means that *Everyday Mathematics* must include a more expansive list of symbols. Each group in society, for example, grocers, scientists, engineers, advertisers, and journalists, has a different set of symbols it considers necessary. Even the way we write numbers can spark debate: *Should it be .1 or 0.1? Is 1/2 better than $\frac{1}{2}$, or is $^1/_2$ the best? Should we write -3, -3, or $^-3$?*

Calculators and computers, which might have been expected to help standardize notation, have actually increased the need for understanding that different symbols can mean the same thing. For example, there are several alternative symbols for multiplication, division, powers, and opposites (inverses). *Everyday Mathematics* provides activities to help children become aware of these alternative notations so that they can adapt to different situations as necessary. The program employs several notations for certain operations so students will become familiar with all common symbols.

Addition and Subtraction Symbols

The only symbols for addition and subtraction are $+$ and $-$. Although the ideas behind the operations are thousands of years old, the symbols first appeared in print in 1498 in a book by the German mathematician Johann Widman. Widman's symbols gradually caught on and are now universally accepted. However, words for these symbols vary: *plus, add*, and *positive* all refer to $+$; *minus, take away*, and *negative* all refer to $-$.

Children in *Everyday Mathematics* see these symbols only after they have had informal experiences with the underlying operations. For example, Pre-Kindergarten and Kindergarten children begin hearing the words *add* and *subtract* in the context of number stories based on their own experiences. Gradually, $+$ and $-$ are introduced in this context to help children link the spoken and symbolic representations. One of the early encounters that Kindergarteners have with the addition symbol occurs when they use ⊞ on their calculators in a counting-on activity. Establishing this informal connection between $+$ and counting supports later use of $+$ in paper-and-pencil representations of addition and the understanding of a rule such as "$+ 3$" in "What's My Rule?" and Frames-and-Arrows activities. Similar counting-back activities use ⊟.

9.2.2 Reading and Writing Number Sentences

Just as English words become meaningful when they are arranged into sentences, mathematical symbols become meaningful in sentences. And just as proper punctuation and grammar make written English easy to read, rules and conventions for writing number sentences ease mathematical communication.

A *number sentence* is an equation or inequality such as $10 = 7 + 3$, $12 \div n = 6$, or $14 > 3$. A number sentence has a left-hand side, a relation symbol, and a right-hand side. Symbols for numbers, unknowns, and operations can appear on each side of the relation symbol. Each side of a number sentence is a *numerical expression*. In the sentences above, 10, $7 + 3$, $12 \div n$, 6, 14, and 3 are expressions. In practice, however, single numbers are usually called just "numbers" or "constants" and expressions usually include one or more operations.

Number sentences can be true, false, or neither true nor false. A number sentence that is neither true nor false is called an *open sentence*. The sentence $5 + 3 = 8$ is true; the sentence $5 + 4 = 8$ is false; the sentence $5 + \_\_ = 8$ is open.

A *number model* is a numerical expression or number sentence that models (represents) some real or hypothetical situation. For example, consider this situation: *Rajiv had 7 pennies and got 3 more. Then he had 10 pennies.* The sentence $7 + 3 = 10$ is a number model of Rajiv's situation. Number models can be based on stories made up by children, on situations invented by you, or on information from everyday life.

An established order of operations eliminates ambiguity about the order in which additions, subtractions, and other operations are to be performed in number sentences. Grouping symbols such as parentheses and brackets can also be used to avoid ambiguity. These rules and techniques are introduced as they become applicable in later grades.

9.2.3 Teaching with Number Sentences and Number Models

In *Pre-Kindergarten* through *Third Grade Everyday Mathematics,* number models are not used to solve problems. Instead, they are used to represent and clarify the quantitative relationships in a problem. Although writing number models may help some children decide how to solve a problem, more importantly, it helps them learn the mathematical-symbol system. Translating a problem into a number model that is manipulated to find an answer comes later in the curriculum, when children begin to learn formal algebra.

When they are first introduced in *Everyday Mathematics,* number models usually appear after a problem has been solved. A typical instructional sequence might be as follows:

1. You pose a problem.
2. Children solve the problem.
3. Children share their solutions and you record them on the board. During the discussion of solutions you write number models or draw situation diagrams on the board. There should be no blanks in the number models or situation diagrams.

Later, the sequence might be as follows:

1. You pose a problem.
2. You and the children discuss the problem and write a number model or draw a situation diagram that corresponds to the problem. The number model or diagram includes a blank or a question mark for the unknown quantity.
3. Children solve the problem. They may use the number model or situation diagram to help them, or they may use another method entirely.
4. Children share their solutions and you record them on the board. During the discussion of the solutions, you fill in the blanks in the number model or diagram.

▶ 9.3 Use Classes and Situation Diagrams

One way to understand something is to examine how it is used. A hammer is used for pounding nails. An umbrella is used for keeping dry in the rain. This is how *Everyday Mathematics* approaches the four basic operations of arithmetic—by examining how they are used. At a certain stage, formal definitions can be valuable, but in the

For more information on situation diagrams, see Section 9.3: Use Classes and Situation Diagrams.

NOTE: The diagrams in *Everyday Mathematics* are adapted from work done by Karen Fuson at Northwestern University.

elementary grades it is better to approach the operations indirectly by looking at how they are used.

Addition, subtraction, multiplication, and division can each be applied in many different situations, but most of those situations can be sorted into just a handful of categories, or *use classes*. In *Everyday Mathematics,* the three basic use classes for addition and subtraction are called *parts and total, change,* and *comparison.* Depending on what is known and what is unknown, each kind of situation can lead to either addition or subtraction problems. Multiplication and division situations are harder to sort out, but several basic use classes can be distinguished: *equal groups, arrays and area, rate and ratio, scaling,* and *Cartesian products.* Each type of situation can lead to either multiplication or division problems depending on what is unknown.

Everyday Mathematics uses *situation diagrams* to help sort out these various kinds of problem situations. These diagrams help children organize the information in simple 1-step number stories. Although they are not formally used with children in Pre-Kindergarten or Kindergarten, a discussion of addition and subtraction use classes and situation diagrams is included here to explain the kinds of problems you and your children will encounter through number stories. Of the multiplication and division use classes, only equal groups and arrays are discussed in this manual. None of these models are intended for use in Pre-Kindergarten or Kindergarten. They are included only to enrich your understanding of each operation and to give you a sense of how early number stories progress in later grades.

9.3.1 Addition and Subtraction Use Classes

Most situations that lead to addition and subtraction problems can be categorized into parts-and-total, change, or comparison use classes.

Parts-and-Total Diagrams

In a *parts-and-total* situation, there is a total quantity that can be separated into two or more parts. For example, the total number of children in a class can be separated into the number of girls and the number of boys. Or the total distance from Chicago to St. Louis can be separated into the distance from Chicago to Springfield and the distance from Springfield to St. Louis.

A parts-and-total diagram has a large rectangle on top for the Total and two or more smaller rectangles below for the Parts as shown below. The rectangles are filled with numbers for particular problems.

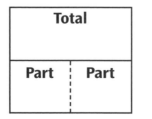
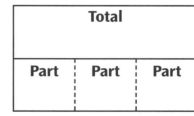

Parts-and-total diagrams

Quick and easy drawings are best. The words "Part" and "Total" can be omitted or replaced with words that better fit the problem situation as in the following examples.

In a situation where all the parts are known but the total is unknown, you can solve the problem by adding the parts.

Example 1: Twelve fourth graders and 15 first graders are on a bus. How many children in all are on the bus?

The parts are known. You are looking for the total.

Possible number model: $12 + 15 = \_$

total number of children on bus	
?	
4th graders	1st graders
12	15

?	
12	15

For a situation in which the total is known but one of the parts is unknown, you can use subtraction to find the unknown part.

Example 2: Thirty-five children are riding on the bus. Twenty of them are boys. How many girls are riding on the bus?

One part and the total are known. You are looking for the other part.

Possible number models:

$20 + \_ = 35$

$35 - 20 = \_$

Total	
35	
Part	Part
20	?

Change Diagrams

A second kind of addition/subtraction situation is *change*. In a change situation there is a starting quantity, a change in quantity, and an ending quantity. For example, a 15-cm-tall plant might grow 5 cm in a week and end up 20 cm tall. Or, you might start with a certain amount of money, spend some, and then have less money at the end. Change situations can lead to either addition or subtraction problems depending on the direction of the change (*change to more* or *change to less*) and what is known or unknown.

A change diagram has a rectangle on the left for the Start quantity, then an arrow above a blank for the Change, and finally a rectangle on the right for the End quantity.

Example 3: Twenty-five children are riding on the bus. At the next stop, 5 more children get on. How many children are on the bus now?

This is a change-to-more situation, or an increase, with the ending quantity unknown.

Possible number model: $25 + 5 = \underline{\ \ }$

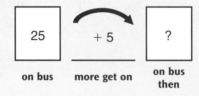

25	+ 5	?
on bus	more get on	on bus then

Example 4: A bus leaves school with 35 children. At the first stop, 6 children get off. How many children are left on the bus?

This is a change-to-less situation, or a decrease, with the ending quantity unknown.

Possible number models:

$$35 - 6 = \underline{\ \ }$$
$$6 + \underline{\ \ } = 35$$

Change

Start		End
35	− 6	?

Example 5: Tom had some money. He bought a magazine for $1.50. Then he had $6.50. How much money did Tom have to start with?

This is a change-to-less situation with the starting quantity unknown.

Possible number models:

$$\underline{\ \ \ \ } - \$1.50 = \$6.50$$
$$\$1.50 + \$6.50 = \underline{\ \ \ \ }$$

Change

Start		End
?	− $1.50	$6.50

Comparison Diagrams

Comparison situations involve two separate quantities and the difference between them. For example, one person might be 60 inches tall and another 70 inches tall; the difference in heights is 10 inches. Or one person might be 25 years old, another 6 years old, and the difference in ages is 19 years. As with change and parts-and-total situations, comparison situations can lead to addition or subtraction depending on what is known and what kind of comparison is being made.

A comparison diagram has a large rectangle on top for the larger Quantity being compared and smaller rectangles below for the smaller Quantity and the Difference.

Example 6: There are 12 fourth graders and 8 third graders. How many more fourth graders are there than third graders?

Here both quantities being compared are known and the difference is unknown.

Possible number models:

$12 - 8 = \_$

$8 + \_ = 12$

4th graders
12

3rd graders	
8	?

difference

Example 7: Vicky is 40 inches tall. Amelia is 4 inches shorter. How tall is Amelia?

Here one of the quantities being compared and the difference are known. The other quantity being compared is unknown.

Possible number models:

$40 - \_ = 4$

$40 - 4 = \_$

$\_ + 4 = 40$

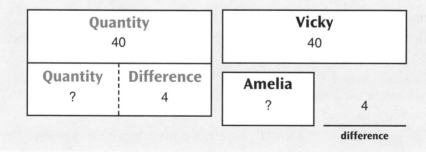

It is important to note that situation diagrams are simply devices to help organize problem solving; they are not ends in themselves. Some children do not need to organize their thinking on paper, and to require them to do so would not be constructive.

Units and Unit Boxes

The importance of including a unit or other label in an answer cannot be over-emphasized. Numbers and operations make the most sense to children when they are thought of in real-world contexts. Encourage children to attach appropriate units of measure or other labels, such as cents, lions, or feet, to the numbers they are using.

Because labeling each number in a situation diagram or other problem can be tedious, *Everyday Mathematics* suggests the use of *unit boxes* for addition and subtraction problems beginning in first grade. These rectangular boxes can be displayed beside the problem or at the top of a page of problems. Unit boxes contain the labels or units of measure used in the problem(s). Unit boxes help children organize their mathematics while keeping a particular context in mind.

Some teachers post a unit box for the day on the board so that children will have a context in which to think about all the abstract numbers used in the day's activities. Or children can supply the context themselves; they can choose topics of current interest or, if they prefer, fanciful or silly labels.

Unit boxes are not a focus in *Pre-Kindergarten* or *Kindergarten Everyday Mathematics,* but identifying the unit in their problems and answers is very important for all children. Be sure to model this in the context of number stories and other activities and to encourage children to get in the habit of including units in these contexts.

9.3.2 Multiplication and Division Use Classes

Multiplication and division arise in many different situations, but most of these situations can be sorted into just a few use classes: *equal groups, arrays and area, rate and ratio, scaling,* and *Cartesian products.* Of these, only equal groups and arrays and area are discussed here, because young children often encounter these types of situations, albeit in very concrete and informal ways.

Equal Groups

Much of the multiplication and division work in the primary grades of *Everyday Mathematics* involves equal groups. In an *equal-groups* situation, there are several groups of objects with the same number of objects in each group. Depending on what is unknown, equal-groups situations can lead to either multiplication or division problems.

In an equal-groups situation where the total is unknown but the number of groups and the number of objects in each group are known, the problem can be solved by multiplication or by acting out the problem with objects and counting the total.

Unit
cents ¢

A unit box

Example 1: A vase holds 5 flowers with 6 petals on each flower. How many petals are there in all?

Possible number model: $5 \times 6 = \underline{\ \ }$

flowers	petals per flower	total number of petals
5	6	?

In situations where the number of groups and the total number of objects are known, the problem is to find the number in each group. In *Everyday Mathematics,* these are called *equal-sharing* problems. Equal sharing is also known as *partitive division*.

Many children solve equal-sharing problems by "dealing out" the objects to be shared.

Example 2: Twenty-eight baseball cards are to be shared equally by 4 children. How many cards does each child get?

Possible number models:

$4 \times \underline{\ \ } = 28$

$28/4 = \underline{\ \ }$

$28 \div 4 = \underline{\ \ }$

children	baseball cards per child	total number of cards
4	?	28

In situations where the number in each group and the total number of objects are known, the problem is to find the number of groups. In *Everyday Mathematics,* these are called *equal-grouping* problems.

Many children solve equal-grouping problems by making as many groups of the correct size as possible and then counting the number of groups.

Example 3: Twenty-four Girl Scouts are going on a canoe trip. Each canoe can hold 3 scouts. How many canoes are needed?

Possible number models:

$3 \times \underline{\ \ } = 24$

$24/3 = \underline{\ \ }$

$24 \div 3 = \underline{\ \ }$

canoes	scouts per canoe	total number of scouts
?	3	24

Equal-grouping problems are also called *measurement division* or *quotitive division*. The term measurement division comes from thinking about using the divisor to "measure" the dividend. For example, consider $26 \div 6$. Think *How many 6s would it take to make 26?* Then imagine measuring off 6-unit lengths on a number line:

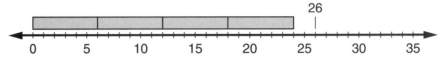

The figure above shows that there are four 6-unit lengths in 26, with 2 units left over. Thus $26 \div 6$ is 4 with remainder 2.

Arrays and Area

Arrays are closely related to equal-groups situations. If the equal groups are arranged in rows and columns, then a rectangular *array* is formed. As with equal-groups situations, arrays can lead to either multiplication or division problems.

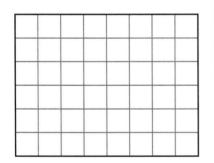

An array of chairs

> **Example 4:** There are 6 rows with 15 chairs in each row. How many chairs are there in all?
>
> Possible number model: $6 \times 15 = \underline{}$
>
> | rows | chairs per row | total chairs |
> |------|----------------|--------------|
> | 6 | 15 | ? |

Arrays are closely related to *area*. An array of square-centimeter tiles with no gaps between the tiles will have an area in square centimeters equal to the number of tiles.

> **Example 5:** The area of a rectangle is 48 cm². The rectangle's length is 8 cm. What is its width?
>
> Possible number models:
>
> $8 \times \underline{} = 48$
>
> $48 \div 8 = \underline{}$
>
> | length (cm) | width (cm) | area (cm²) |
> |-------------|------------|------------|
> | 8 | ? | 48 |

▶ 9.4 Algorithms

Computational algorithms are not a focus in *Pre-Kindergarten* and *Kindergarten Everyday Mathematics*. However, the question of whether and how algorithms should be taught in elementary school mathematics is a complex and controversial topic, so an overview of the *Everyday Mathematics* approach to algorithms is included in this section.

9.4.1 Algorithms and Procedures

As a teacher, you establish many procedures and routines to help your classroom run smoothly. For example, in the beginning of the year, you probably discuss the proper procedures for hanging up coats, lining up, and using materials. *Everyday Mathematics* encourages you to establish similar, but more mathematical, routines such as keeping a weather record or class calendar.

An *algorithm* is a well-defined, step-by-step procedure guaranteed to achieve a certain objective, often with several steps that "loop" as many times as necessary. For example, an algorithm for multiplication will produce the correct product no matter what the factors are.

A good algorithm is efficient, unambiguous, and reliable. Although you may be most familiar with the traditional elementary school procedures for adding, subtracting, multiplying, and dividing, there are many other algorithms both in mathematics and in real life. A computer program is an algorithm that specifies what a computer is to do at each step. The instructions for operating calculators or complicated equipment, such as FAX machines and VCRs, are forms of algorithms.

Formal algorithms are not introduced in Pre-Kindergarten or Kindergarten. In later grades, though, *Everyday Mathematics* includes a variety of both traditional computational algorithms and children's invented procedures. Inventing procedures is valuable because it:

- Promotes conceptual understanding and mental flexibility, both of which are essential for effective problem solving;
- Helps students learn about our base-ten place-value (decimal) system of numeration;
- Involves solving problems that the solver does not already know how to solve. Thus, asking children to devise their own computational methods provides valuable experience in solving nonroutine problems.

Traditional algorithms have advantages, too. They are generally efficient and can help children understand both the decimal number system and the underlying operations. Traditional algorithms also provide a common vocabulary for further development of mathematical ideas.

In addition to studying specific algorithms in *Everyday Mathematics*, children engage in activities to help them understand algorithms in a more general sense. Included are:

- Understanding specific algorithms or procedures provided by other people;
- Applying known algorithms to everyday problems;
- Developing algorithms and procedures when necessary;
- Realizing the limitations of algorithms and their procedures so that they are not used inappropriately;
- Adapting known algorithms to fit new situations.

Mathematics advances in part through the development of efficient procedures that reduce difficult tasks to routine exercises. An effective algorithm will solve an entire class of problems, thus increasing the user's mathematical power. The authors of *Everyday Mathematics*

NOTE: The term *algorithm* comes from the name *al-Khwarizmi*. Muhammad ibn Musa al-Khwarizmi (c. 780–850) was one of the greatest mathematicians of the Arab-Islamic world. We also have al-Khwarizmi to thank for the word *algebra*, which comes from *Hisab Aljabr w'al-muqabalah*, the title of one of his books.

have found that the study of paper-and-pencil computational algorithms at appropriate times can be valuable for developing algorithmic thinking in general.

9.4.2 Computational Algorithms: The *Everyday Mathematics* Approach

The *Everyday Mathematics* authors have been asked about the role of computational algorithms in elementary school mathematics. Before we address this issue, consider the following stories told by Professor Zalman Usiskin of the University of Chicago:

Scene 1: An Office Hal is preparing an end-of-the-month sales report. This involves doing many calculations, which he does, churning out each computation on paper. In walks the boss, horrified, saying, "Hal, why aren't you using a calculator? You're wasting valuable time!"

Scene 2: A Fourth-Grade Classroom The class is working on a page of difficult computational problems. Susie gets out her calculator and starts completing the assignment. The teacher walks over to Susie, horrified, saying, "Susie, put that calculator away or you'll get done too quickly!"

These two scenarios highlight the need to rethink the school mathematics curriculum in light of the widespread availability of calculators and computers outside of school. Children certainly still need:

- To know the meanings and uses of all the arithmetic operations in order to function in the practical world and to succeed in mathematics in high school and beyond;
- To know the basic addition and multiplication facts automatically, especially to help solve mental-arithmetic problems in our technological society;
- To understand and be able to apply paper-and-pencil algorithms for addition, subtraction, multiplication, and division of whole numbers, decimals, and fractions, especially in an environment of standardized testing.

Today's elementary school children also need to be prepared to be productive workers in the second half of the 21st century. Among other things, this means they need a conception of computation that takes into account advances in technology. For example, skill at judging the reasonableness of results is especially important for anyone using technology, whether sophisticated computer spreadsheets and modeling programs or simple four-function calculators. Estimation and approximation skills are also important both because many everyday applications of mathematics require quick, approximate answers and because one good way to judge whether a result is reasonable is to compare it to a sensible estimate. For all these purposes, mental arithmetic, both exact and approximate, is more useful than ever.

Along with increased attention to estimation and approximation, the broader approach to computation in *Everyday Mathematics* also includes paper-and-pencil algorithms taught with both efficiency and understandability in mind. That is, children are expected to know both *how* to add, subtract, multiply, and divide using paper and pencil methods and also *why* the methods they are using work.

Research carried out in the past 30 years by Kurt Van Lehn and others has shown that many children develop "buggy" algorithms that resemble standard procedures but do not work properly. In subtraction, for example, some children always subtract the smaller digit from the larger digit. Van Lehn has shown that bugs such as this develop because children are trying to carry out procedures they don't understand and can't remember well enough to reproduce accurately. Procedures that are well understood, on the other hand, are more easily recalled, are more easily "repaired" when they are not recalled accurately, and are more easily modified to fit new situations.

Children who solve mathematics problems using methods that they understand come to believe that mathematics is logical, that if they work at mathematics they can figure it out, and that doing mathematics can be enjoyable. Such beliefs are much more productive than those held by adults who believe that mathematics is a grab-bag of procedures that often don't make sense, that in mathematics more than other fields you either "get it" or you don't, and that the study of mathematics is often not much fun.

Because there are many paper-and-pencil methods that are both efficient and understandable, the authors of *Everyday Mathematics* believe that children should be exposed to paper-and-pencil algorithms for these reasons:

- Exploring different algorithms builds estimation skills and number sense and helps children see mathematics as a meaningful and creative subject.
- There are situations in which the most efficient or convenient way to carry out a computation is with paper and pencil.
- If taught properly for understanding, but without demands for "mastery" by all children by some fixed time, paper-and-pencil algorithms can reinforce children's understanding of our number system and of the operations themselves.

In the debate about algorithms, *Everyday Mathematics* takes a moderate position, combining elements from both the child-centered, invented-algorithms approach and the subject-matter-centered, traditional-algorithms approach. During the early phases of learning an operation, *Everyday Mathematics* encourages children to invent their own procedures. Children are asked to solve arithmetic problems from first principles about situations in which operations are used, before they develop or learn systematic procedures for solving such problems. This helps them to understand the operations better and also gives them valuable experience solving nonroutine problems.

Later, when children thoroughly understand the concept of the operation, several alternative algorithms are introduced. Some of these algorithms are based on approaches that many children devise on their own. Others are less likely to be discovered by children but have a variety of desirable characteristics. As children move through the grades, they are urged to experiment with various algorithms in order to become proficient at using at least one alternative.

NOTE: In *Mind Bugs: The Origins of Procedural Misconceptions*, cognitive scientist Kurt Van Lehn said this about using the traditional subtraction algorithm in some of his research:

> [O]rdinary multidigit subtraction . . . is a virtually meaningless procedure [for] most elementary school children. . . . When compared to procedures they use to operate vending machines or play games, subtraction is as dry, formal, and as disconnected from everyday interests as the nonsense syllables used in early psychological investigations were different from real words. This isolation is the bane of teachers. . . .

Data and Chance

Contents

Probability ideas are extended and made more precise throughout the rest of *Everyday Mathematics*. The *Probability Meter,* a number-line device for recording probabilities, is introduced in Grade 5.

Understanding statistics and probability is more important now than ever before. In a world inundated with numbers, citizens and consumers need to understand claims about data and probabilities in journalism and advertising. Workers need to know how to gather, display, and analyze data in order to work efficiently and effectively. Even many recreational activities such as fantasy sports leagues involve data and chance. Statistics and probability have become prominent in the elementary school curriculum, both because of their current importance and as a source of contexts for practicing arithmetic and other skills.

▶ 10.1 Probability

Everyday Mathematics authors believe that most children need to be exposed to concepts and skills many times in many different ways, often only briefly, before they are able to master them. The treatment of probability in the curriculum is a good example of this approach. Children play informal games and engage in activities involving the idea of fairness and the use of random-number generators such as cards, number cubes, and spinners. The first step toward a more formal treatment occurs in *Third Grade Everyday Mathematics*.

10.1.1 Why Study Probability?

Most people are aware that our world is filled with uncertainties. Although there are some things that we can be sure of, for example, that the sun will rise tomorrow or that it will be hot this summer in Florida, we also know that there are degrees of uncertainty and that some things are more likely to happen than others. We know that there are also uncertain occurrences, such as weather patterns, that can be predicted with increasing accuracy. These qualitative ideas of probability—*impossible, possible, likely, certain*, and so on—are the basis for the mathematical treatment of probability in *Everyday Mathematics*.

Few people understand how to calculate the chance that something will take place. Yet many decisions in our personal lives, from the relatively trivial *Should I take an umbrella with me?* to the vitally important *Should I undergo surgery?* are based on probabilities. Probability is more useful in daily life than are most other branches of mathematics and fully deserves the greater prominence given to it in most contemporary elementary school mathematics curricula.

10.1.2 The Language of Chance

Because children should become comfortable talking about chance events as early on as possible, *Everyday Mathematics* begins by focusing on vocabulary development. Some of the many terms introduced are *sure, certain, probably, 50-50, unlikely,* and *impossible.* These terms should not be taught formally. Through repeated use, children will gradually make them part of their vocabularies. Many children are familiar with terms like *forecast* and *predict,* but not with the term *probability.* Probability is a difficult word and need not be used at first.

All children have had experience comparing the chances of various outcomes of a random process. They understand everyday statements like *Rain is more likely than snow today.* They may also understand that getting a sum of 7 is more likely than getting a sum of 3 when two dice are rolled. Such informal comparisons are a good place to begin, because they provide a context in which the language of chance can be intuitively introduced. Discuss the fact that some things are certain to happen and other things are certain to not happen. The most interesting things are in between, neither certain nor impossible. Point out that if we think hard enough, we can often say which of these uncertain things are more likely to occur than others.

Randomness

Throughout *Everyday Mathematics,* many activities rely on spinning spinners, drawing from card decks, rolling dice, and flipping coins. All of these are procedures for generating random results, but randomness is not formally defined until fifth grade. This is because randomness is simple to describe with words such as *haphazard, unpredictable, without pattern,* and *chaotic,* but difficult to define formally and hard to verify in practice. Technically, a *random outcome* is an event selected from a set of outcomes, all of which have an equal probability of being selected. There are several reasons why randomness is hard to verify in practice.

First, there is the problem of assuring truly equal probabilities. Many variables affect this, such as position of a spinner, weight distribution in a die, and thoroughness of the shuffle of a card deck. These problems

For more information, see Section 10.4.1: Random-Number Generators.

Two 6-sided dice

For more information on rolling two dice, see Section 10.4.1: Random-Number Generators.

A *fair* spinner: The probability that a spin will land in any one of the three regions is $\frac{1}{3}$.

An *unfair* spinner: The probability that a spin will land in any one of the three regions is not $\frac{1}{3}$.

affect classroom activities that rely on randomly generated numbers, but they are essentially beyond control. In *Everyday Mathematics,* random-number generators are trusted to provide numbers that are random enough to serve their purpose.

The second problem in verifying random results is an individual's perception of what such results should look like. Imagine a list of 1,000 randomly generated single-digit numbers. Somewhere in the list there are six consecutive 3s. Is this a problem? Most people would think so; it is counter to the notion that random means "all shook up." Six 3s in a row seems to be a pattern, and therefore the list is suspect. Similarly, if you flip a coin 8 times and get 8 HEADS, the coin seems suspect.

Results like these lead people to believe that previous outcomes can affect the next outcome. For example, one might think *After 8 HEADS in a row, it seems that I should expect TAILS on the next toss, because I believe that on average, a fair coin will land TAILS half the time. TAILS are now overdue.* The belief that a fair coin will land TAILS half the time is correct *on average, in the long run.* However, it is incorrect to think that the previous eight HEADS affect the ninth toss, for which there is still a 50-50 chance of getting HEADS (or TAILS). If you see children acting as though past results affect the probability of future outcomes, you might ask them about their thoughts on the matter.

10.1.3 Making Predictions

In most of the probability activities in *Everyday Mathematics,* children make a prediction about the likelihood of a particular outcome of some random process such as rolling a die or flipping a coin. Then they check their predictions by performing an experiment that involves collecting, organizing, and interpreting data. Some activities call for students to compare the likelihood of several possible outcomes. Activities in later grades ask students to estimate the chance that something will happen by assigning it a numerical value. For example, when a coin is tossed, the chance of its landing HEADS up is 1 out of 2 or $\frac{1}{2}$ because there are two ways the coin could land, one of which is HEADS up. When a single die is rolled, the chance of getting an even number is 3 out of 6, or $\frac{3}{6}$, because there are three even numbers {2, 4, 6} out of the six ways the die can land {1, 2, 3, 4, 5, 6}.

All outcomes are equally likely for some situations such as tossing a fair coin, rolling a fair die, and spinning a spinner that is divided into equal parts. In other situations, the outcomes are not equally likely. For example, when two 6-sided dice are rolled, a sum of 7 on the top faces is more likely than a sum of 4. In experiments with unequally divided spinners, most children will probably conclude quickly that the spinner is more likely to land on the larger regions than on the smaller ones. Spinners are extremely useful for helping students to visualize the idea of chance.

Many random processes lend themselves to intuitive predictions because their outcomes follow very definite laws of chance. Coin tosses and spinner experiments are good examples of these. Other processes do not lend themselves to such precise analysis. Predicting the weather is much harder than predicting the outcome of a coin toss.

The Law of Large Numbers

In the long run, *Everyday Mathematics* aims to help children understand that the more often they repeat an experiment, the more reliable their predictions will be. For example, if a coin is tossed 10 times, it is possible, but not certain, that it will land HEADS up about half the time. If you try it, you may be surprised at how often you obtain a 7-3 or 8-2 split. But if the coin is tossed 100 times, it is more likely to land nearer to a 50-50 split, as the occurrences of HEADS and TAILS tend to "even out" with more tosses.

Children have a variety of experiences throughout *Everyday Mathematics* that illustrate this important idea, known to mathematicians as the *law of large numbers*. For example, in *Third Grade Everyday Mathematics,* children participate in a block-drawing experiment. Children are asked to figure out how many blocks of different colors are hidden in a bag by examining the results of repeatedly drawing a block from the bag. The more times they draw a block, the more likely it is that they will make the correct guess.

10.2 Data Collection, Organization, and Analysis

Collecting, organizing, and presenting data in tables and graphs has become increasingly important in our complex world. Even young children can participate in gathering information, displaying it, and making counts and comparisons. Children's initial data explorations should be informal, allowing them to collaborate with you and with one another to decide on methods of collecting, representing, and making sense of their data.

10.2.1 Formulating a Question

Ordinarily, data are collected and analyzed to describe a situation and/or to make predictions. The process almost always begins with a question. When we want to know something, a good strategy is to gather information. Then we look at the information—the *data*—in various ways to determine whether we found what we wanted to know.

There are two important reasons to take time to formulate a question for data exploration. The first is motivational. Data-collection activities are usually more meaningful to children if they are connected to a real-life problem or involve situations that children really care about. In *Kindergarten Everyday Mathematics,* the Survey Routine suggests a way to incorporate data collection and display, based on questions that interest children, into your regular routine. Throughout the grades, *Everyday Mathematics* presents many other problem situations that require data collection and analysis. You are encouraged to personalize them and to add your own.

(in) perspective

In *Fifth Grade Everyday Mathematics*, pairs of students each take small samples from a bowl of multicolored candy and count how many of each color they have. The class then pools the results from each pair to form one large sample, thereby concluding that a large sample produces a better estimate of the color distribution than does a small sample.

An example of personalization comes from a Kindergarten class. A number of children didn't know how to tie their shoes, always relying on the teacher to do this for them. The children decided it would be much more efficient to find out who among them could tie shoes so that they could help those that could not. This led to a survey, a tally, and a display of the collated data, as well as a solution to a problem meaningful to the children in the class.

A second reason to take time to formulate a question for data exploration is to clarify the essential information that can lead to an answer. In the shoe-tying survey, for example, is it important to know what color the shoes are or how long the laces are? If you want to know who runs the fastest, does hair color matter? Does distance matter? What about footwear or clothing? Even if the questions sometimes seem silly, it is important to ask them to help children develop habits of thinking about the possible effects various factors may have on the data they collect.

10.2.2 Collecting and Recording Data

Everyday Mathematics uses many sources of data and a variety of collection procedures, such as the following:

- Counting and measuring in the classroom;
- Observing and measuring at home;
- Taking surveys at school, including surveys of other classes;
- Collecting data from such sources as TV, newspapers, magazines, encyclopedias, and the Internet.

In *Pre-Kindergarten* through *Third Grade Everyday Mathematics,* the most common data are counts, and the usual goal is to examine the frequency of various occurrences. *How many . . . ?* is the classic beginning to the questions that are formulated by children: *How many of each kind of Halloween candy did you get? How many brothers and sisters do you have? How many pets are in your family?* Investigations of this sort genuinely interest children and can be used to build a foundation for later more sophisticated work in statistics and probability. For young children, it can be useful to begin data collection endeavors even more simply, with questions that children can answer with *yes* or *no.* As they become comfortable with the skills and concepts involved, even young children will be able to manage collecting data on questions with more varied responses.

Children love to conduct surveys to generate data. They may think of a question they want every class member to answer such as *Are you afraid of the dark?* They can record each child's response on a class list, "writing" the responses as best they can. Children are often very motivated to graph the results of their surveys and share them with the class. Some children enjoy thinking of different ways to display their results.

Data activities also include games such as first grade's *Dice Roll and Tally,* in which results are kept with tally marks. Other investigations are formatted as Projects and Explorations, such as the second grade's "How Far Can I Run in 10 Seconds?" activity. Many opportunities arise naturally in the course of classroom life.

Data analysis begins as the data are collected. If the information is not recorded in an organized table or chart, children will likely end up with an indecipherable heap of numbers instead of useful information. *Everyday Mathematics* provides various tools to help with the initial collection and organization of data, including masters, bulletin-board displays, and, for children in Grade 1 and beyond, journal pages and suggestions for the Class Data Pad.

10.2.3 Organizing and Displaying Data

The tools in *Everyday Mathematics* provide some organization during data collection, but it is also important for children to design their own ways of recording and displaying data. Organization can help you "see the data *better,*" while reorganizing it can help you "see the data *differently*" in a way that may better suit your needs. Children are encouraged to make and observe a wide variety of data displays.

Two simple methods for organizing data are:

- To arrange the data in order from the smallest value to the largest;
- To sort the data by one or more characteristics.

When the data come from children's characteristics, this can be done concretely in the classroom. For example, you could order children's age data by having them line up by age. Or you could organize children by gender and then handedness. Direct all boys to move to the north wall of the room and all girls to the south wall; then have all right-handers move to the east wall and all left-handers to the west wall.

Several types of data displays are described in the following sections. All displays need not be neat and nicely labeled, especially tally tables or line plots. If you or the children sketch many plots quickly, they can "see" the data in several different ways. After they analyze data, ask children to report on their findings in some way. In Pre-Kindergarten and Kindergarten, this analysis and reporting is typically done as a group process.

Data Tables

Tables are one of the most basic formats for the display of data. Newspapers, reference books, scientific articles, Web sites, and some publications are filled with data tables. Tables have specific uses, such as tally tables, lists, and the in/out tables used in "What's My Rule?" activities. In later grades, tables of numbers, arithmetic facts, and statistics such as the ones on the next page are also used extensively to help children improve their mental-arithmetic skills.

in perspective

Beginning in *Third Grade Everyday Mathematics,* children explore sampling when collecting and analyzing data. A *sample* is a relatively small part of a group chosen to represent the larger group being studied. The larger group is the *population.* An important aspect of certain samples is that they are random. A *random sample* is taken from a population in a way that gives all members of the population the same chance of being selected. Large samples give more precise estimates of the population's characteristics than do small samples.

chapter 10

World's Largest Urban Agglomerations Projected 2015 Populations	
City, Country	**Population**
Tokyo, Japan	36,214,000
Bombay (Mumbai), India	22,645,000
Delhi, India	20,946,000
Mexico City, Mexico	20,647,000
Sao Paulo, Brazil	19,963,000
New York City, U.S.	19,717,000
Jakarta, Indonesia	17,498,000

Source: World Almanac, 2005

NBA Eastern Conference Standings				
7 March, 2005	**W**	**L**	**PCT**	**GB**
Miami	45	16	0.738	0.0
Detroit	36	22	0.621	7.5
Boston	31	29	0.517	13.5
Washington	33	25	0.569	10.5
Cleveland	31	27	0.534	12.5
Orlando	31	27	0.534	12.5
Chicago	29	27	0.518	13.5
Philadelphia	29	30	0.492	15.0
Indiana	29	30	0.492	15.0
New Jersey	26	34	0.433	18.5
Toronto	25	34	0.424	19.0
New York	25	34	0.424	19.0
Milwaukee	24	33	0.421	19.0
Charlotte	12	45	0.211	31.0
Atlanta	10	48	0.172	33.5

Source: www.nba.com

Line Plots and Bar Graphs

Line plots are used extensively to organize and display data. A *line plot* is a sketch of data in which checks, Xs, stick-on notes, or other marks above a labeled line show the frequency of each value. A line plot can be thought of as a rough sketch of a bar graph.

Bar graphs are excellent for displaying *how much* or *how many* and can be drawn vertically or horizontally like the graphs below.

A line plot
(Number of Children vs Number of Siblings)

NOTE: Line plots are also called *sketch graphs, dot plots*, or *pictographs* when the tally marks are pictures. Bar graphs are sometimes called *bar charts*.

A graph made from squares of paper arranged in bars

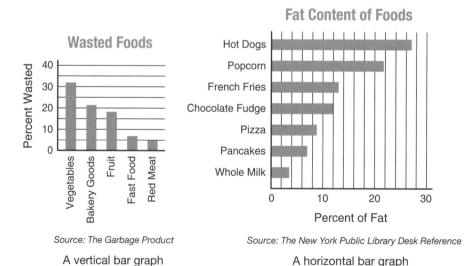

A vertical bar graph

A horizontal bar graph

Source: The Garbage Product

Source: The New York Public Library Desk Reference

In Pre-Kindergarten and Kindergarten, graphs are often made very concretely by accumulating small pictures or squares of paper into bars or by making stacks with different numbers of connecting cubes to show the number of each response. In the curriculum, these are generally referred to as bar graphs, although many would say that they are technically picture graphs, pictographs, or line plots, depending on how the data are represented. With children's input, be sure to label the important parts of a graph, including the title, the axes, and the scales for numbering the axes.

Several teachers have expressed concern that *Everyday Mathematics* does not distinguish between *bar graphs* and *histograms*. This is because the authors view a histogram as a specific kind of bar graph and do not believe that children benefit from such fine distinctions. However, we briefly describe the differences here because some state objectives and tests distinguish between the two, as do some spreadsheets and data analysis applications for computers.

Bar graphs are useful for comparing counts, or frequencies, of data. Sometimes the data are *categorical,* such as the food types in the "Wasted Foods" graph on page 66. Usually, each category is assigned its own bar in a graph so frequencies or other information about the categories can be compared. But you could combine categories to get a different picture of the data. For example, you could make a new category called "probably healthy foods" that combines vegetables, fruit, and red meat, and another category called "questionably healthy foods" that combines bakery goods and fast food. A graph with two bars could then compare waste based on healthiness of foods.

For *noncategorical* data, such as measurements, there are likely to be so many distinct data values that they need to be collected into intervals or else there would be too many bars on the graph. A *histogram* is a fancy name for a bar graph of noncategorical data. To make a histogram, you decide on a fixed interval, or scale, on the horizontal axis and count all of the values in each interval. For example, to display a histogram of the heights of all the children in your school, you might decide to group them by 4-inch intervals: 30–33 inches, 34–37 inches, and so on. In *Everyday Mathematics,* this histogram is still called a bar graph.

In any bar graph, if the scale used on the axis displaying the counts or frequencies is too small or too large, the "look" of the data can be distorted, as in the "Favorite Flavors of Ice Cream" bar graphs below.

Weights of 91 Cars (Sedans)

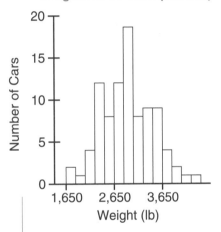

A histogram of car weights: Scale 200 pounds. Eighteen cars weighed between 2,850 and 3,050 pounds.

Favorite Flavors of Ice Cream

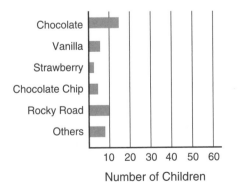

A bar graph with too large a scale

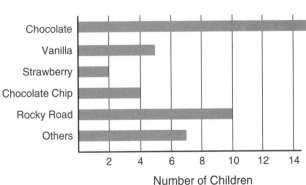

A bar graph with too small a scale

chapter 10

NOTE: In bar graphs of categorical data, it does not matter if the bars touch each other. In bar graphs of quantitative data, adjacent bars share a common endpoint, so they touch.

 perspective

Students in *Fourth* through *Sixth Grade Everyday Mathematics* learn how to read and construct several other types of graphs, including circle graphs, stem-and-leaf plots, step graphs, and both stacked and side-by-side bar graphs.

Computer or graphic calculator programs may distinguish between bar graphs and histograms. The main reason is that before you enter the data, you usually need to tell the program whether it is categorical or noncategorical. Better programs then let you manipulate the scales of both the frequency counts and the bar widths of histograms. If you have access to such a program it is a wonderful way to show older children how easily the "look" of a graph can affect the way the data are perceived.

Line Graphs

Line graphs are good applications of ordered pairs, which are introduced in *Third Grade Everyday Mathematics.* These graphs are particularly good for showing how data change over time, and time is often one of the variables used and labeled. Drawing and analyzing line graphs gives students good practice in working with the coordinate plane.

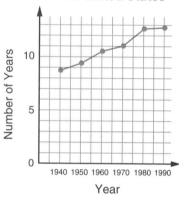

Median Number of Years of School Completed by Peoples Age 25 or Over in the United States

Source: 1995 Digest of Education

A line graph

10.2.4 Data Analysis

To many people, data analysis is synonymous with statistics. In *Everyday Mathematics,* however, this is not the case. For our purposes, *data analysis* means the examination and explanation of data. A good data analysis for a first grader can be summed up in a single well-phrased comment, such as *More than half the people in class are girls.* Statistics may be completely irrelevant in such an analysis. A *statistic* is simply a number used to describe some characteristic of one or more data sets and may not necessarily shed any particular light on the situation being examined.

One of the most common statistics is the *average,* or *mean,* of a set of data. Finding the mean requires adding a set of numbers and then dividing, tasks too difficult for most young children. Yet a lack of arithmetic skills should not bar students from data analysis of a more general nature.

When leading a discussion about a finished graph with young children, you might begin with an open-ended question such as *What did we find out?* Then continue with more specific questions such as *Which had the most responses? The least? Did a lot more say "yes" than "no"? Can you figure out how many more? How did you figure it out?* One advantage of graphs made from objects or slips of paper for young children is that they can touch and manipulate the graphs as they try to understand them and figure out answers to questions such as those above.

Beginning in first grade, *Everyday Mathematics* provides activities for children to study two general attributes of data at increasingly sophisticated levels: useful *landmarks* within a data set and the *spread and pattern* of the set as a whole. These are described below, even though you probably won't use them directly with your class.

Landmarks of Data Sets

Once data have been organized, take every opportunity to have children discuss things they notice about the data. The following terms are commonly used to describe features of *ordered,* or *sorted,* data. These statistics are called *landmarks* in a data set because they show important features of the data.

- *Maximum* – the *largest* data value observed;
- *Minimum* – the *smallest* data value observed;
- *Range* – the *difference* between the maximum and minimum values;
- *Mode* – the *values observed most often;* the most popular or frequent data value or values;
- *Median* – the *middle data value* or, if there is an even number of values, the number halfway between the two middle data values.

Children can use landmarks as reference points when they discuss other features of the data, just as cartographers use landmarks as reference points when they discuss the lay of the land on maps.

Note that finding a median may require averaging the two values nearest the middle. This is probably the first use of average that children encounter other than as a descriptive term for data found in newspapers, TV, and other media. Children often develop the idea of an average in the context of finding a median. The question *What do we do if there is no single middle value?* leads to an important discussion about what is a fair value between two others. One approach to finding that fair value is to point to a spot on a number line. Another is to guess a value and check if its differences from the two nearest values are equal. Some children may develop the common algorithm of averaging on their own.

Some data sets may have no landmarks other than the mode. For example, a survey of favorite hair color would not lead to a largest or average color but just the most popular color among the people who are surveyed.

Spread and Pattern of Data Sets

Encourage children to talk about the spread and pattern, or distribution, of the data in tables or graphs. Terms such as *clump, hole, bump, way-out number,* and *all-alone number* are fine for describing how data values are arranged in a table or along a number line. Sometimes these characteristics can spark interesting explorations. Data that are clumped too closely together may suggest the need to ask a more discriminating question or to change the scale in a display.

chapter 10

The range of a data set can be useful in comparing the spreads of different sets of similar data. However, taken by itself it can hide the clumps or holes or singularities that make a data set really interesting.

In *Everyday Mathematics,* children discuss landmarks, spread, and patterns of *raw* data, that is, data as they are recorded, and of *ordered* data, or data that are numerically ordered or grouped by categories. Children also discuss their data qualitatively without using landmarks such as median or range, noting where the data bunch together or spread out. Exploring reasons for the "shape of the data" can lead to a better understanding of the data set in question and the data analysis process in general. Formal treatment of averages and other statistics begins in Grades 4 through 6.

Remember that a typical reason for analyzing data is to solve a problem, make a prediction, or arrive at a decision. Never finish a data activity before children have had an opportunity to summarize, discuss, report, or reach some sort of conclusion. Think of data analysis as a process with several stages: gathering the data, displaying the data, analyzing the data, and looking back. In some ways, the last step—to achieve closure—is most important.

▶ 10.3 Using Data and Probability

Everyday Mathematics is committed to developing mathematics through applications, and virtually any number drawn from an application is a piece of data. In Pre-Kindergarten through Grade 3, each year of the program has at least one routine centered around uses of data and/or probability:

- The *Weather Observation Routines* (in Pre-Kindergarten and Kindergarten);
- Explorations (*Group Tally of Penny Dates* in Grade 1);
- Projects (the *Collections Project* in Grade 2);
- Games (the *Block-Drawing Game* in Grade 3).

In *First* and *Second Grade Everyday Mathematics,* children also have special Data Days on which they collect data and work with data sets. They put data in order; observe the spread or range from minimum to maximum; make graphs; estimate representative, typical, or middle measurements; and count to the middle to find the median of each data set.

You probably do not need specific suggestions for data sets as much as you may need suggestions for applications in other subjects. Children are naturally interested in surveying topics like favorite colors, favorite foods, pets, and handedness. You know better than anyone else what interests the children, so use your best ideas and theirs. The goal is to have children understand data exploration as a *sensible process.* Can they ask sensible questions? Can they make sense of graphs? Can they make sensible graphs? If so, then they are intelligent users of data and probability.

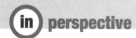

in perspective

In *Fourth* through *Sixth Grade Everyday Mathematics*, students continue to collect, organize, and analyze data, as well as explore probability. In Grades 4 and 5 most of the data analysis occurs within the context of the World Tour and American Tour, respectively. In Grade 6, data analysis and probability are explored in individual lessons.

10.4 Data and Chance Tools and Techniques

Along with measurement tools for collecting data discussed in Section 12.10 and the tables and graphs for representing data described in Section 10.2.3, random-number generators play an important role in *Everyday Mathematics,* especially in the context of games.

10.4.1 Random-Number Generators

Everyday Mathematics uses a variety of devices to generate random outcomes. These tools are integral to the success of many games. Often these devices do not generate perfectly random outcomes, but they are good enough for most purposes. Several tools for helping children generate random outcomes are listed below. For Pre-Kindergarten and Kindergarten children, dice and spinners are the most frequently used random number generators. Decks created from simple number cards are also often used for games in *Pre-Kindergarten* and *Kindergarten Everyday Mathematics.*

Dice

Use a regular die to generate the numbers 1 through 6. Use a polyhedral die (with 12 or 20 sides) to extend the range of numbers to be generated. Note that rolling more than one die and adding the resulting number of dots produces a nonuniform distribution of possible outcomes. For example, if you roll two standard dice, the 36 possible ways for them to land are shown below. Only one of the 36 has a sum of 2 (two 1s), but six of the 36 have a sum of 7 {[1,6], [2,5], [3,4], [4,3], [5,2] and [6,1]}. Therefore, the chance of rolling a sum of 7 is much greater than the chance of rolling a sum of 2. This is what is meant by a *nonuniform distribution*. Shaking a die in a cup may lead to slightly more random results than throwing the die by hand.

					6+1					
				5+1	5+2	6+2				
			4+1	4+2	4+3	5+3	6+3			
		3+1	3+2	3+3	3+4	4+4	5+4	6+4		
	2+1	2+2	2+3	2+4	2+5	3+5	4+5	5+5	6+5	
1+1	1+2	1+3	1+4	1+5	1+6	2+6	3+6	4+6	5+6	6+6
2	3	4	5	6	7	8	9	10	11	12

Sums of two dice

Egg Cartons

Label each egg-carton cup with a number. For example, you might label the cups 0 through 11. Place one or more pennies, beans, or centimeter cubes inside the carton, close the lid, shake the carton, and then open it to see in which cups the objects have landed. Randomness depends on how thoroughly the carton is shaken. This is probably the least random method of the list.

chapter 10

The Everything Math Deck

This deck of cards is used beginning in *First Grade Everyday Mathematics*. It consists of four sets of number cards 0 through 10 and one set of number cards 11 through 20. Fractions are on the reverse side of the 0 through 10 cards. You can limit the range of numbers to be generated simply by removing some of the cards from the deck. For a uniform distribution of numbers 0 through 20, for example, use only one set of 0 through 10 cards and the set of 11 through 20 cards. To use the cards, simply shuffle and draw. The better the shuffle, the more unpredictable the draw will be.

Spinners

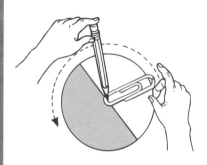

Spinners are used throughout *Everyday Mathematics,* usually in games. They are extremely useful for helping children visualize the idea of chance. There are many commercially available spinners, though it is not necessary to purchase them. Children can use a pencil and paper clip with a spinner mat as shown in the margin. Use either a large (about 2-inch) or standard (about 1-inch) paper clip for the part that spins. The larger size is preferred because it spins more easily. Make a mark, as a pointer, at one end of the paper clip using a permanent felt-tip marker.

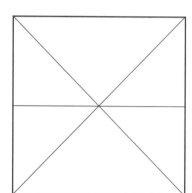

The spinning mat may be drawn on cardstock or paper. Sometimes a mat is supplied as a master or journal page. If you make your own mat, start with a circle or square large enough to accommodate the paper clip. Mark the center of the circle, choose the number and sizes of the regions, and then measure and draw the appropriate angles. For example, six equal regions would each measure $360° \div 6 = 60°$. You can use shapes other than circles for the spinner, and the regions do not have to be the same size, as in the squre mat in the margin.

Before spinning, tape the mat to a level surface. You need only two small pieces of tape, one at the top and one at the bottom. To spin, place the tip of a pen or pencil on the center of the circle and within the paper clip as shown in the diagram. Flick the paper clip about halfway between the center of the circle and the tip of the paper clip, as flicking the paper clip near the pointer end generates less of a spin.

Standard Playing Cards

Use the 2 through 9 cards, the aces for 1s, and the queens for 0s. Draw one card to get a 1 in 10 chance for each one of the digits 0 through 9. Draw two cards to make 2-digit numbers, three cards for 3-digit numbers, and so on. If more than one card is drawn, you need to decide whether to replace it before another card is drawn. If the first card is replaced in the deck and the deck is reshuffled, the probability will remain the same for each draw. If the card is not replaced, the chance of drawing that digit decreases.

11 Geometry

Contents

Geometry, the study of visual patterns of objects in space, is a natural and deeply intuitive part of mathematics for children. From birth, children need to make sense of forms and shapes, such as a mother's face, their own bodies, shapes that move, shapes that don't, curved things, and sharp things. Then, with a wealth of informal knowledge about spatial objects, they come to school. The teacher's role is first to acknowledge and value what children already know and then to help them "notice" what they see and to organize their perceptions into a meaningful system.

The word *geometry* derives from Greek words for "earth" and "measure," which gives a clue about the first geometric activity of humans. The earliest records of geometric thinking, from the Egyptians, Babylonians, and Chinese, confirm that it centered on solving practical problems, such as laying out fields, finding areas and volumes, and constructing houses and temples.

The Greeks are credited with formalizing geometry. In high school, most of us encountered the geometry of Euclid with its axioms and theorems. And, for many, this was a mystifying experience. This was due in part to the inappropriate structure and content of many of these geometry courses—a situation that is slowly changing as new approaches to secondary school geometry instruction are being developed. But, an equally compelling reason is that many students have little or no formal experience with geometry prior to their high school courses. The *Everyday Mathematics* curriculum places significant emphasis on this part of mathematics beginning in Pre-Kindergarten and Kindergarten.

Students investigate geometry through many hands-on experiences, including manipulating pattern blocks; building shapes with straws; tracing, cutting out, and folding shapes; forming figures on geoboards; and constructing figures with compasses, straightedges, and protractors.

–Adapted from *Everyday Teaching for Everyday Mathematics*™ by Sheila Sconiers

This chapter first describes common 1-, 2-, and 3-dimensional objects. Next, it discusses some operations on these objects and some relationships that the objects have with one another. The chapter concludes with an outline of the approach used in *Everyday Mathematics* for teaching geometry.

▶ 11.1 Dimension

Dimension is a tricky word. One meaning refers to the size of an object, as in the dimensions of a room or of a piece of paper; another meaning, the one implicit in terms like *3-dimensional,* refers to how much information is required to specify an exact location. For example, a checkerboard is *2-dimensional* because two pieces of information can specify a particular square: its row and its column. A line is *1-dimensional* because a point on it can be located using one number—its distance from an origin. An opera house is *3-dimensional* because a seat in it can be determined using a row number, a seat number, and a floor level.

We live in 3-dimensional space, *3-D space.* The objects that constitute our physical experience are all 3-dimensional. Objects in other dimensions, such as lines, triangles, and circles, are abstractions that do not physically exist in the way dogs, cellular telephones, and pencils exist. Even the checkerboard, which was called 2-dimensional a moment ago, is really 3-dimensional; it has length, width, and depth. The 2-dimensional surface of the checkerboard is an abstraction.

Many 1- and 2-dimensional abstractions are so useful in the 3-dimensional world that we name them and study their properties. You can model them with wood or plastic, with drawings, and with special manipulatives. But the models are always 3-dimensional, not the "real" thing. Even a drawing made with ink has length, width, and depth.

The following sections discuss objects in dimensions 0 through 3 and describe how children examine them in *Everyday Mathematics* activities.

NOTE: Both *3-D* and *3D* are widely used shorthand for 3-dimensional. If you ever search the Web for information about 3-D objects, try both.

NOTE: Although the objects of geometry are presented here from less complicated to more complicated, children encounter them in the opposite order in *Everyday Mathematics*, a more developmentally appropriate order in which 1- and 2-dimensional objects are introduced informally as parts of 3-D objects. For example, a line segment is modeled by an edge of a box and a rectangle by four adjoining edges of a box. For more information on developmental stages in the learning of geometry, see Section 11.9.1: The van Hiele Levels.

▶ 11.2 Points

Point is an undefined term in geometry, so no one can say exactly what it is. Nevertheless, most people have some idea of what a point is and what it is not. A point cannot be broken into pieces; it is one indivisible thing and so it has 0 dimensions. Because a point has no parts, no information is needed to specify which part of a point is being referred to; it cannot be measured.

You can model a point by drawing a *dot* on a piece of paper. If you get a finer pen and draw a smaller dot, then you have a better model of a point. But no matter how small you make your dot and no matter how fine your pen's tip, you still cannot draw a true point. Even the smallest dot of ink has length, width, and depth, and therefore it is not a point.

● ● ● ·

Models of points

Another way to think about a point is as a *location,* or an exact position. On a map or other reference frame, a point marks where something is. For example, there is a point on a number line that is exactly 3 units from the origin. In fact, there are two such points, one at $+3$ and one at -3. In *Kindergarten Everyday Mathematics*, children use points as locations when they follow maps and count steps to get from one classroom to another. Children also locate points on number lines beginning in Kindergarten. *Length* is the distance between two points, so children imagine points as locations on objects every time they measure a height, width, or depth. Points on maps are used to estimate distances, and children learn about map scale beginning in Grade 3.

NOTE: *Synthetic* geometry is the study of geometric objects without concern for their position on a line, in a plane, or in space. *Analytic* geometry is the study of geometric objects on a number line, coordinate plane, or 3-D coordinate grid.

Sometimes a location is considered a point, but its position is not important. For example, the vertices (corners) of a polygon are the points where two sides meet, but unless the polygon is on a coordinate system, the position of a vertex is of little interest. Yet the fact that the point is a vertex *is* interesting, because the vertex often receives a name and that name contributes to a name for the whole polygon. On geometric objects, points are usually named with capital letters, such as point *A,* point *B,* and so on. Naming geometric figures using the names of points begins in Grade 2, for example, "triangle *ABC.*"

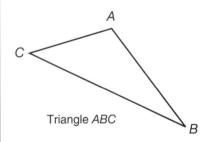

Triangle *ABC*

There are other uses and models of points not discussed here. The aim is simply to give you some ways to think about points and to help you realize how often they are used in the 3-dimensional world.

▶ 11.3 Lines, Segments, and Rays

Line is another undefined term, but, again, one for which most people have good intuition. You can model a line with a pen and ink, by folding a piece of paper, or by pulling a piece of string taut.

A *line* is made up of infinitely many points extending forever in opposite directions. "Forever" is an important word here; it means that a line has no ends. If you started marking off unit intervals on a line, you would never finish, no matter how many intervals you marked. One-dimensional figures on a line are called *linear figures.* Zero-dimensional points make up 1-dimensional figures.

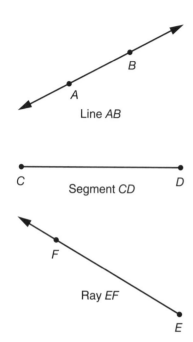

Line *AB*

Segment *CD*

Ray *EF*

A line is 1-dimensional in that one number is enough to specify any point on a line relative to an origin. One-dimensional objects on a line have length, but no width or depth.

A drawing of a line has arrowheads on its "ends" to indicate that it does not stop. A line is named using any two points on it, as in line *AB* in the margin. Shorthand for "line *AB*" is $\overleftrightarrow{AB}$.

Now think about any two points on a line. No matter how close together they are, there are infinitely many points on the line between them. Mathematicians say lines are *dense*, meaning that between any two points on a line there is always another point. The fact that each point on a line can be associated with a number is a key to understanding why our real-number system does not run dry. Just as there is always a point between any two points on a line, there is always a number between any two numbers.

A *line segment,* or *segment* for short, is a part of a line between and including two different endpoints. Although you cannot measure the length of a line, a segment has a finite length that you can approximate. A segment is labeled using any two points on it, as in line segment *CD* in the margin. Shorthand for "line segment *CD*" is $\overline{CD}$.

A *ray* is a part of a line with only one endpoint and all the points on the line to one side of the point. For this reason, rays are sometimes called *half-lines.* Like a line, a ray has no measure. A drawing of a ray has an arrowhead at the "end" opposite its endpoint. A ray is labeled using the name of the endpoint and another point on it, as in ray *EF* in the margin. Shorthand for "ray *EF*" is $\overrightarrow{EF}$.

▶ 11.4 Planes and Plane Figures

Plane is yet another undefined geometric term for which most people have some intuition. A tabletop, a smooth floor, and the surface of a calm body of water all suggest planes.

A *plane* extends forever in every direction in two dimensions. There are infinitely many points and infinitely many lines in a plane. Two-dimensional objects that are entirely contained in a plane are called *plane figures* or *planar figures.* And just as 0-dimensional points make up 1-dimensional objects like lines, both 0-dimensional and 1-dimensional objects make up plane figures.

A plane is 2-dimensional in that two numbers can specify any point in a plane relative to an origin. Two-dimensional objects in a plane have length and width, but no depth. Like a line, a plane cannot be measured.

The next three sections discuss some of the common planar figures that children explore in *Everyday Mathematics:* angles, polygons, and circles.

11.4.1 Angles and Rotations

In mathematics, an *angle* consists of two rays that have the same endpoint, called the *vertex* of the angle. The rays are called the *sides* of the angle. An angle usually takes the name of its vertex, as in angle *A* in the margin. Sometimes the name of an angle contains three points—a point on one ray, the vertex, and a point on the other ray—as in angle *BAC* in the margin. And sometimes an angle is named with a number in the region between the rays, as in angles 1 and 2 in the margin. Shorthand for "angle *A*" is ∠*A*.

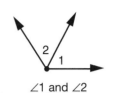

ray

Angle *A* or ∠*A*   ∠*BAC* or ∠*CAB*

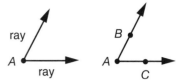

∠1 and ∠2

Sometimes it is convenient to think of the sides of an angle as line segments, for example, "the angles of a square," but strictly speaking, the sides of an angle are rays, each continuing without end. In *Everyday Mathematics,* angles are often modeled using segments because they are introduced in Grade 1 as features of solids and in Grades 2 and 3 as features of polygons. In Grades 4 through 6, angles are studied as features of polygons and polyhedrons.

It is often useful to think of an angle as being formed by starting with the two rays or segments pointing in the same direction and then rotating one ray or segment around the common endpoint. In first grade, children model angles in this manner by bending a straw and rotating one of the sides around the bend.

Angles are most commonly measured in *degrees*. One complete rotation, a full circle, measures 360 degrees. Shorthand for "360 degrees" is 360°. If a child begins with both parts of a bent straw together and then rotates one of the parts 1 quarter of the way around the bend, the resulting figure models an angle of 360° ÷ 4 = 90°. If the rotation continues another 1 quarter of the way around the bend, the straw is straight and models an angle of 180°. A further 1-quarter rotation models an angle of 270°. A final 1-quarter rotation returns the straw to its starting position, an angle of 360°, which looks like an angle of 0°.

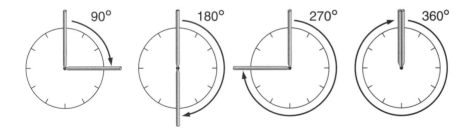

An analog clock also shows angles. At 12 o'clock, the overlapping hands model an angle of 0° or 360°; at 3 o'clock, an angle of 90° or 270°; at 6 o'clock, an angle of 180°; and at 9 o'clock an angle of 270° or 90°.

90°

180°

270°

360°

Angles are categorized according to their measures as follows:

- An *acute* angle measures less than 90°.
- A *right* angle measures 90°.
- An *obtuse* angle measures between 90° and 180°.
- A *straight* angle measures 180°.
- A *reflex* angle measures between 180° and 360°.

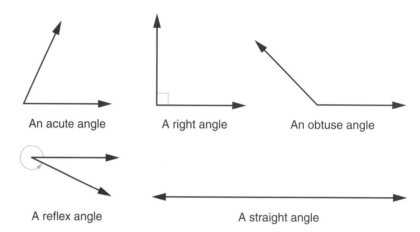

An acute angle   A right angle   An obtuse angle

A reflex angle   A straight angle

NOTE: The region between the rays of an angle is not part of the angle. If the angle measures between 0° and 180°, the region is called the *interior of the angle*. However, people commonly refer to both the angle proper and its interior as "the angle."

Children in Pre-Kindergarten and Kindergarten do not talk about angle measures or types of angles, although they may notice and informally describe different angle types as they describe properties of various shapes. Children in Grades 1 through 3 are not expected to learn the categories of angles, but they manipulate angles of each category. Students in Grades 4 through 6 examine angles more closely as they measure angles with protractors, construct angles with a compass and straightedge, and learn about categories and relationships of angles.

11.4.2 Polygons (*n*-gons)

A *polygon* is a 2-dimensional figure formed by three or more line segments that meet only at their endpoints to make a closed path. The sides may not cross one another. The segments are the *sides* of the polygon. The endpoints are *vertices,* or *corners.* Each pair of adjacent sides defines an interior *angle of the polygon.*

NOTE: The region inside a polygon is not part of the polygon. The polygon is just the line segments. *Polygonal region* is a name for both the polygon and the region inside. However, people commonly ignore the difference, saying, for example, that a cracker is a square or that a piece of paper is a rectangle. Do not hold children responsible for knowing the difference.

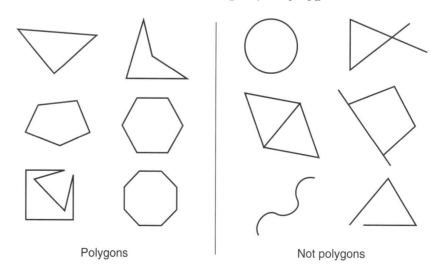

Polygons   Not polygons

The term *polygon* comes from the Greek *polu-,* "many," and *-gonon,* "angled." Polygons are named according to the number of angles (or sides or vertices) they have. A 12-gon is a polygon with 12 sides. In general, an n-*gon* is a polygon with *n* sides.

A dodecagon, or 12-gon

A few *n*-gons have their own names, as shown in the table in the margin. Children in Grade 3 classify triangles and quadrilaterals by special features such as parallel sides, right angles, and sides or angles of equal measure. Triangles and quadrilaterals are discussed in more detail in the next two sections.

Number of Angles	Name
3	triangle
4	quadrangle or quadrilateral
5	pentagon
6	hexagon
7	heptagon
8	octagon
9	nonagon
10	decagon
12	dodecagon

Triangles

A *triangle* is a 3-sided polygon. A triangle is usually named for its three vertices as in triangle *ABC*. Shorthand for "triangle *ABC*" is △ *ABC*.

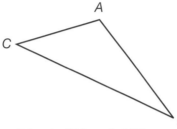

Triangle *ABC* or △ *ABC*

Triangles may be classified in three ways according to side lengths:

- A *scalene triangle* has no two sides with the same length.
- An *isosceles triangle* has two sides of equal length. This makes two of the angles equal in measure.
- An *equilateral triangle* has all three sides of equal length. This makes all the angles equal in measure (60° each), so an equilateral triangle is also an *equiangular triangle*. Every equilateral triangle is also an isosceles triangle.

A scalene triangle   An isosceles triangle   An equilateral triangle

A triangle may also be classified according to its angles:

- An *acute triangle* has every angle measure less than 90°.
- A *right triangle* has a right angle.
- An *obtuse triangle* has an angle with measure greater than 90°.

An acute triangle   A right triangle   An obtuse triangle

in **perspective**

In *Fourth* through *Sixth Grade Everyday Mathematics,* the exploration of polygons is extended to include transformations of polygons by slides, flips, and turns (translations, reflections, and rotations), and classifications of polygons as regular, concave, and convex. Polygons are also studied in the coordinate plane as part of analytic, or coordinate, geometry.

NOTE: Unlike quadrangles, which are also called quadrilaterals, triangles are not usually called "trilaterals."

chapter 11

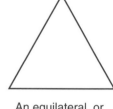

Any triangle can be given two names, one for its sides and the other for its angles. Some examples are shown below.

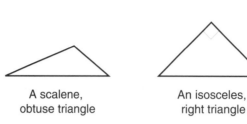

| A scalene, obtuse triangle | An isosceles, right triangle | An equilateral, or equiangular, triangle |

During the primary grades, children learn some of the triangle categories, label vertices, write and read names for triangles, and write and read names for their sides.

Quadrangles (Quadrilaterals)

A *quadrangle,* or *quadrilateral,* is a 4-sided polygon. *Diagonals* of a quadrangle are line segments connecting opposite vertices. Some quadrangles have special features and names:

- A *trapezoid* is a quadrangle with exactly one pair of parallel sides. In an *isosceles trapezoid,* the two nonparallel sides are the same length.

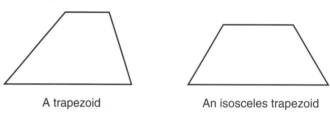

A trapezoid   An isosceles trapezoid

- A *kite* is a quadrilateral with two adjacent sides of one length and two other sides of a different length. The diagonals of a kite are perpendicular.

- A *parallelogram* is a quadrangle with two pairs of parallel sides. Both parallelograms and kites have pairs of equal-length sides, but in kites the equal-length sides are adjacent, not opposite. The diagonals of a parallelogram intersect at their midpoints, or *bisect* each other.

- A *rhombus* is a parallelogram with all sides the same length. The diagonals of a rhombus bisect each other and are perpendicular.

Rhombuses

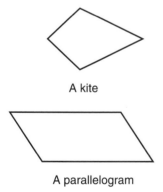

A kite

A parallelogram

In Grades 4 through 6, students find areas of triangles, use triangles in tessellations, and represent triangles analytically by graphing them in the coordinate plane. In Grade 6, they learn about one of the most profound discoveries in the history of mathematics, the Pythagorean theorem.

in perspective

- A *rectangle* is a parallelogram in which all angles are right angles. Diagonals of a rectangle are equal in length.
- A *square* is a rectangle with all sides the same length. It is also a rhombus with four right angles. Diagonals of a square are equal in length, bisect each other, and intersect at right angles.

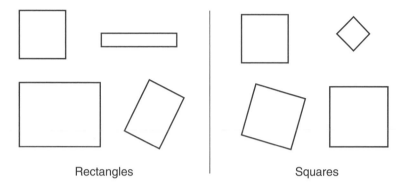

Rectangles   Squares

Some definitions depend on previously defined quadrangles. For example, a rectangle is first a parallelogram, then a parallelogram with right angles. This means that all the features and properties of parallelograms are also features and properties of rectangles, along with new ones specific to rectangles.

This diagram shows the *Everyday Mathematics hierarchy of quadrangles*. Pick any quadrangle in the hierarchy. It has all the properties of any quadrangle on a path leading to it. For example, a square is a rectangle, a rhombus, a parallelogram, and a quadrangle.

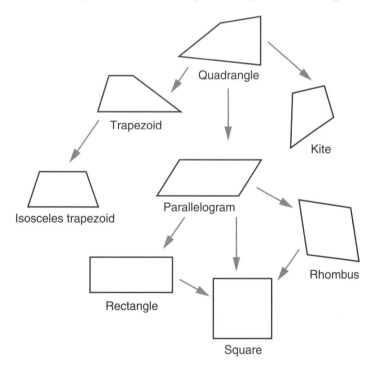

The authors hope the hierarchy of quadrilaterals may be useful to you, but you are not expected to use it with children. Many children in any grade of elementary school may not have reached the stage of geometric understanding necessary to make sense of the hierarchy.

NOTE: Definitions of geometric objects are not carved in stone. For example, some people define a *trapezoid* as a quadrilateral with at least one pair of parallel sides. So a parallelogram is also a trapezoid under this definition. Similarly a *kite* is sometimes defined as a quadrilateral with two different pairs of adjacent sides having the same length. So a rhombus is also a kite under this definition. *Everyday Mathematics* uses the narrower definitions to help children focus on unique properties of the figures.

For more information on the stages of geometric understanding, see Section 11.9.1: The van Hiele Levels.

Other Features of Polygons

Although children in Pre-Kindergarten through Grade 3 explore polygons with the following features, defining them at that time is not especially helpful. In Grades 4 through 6, the terminology becomes more useful, especially in compass-and-straightedge constructions and when talking about tessellations.

- A *regular polygon* is a polygon in which all sides are the same length and all angles have the same measure. If a polygon is regular, then it is possible to draw a circle that passes through all its vertices. Equilateral triangles and squares are regular polygons.

- A *convex polygon* is a polygon on which no two points can be connected with a line segment that passes outside the polygon. Each angle of a convex polygon measures less than 180°.

- A *concave,* or *nonconvex, polygon* is a polygon that is not convex. At least one line segment drawn to connect points on two different sides contains at least one point that is outside the polygon. At least one angle of a concave polygon has a measure greater than 180°.

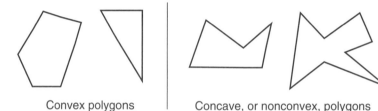

Convex polygons   Concave, or nonconvex, polygons

Most children have little difficulty distinguishing convex and nonconvex polygons, but they may not be able to clearly explain the difference.

11.4.3 Circles and Pi (π)

A *circle* consists of all the points in a plane that are the same distance from a given point in the plane called the *center* of the circle. Many physical objects have circular shapes, although none are likely to be perfectly circular. Features of a circle include the following:

- A *radius* is a segment connecting the center of a circle and any point on the circle. The radius is also the length of that segment.

- A *chord* is a segment with endpoints on a circle.

- A *diameter* is a chord through the center of a circle. The diameter is also the name of the length of such a chord. The diameter of a circle is twice its radius.

- The *circumference* is the distance around a circle, or its perimeter.

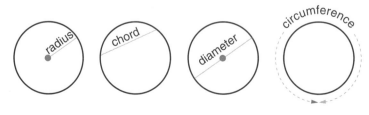

NOTE: As with angles and polygons, the interior of a circle is not part of the circle itself. Sometimes the circle and its interior are together called a *disk,* or simply a *circular region.* As with the other figures, do not expect children to make this distinction.

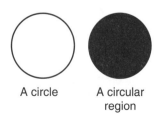

A circle   A circular region

Another way to think of a circle is as a regular *n*-gon where *n* is infinitely large. For example, start with a square, not a very good approximation of a circle, but a start. Next, double the number of sides of the square to obtain a regular octagon; this is closer to a circle. Next, double the number of sides again to obtain a regular 16-gon; this is closer still. Doubling a few more times would give a figure that could be distinguished from a circle only with a magnifying glass. Double infinitely many times and the result would actually be a circle.

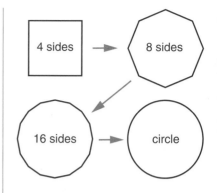

Pi is the ratio of the circumference of a circle to its diameter. This ratio, represented by the Greek letter π, is the same for all circles. If *C* is the circumference and *d* is the diameter of a circle, then:

$$\frac{C}{d} = \pi \qquad \text{or} \qquad C = \pi d$$

Pi is also the ratio of the area A of a circle to the square of its radius *r*:

$$\frac{A}{r^2} = \pi \qquad \text{or} \qquad A = \pi r^2$$

Pi is an irrational number; its decimal does not repeat and never ends. Two common approximations for pi are 3.14 and $\frac{22}{7}$.

11.5 Space and 3-D Figures

Space is one more undefined geometric term about which people have plenty of intuition. Space is the 3-dimensional, or 3-D, world we live in. Everything around us is space.

Space extends forever in three dimensions. There are infinitely many points, infinitely many lines, and infinitely many planes in space. *Spatial figures* are objects in space, and they come in infinitely many shapes, sizes, and orientations.

Having good *spatial sense* means you can mentally manipulate 1-, 2-, and 3-dimensional objects in space and describe their orientations. Spatial sense is important in constructing 3-D objects, in representing 3-D objects in two dimensions by drawing on paper or on a computer screen, and in interpreting drawings of 3-D objects. Video games often demand a well-developed spatial sense of the latter kind, at least if you want to win.

11.5.1 "Solid" Figures

The items listed below are models for familiar 3-D mathematical shapes. The items in the left column are "hollow." The items in the right column are "filled up."

empty box with lid	brick
basketball	baseball
empty ice-cream cone	filled ice-cream cone
empty food can	rolling pin

All these objects are solid in the sense that they can be felt when touched. All concrete models of 3-dimensional figures are solid in this sense. For example, a cube can be modeled by a construction made

NOTE: Another definition of the *circumference* of a circle is the limit of the perimeter of a regular *n*-gon as *n* gets infinitely large.

(in) perspective

In third grade, children begin an inquiry into the relationship between the diameter and the circumference of a circle. They roll food cans to find circumferences, measure across the tops of the cans to find diameters, and display the results in a table. From these results, they discover that the circumference of a circle is consistently about 3 times its diameter. This is a first approximation of π, and a pretty good approximation at that.

chapter 11

of drinking straws, by an empty box, or by a die. All three models are solid, but each highlights a different mathematical aspect of cubes. The drinking-straw model emphasizes a cube's edges, the box emphasizes the surfaces of a cube, and the die emphasizes a cube and its interior.

To be consistent with definitions in 0, 1, and 2 dimensions, *Everyday Mathematics* defines a *geometric solid* as all the points on the surface of a 3-dimensional figure. According to this definition, a geometric solid is actually just the "skin" of 3-D objects. Common 3-dimensional figures such as cones, pyramids, spheres, cubes, cylinders, and prisms do not include the points in their interior. That's why the objects listed in the left column on page 83 are better models for a prism, sphere, cone, and cylinder, respectively, than the objects in the right column.

Yet perhaps even more so than for plane figures, people commonly think of solids as solid through and through. So, just as with the difference between a polygon and a polygonal region, do not expect children to distinguish between the proper definition of a cone versus the solid and its interior. When the distinction eventually becomes mathematically relevant, it can be made and understood easily enough.

11.5.2 Polyhedrons

A *polyhedron* is a 3-dimensional shape formed by *polygons* and their interiors and having no holes. The word polyhedron comes from Greek words meaning "many bases" or "many seats." Polyhedrons include cubes, pyramids, prisms, and many other shapes. Features of polyhedrons include the following:

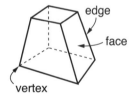

edge
face
vertex

An irregular polyhedron

For more information, see Section 11.6.2: Congruence and Similarity.

- *Faces* are the polygonal regions that make up a polyhedron. Although faces are always regions, they are often called by the name of the polygon defining the region. For example, it's common for a face that is a triangular region to be simply called a triangle.
- An *edge* of a polyhedron is a line segment where two faces meet.
- A *vertex,* or *corner,* of a polyhedron is a point where three or more edges meet.

In a *regular polyhedron,* all the faces are congruent, that is, the same shape and the same size; and the same number of faces join at the same angles at each vertex. Although there are infinitely many regular polygons, there are only five regular polyhedrons, which are illustrated here. The regular polyhedrons are also known as the *Platonic solids.*

| A tetrahedron (4 equilateral triangles) | A cube (6 squares) | An octahedron (8 equilateral triangles) | A dodecahedron (12 regular pentagons) | An icosahedron (20 equilateral triangles) |

Prisms

A *prism* is a polyhedron with two congruent and parallel polygonal regions for *bases*. The bases are connected by line segments with endpoints on corresponding edges of the bases. These segments form parallelograms and their interiors called *lateral faces*. Lateral faces intersect at *lateral edges*.

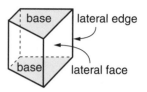

A prism

Prisms are usually named according to the shape of their bases. If a prism has a triangular region for a base, it is called a *triangular prism*. If a prism has a pentagonal region for a base, it is called a *pentagonal prism*. Emerald crystals often take the form of *hexagonal prisms*.

Pyramids

A *pyramid* is a polyhedron consisting of a polygonal region for a *base,* a point *(apex)* not in the plane of the base, and all of the line segments with one endpoint at the apex and the other on an edge of the base. The *lateral edges* of a pyramid are the segments from the vertices of the base to the apex. The lateral edges form triangles, and the triangular regions are the *lateral faces* of the pyramid.

A crystal

Like a prism, a pyramid is usually named according to the shape of its base. The famous Pyramids at Giza, Egypt, are square, right pyramids. A triangular-based pyramid is also known as a *tetrahedron*.

All prisms and pyramids are polyhedrons, but not all polyhedrons are prisms or pyramids. For example, three of the five regular polyhedrons shown on page 84 are neither pyramids nor prisms.

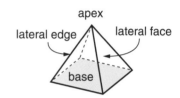

A pyramid

11.5.3 Solids with Curved Surfaces

All the faces of a polyhedron are flat. Three interesting geometric solids with curved surfaces are spheres (entirely curved), cylinders (two flat surfaces and one curved surface), and cones (one flat surface and one curved surface).

Spheres

A *sphere* consists of all the points in space at an equal distance, the *radius,* from a given point at its *center*. A sphere is modeled by a basketball.

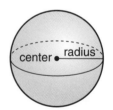

A sphere

Cylinders

A *cylinder* is a geometric solid with two congruent, parallel, circular regions for bases and a face formed by all the segments with an endpoint on each circle. These segments are parallel to a segment with endpoints at the centers of the circles. Food cans with top and bottom on, but no food inside, are models of cylinders.

NOTE: A cylinder resembles a prism in every way except that the former has circular bases and the latter has polygonal bases.

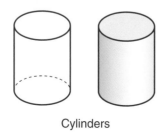

Cylinders

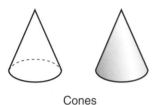

Cones

Cones

A *cone* is a geometric solid with a circular base, a point *(apex)* not in the plane of the base, and all of the line segments with one endpoint at the apex and the other endpoint on the edge of the base. Together, these line segments form the *lateral face* of the cone.

In *Pre-Kindergarten* through *Fourth Grade Everyday Mathematics*, children explore geometric solids by manipulating blocks available in most classrooms, paper models constructed from blackline masters, and a variety of real-life materials such as shoe boxes and tin cans. More formal definitions such as those above and on the previous page are introduced in Grades 5 and 6.

11.5.4 Connecting 2-D and 3-D

A goal of the geometry strand at all levels of *Everyday Mathematics* is to help students see connections between 2-dimensional figures, such as polygons and curves, and the corresponding polyhedrons and curved surfaces in three dimensions. Children work toward this goal by building 3-dimensional models using materials such as marshmallows, toothpicks, straws, twist-ties, paper, and clay. Beginning in Kindergarten and first grade, these constructions help children develop good connections between 1-dimensional line segments, 2-dimensional polygons, and 3-dimensional figures having polygonal regions as faces.

▶ 11.6 Geometric Relations

Just as numbers can be related to one another in various ways, for example, $5 > 2$, $\frac{6}{2} = 3$, and $5 \neq 3$, geometric objects can likewise be related to one another. For example, if two figures are exactly the same size and shape, we say they are *congruent*. In the following sections, we discuss several interesting geometric relations.

11.6.1 Perpendicular and Parallel

Two lines in a plane either cross or do not cross. Lines that cross each other are said to *intersect*. When two lines intersect, they form several angles. When the angles formed are right angles, the lines are *perpendicular*. The symbol ⌐ is often included in a drawing of perpendicular lines to indicate a right angle. The symbol ⊥ means *is perpendicular to*.

Lines in a plane that never cross are *parallel*. Parallel lines are always the same perpendicular distance apart, as shown below for parallel lines *AC* and *DF*. Many objects in our everyday world suggest parallel lines: window gratings, highway lane markings, and lines on notebook paper. The symbol ‖ means *is parallel to*.

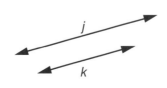

Line *j* is parallel to line *k*, or *j* ‖ *k*.

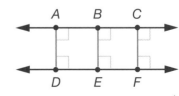

$\overline{AD}$, $\overline{BE}$, and $\overline{CF}$ have equal measure.

Line *n* is perpendicular to line *m*, or $n \perp m$.

Skew lines are neither intersecting nor parallel. For example, an east-west line on the floor of a room and a north-south line on the ceiling are skew. Skew lines cannot be in the same plane.

Planes, or figures in planes, such as line segments and squares, can also be parallel or intersecting. If two planes intersect at right angles, they are perpendicular, and two squares, one in each of those planes, are also perpendicular. Opposite faces of a cube are parallel, and adjacent faces are perpendicular.

Beginning in first grade, children are introduced to the ideas of parallel and perpendicular through the exploration of solids, their faces, and their edges. Drawing and naming parallel and perpendicular line segments begins in second grade.

11.6.2 Congruence and Similarity

Congruent figures are exactly the same size and shape. They can be as simple as line segments or as complicated as polyhedrons. The symbol ≅ means *is congruent to*.

Congruent figures do not have to be oriented the same way to be congruent. They may be rotated, flipped, or otherwise arranged, as shown in the drawings below.

Congruent segments   Congruent polygons

Congruent polyhedrons

Similar figures are the same shape but not necessarily the same size. For example, any two squares are similar, as are any two equilateral triangles, or the two polyhedrons in the drawings below.

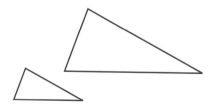

Similar triangles

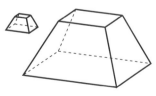

Similar polyhedrons

Skew lines can be modeled with two pencils.

Parallel faces   Perpendicular
of a cube   faces of a cube

NOTE: In theory, even two rocket motors could be congruent; the same blueprints could be used to build both. But as in most real-life applications of geometry, the motors could not be exactly the same, as each would have nicks and marks the other would not. Only abstract geometric objects can be congruent.

NOTE: In theory, two copies of Michelangelo's statue of David could be similar. But in reality, they are likely to have minor differences in shape. Like congruence, similarity is possible for only abstract geometric objects.

preimage / image

A transformation

For more information, see Section 11.8.1: Line Symmetry.

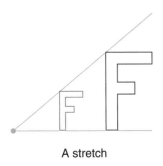

A stretch

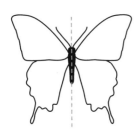

For more information, see Section 11.7: Transformations.

chapter 11

► **11.7 Transformations**

A *transformation* is an operation on a figure that produces a new figure. The original figure is called the *preimage;* the figure produced by the transformation is called the *image.* The transformations usually studied in elementary school mathematics produce images that have either the same shape as the preimages or both the same size and the same shape as the preimages.

In *Kindergarten* through *Third Grade Everyday Mathematics,* children explore reflection images. Students in Grades 4 through 6 explore the other isometries and size changes.

Flips, Turns, and Slides

An *isometry* is a transformation in which a preimage and image are congruent. In *Everyday Mathematics,* children investigate three isometries: reflections (flips), rotations (turns), and translations (slides), each of which is illustrated below.

A reflection (flip)   A rotation (turn)   A translation (slide)

Size Changes (Stretches and Shrinks)

In a *similarity transformation,* the image of a figure stays the same shape but changes size. The name comes from the fact that the image is *similar* to the preimage. Children do not encounter similarity transformations in *Everyday Mathematics* until Grade 4.

► **11.8 Symmetry**

A figure is symmetric if you can transform it and the image looks exactly like the original. For example, a butterfly has reflection symmetry, or line symmetry, because you can fold it and the two halves (wings) align perfectly. A starfish has rotation symmetry because you can turn one arm to where the next one was and it looks the same. A strip of wallpaper border has translation symmetry if a tracing of one part slides over and exactly matches another part of the pattern.

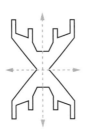  

Line symmetry   Rotation symmetry   Translation symmetry

11.8.1 Line Symmetry

A figure has *line symmetry* if there is a line that divides it into two halves that are reflection images of each other. They are the exact size and shape, but have opposite orientation. The line is called a *line of symmetry* of the figure, but no part of it is necessarily part of the figure. The two halves look exactly the same but face in opposite directions.

To check a figure for line symmetry, fold, or imagine folding, the figure on a line. If the halves match, the fold is a line of symmetry. An isosceles trapezoid has one line of symmetry. Figures may have more than one line of symmetry. A square has four lines of symmetry. A circle has infinitely many lines of symmetry through its center.

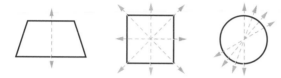

A solid figure has *bilateral symmetry* if there is a *plane* that divides it into two haves that are reflection images of each other in space. For example, each half of a human face is the mirror image of the other half, more or less. Other living things have this sort of bilateral symmetry, as do many human-made objects such as car grilles and traffic lights. Verifying bilateral symmetry is trickier than verifying line symmetry because it's very difficult to fold solid figures.

11.8.2 Other Symmetries

Sometimes people think a figure has line symmetry when it doesn't. They may think, for example, that there is a way to fold the parallelogram at right so that the two halves match.

Parallelograms that are not rectangles do not have line symmetry, but they do have *rotation symmetry*. If a parallelogram is given a half-turn around its center (where the diagonals bisect), it will look unchanged. Other figures take less turning to show rotation symmetry. For example, a regular pentagon looks the same after 1 fifth of a full turn around its center.

To test for rotation symmetry, turn, or imagine turning, a figure around a point. If it coincides with itself before a full rotation of 360°, then it has rotation symmetry. The number of times a figure coincides with its preimage during one full rotation is called its *order of rotation symmetry*. The pentagon in the margin has order-5 rotation symmetry.

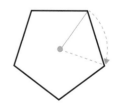

Line symmetry and rotation symmetry are not the only kinds of symmetry. Some *tessellations,* or tilings of a plane, involve symmetry based on translation (slide) symmetry. In general, *tessellations* can be simple or complicated combinations of several isometries.

In *Kindergarten* through *Third Grade Everyday Mathematics,* children focus on line symmetry, but they may notice other symmetries when they are working with pattern blocks or looking for mathematics in

For more information, see Section 11.7: Transformations.

their world. Many corporate logos, for example, have line symmetry or rotation symmetry. Some figures have both, as do the star and pentagon below.

▶ 11.9 Teaching Geometry

Children in *Pre-Kindergarten* and *Kindergarten Everyday Mathematics* play with models of shapes, manipulate pattern blocks, cut shapes out of paper, and look for shapes in their everyday environment. This informal approach is intended to let children's curiosity lead them toward recognizing features of polygons and other geometric figures. Vocabulary is introduced as necessary in order to identify groups of shapes by name. Informally, many common shapes that young children recognize are embedded in solids. For example, a square is a face on a cube, a rectangle is a face on a box, and a circle is the rim of a can.

The approach of using concrete manipulations leading to the recognition of key features and the naming of objects continues throughout the grades. Children in Grade 3 reach a point when they know the names of most common polygons. They are also able to informally classify triangles and quadrilaterals by describing such characteristics as parallel sides, equal sides, right angles, and equal angles.

11.9.1 The van Hiele Levels

The *Everyday Mathematics* curriculum is based on research that has been carried out by the authors and others over several decades. In geometry, some of the most important research was done in the late 1950s by two Dutch researchers, Dina and Pierre van Hiele.

The van Hieles identified five stages in the development of geometric understanding. During the first stage, children approach shapes holistically. A triangle is a triangle because its overall shape is like other objects that are also called triangles. At this stage, shapes are not broken down into parts; line segments, vertices, and angles of the triangle are not considered separately. Instead, the child grasps the whole figure at once. At this visualization stage, children can benefit from hands-on work with pattern blocks, geometric solids, geoboards, straws and connectors, and real objects from their everyday environment.

During the second stage of geometric understanding, children begin to notice the individual elements that make up geometric figures. They see that a triangle has three sides and three corners and that a square has four sides all the same length and four right angles. At this stage, children continue hands-on work and begin to compare, measure, sort, and describe shapes. They can also begin to learn the names for the parts of geometric figures: side, angle, face, edge, and so on.

In the third stage of geometric understanding, children begin to move beyond the analysis of single shapes and start thinking about relationships among different shapes. They can, for example, understand that squares are rectangles because they meet the minimal requirements of four sides and four right angles. Children also begin to understand hierarchical classification schemes like the one for quadrilaterals in Section 11.4.2. They also begin formulating simple chains of reasoning. If the context is not too abstract, children at this stage can work with definitions of geometric objects and properties. This is also the stage of informal proof, which is the highest level expected of children in elementary school geometry.

Beyond the informal proof stage, the van Hieles identified two further levels. One is the level of deductive reasoning, the level at which high school geometry is traditionally taught. The highest level is the formal axiomatic geometry of professional mathematicians, a level most of us would not even recognize as geometry.

11.9.2 Solid versus Plane Geometry

Which is less abstract, a cube or a square? In a purely mathematical sense, both are equally abstract. But in a practical sense, a cube is less abstract than a square. Good, concrete models for cubes are commonplace; a sugar cube, a die, or a lump of clay pressed into shape are all excellent representations of a cube. A square, on the other hand, is not so easily modeled. The face of a cube is a model for a square region, not a square. You can use straws to build a model of the square, but everyday objects that are good models of squares, circles, triangles, and other plane figures are hard to find.

So, odd as it may sound, solid geometry is more concrete than plane geometry. For this reason, *Everyday Mathematics* includes work with spheres, prisms, cylinders, and other 3-dimensional figures much sooner than in a traditional curriculum.

11.10 Geometry Tools and Techniques

The study of geometry in *Everyday Mathematics* involves many hands-on experiences, such as manipulating pattern blocks and attribute blocks, working with geometric solids and building blocks, tracing shapes from templates, working with geoboards, cutting out shapes, folding shapes, drawing shapes with straightedges or compasses, constructing shapes out of straws, and constructing 3-dimensional figures from 2-dimensional nets (flat figures that can be folded to form closed, 3-dimensional solids). The following sections highlight some of the most widely used tools.

11.10.1 Pattern-Block Template

Pattern-Block Templates are used for exploring plane figures. Children are encouraged to use the templates to make designs in a variety of activities and contexts. In Kindergarten, children use the templates to record their pattern block patterns and designs. In first grade, children are asked to estimate how many triangles,

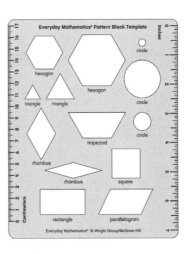

Beginning in fourth grade, students do detailed explorations of categories of triangles and quadrangles using a Geometry Template that contains more varied shapes than Pattern-Block Templates. The Geometry Template also includes inch and centimeter scales, a percent circle for making circle graphs, and two protractors.

squares, or other figures it will take to "fill up" a piece of paper. They check their guesses by drawing the shapes using the templates. This informal introduction to area develops valuable background for formal definitions later. Children in Kindergarten through third grade also use their Pattern-Block Templates, rather than compasses, to draw circles.

11.10.2 Pattern Blocks and Geometric Solids

Pattern blocks help children learn the names and features of geometric objects. In Kindergarten and first grade, children identify categories of shapes and colors of pattern blocks. Beginning in first grade, children are encouraged to find different ways of categorizing blocks on their own, that is, to create multiple perspectives of a given set of blocks. This ability to think about the same things in different ways is important for many problem-solving activities. Science educators also identify classification as one of the most important processes of science.

As young children build with all types of blocks, they have meaningful, concrete experiences with a variety of 3-dimensional objects. Through their block play, children discover and compare some of the properties of different blocks. They also spontaneously use position vocabulary (*over, under, in,* and so on) and explore transformations (flipping, turning, and sliding blocks) and symmetry as they build. *Kindergarten Everyday Mathematics* also introduces children to measurement, in part, through the use of geometric solids and building blocks. In later grades, children use both metric and U.S. customary rulers to measure the lengths of block edges and the heights and lengths of structures they build using several blocks. Such uses of models of geometric solids continue as a basis for the study of 1- and 2-dimensional geometry through third grade.

Measurement

Contents

Measurement is one of the most widespread uses of mathematics in daily life. Even very young children show considerable interest in measurement. Questions such as *How tall is my block building? How long can we make this block train? How much water until the sink overflows?* and *How long until lunchtime?* are spontaneously pursued by preschool and primary-grade children. Older children continue to be curious about how much, how long, how far, and the like. Many become fascinated with measures and ways of determining them, whether it is the height of a tall building or the amount of water in a swimming pool. *Everyday Mathematics* recognizes and capitalizes on children's natural curiosity about measurement and measures. Throughout the grades, children engage in interesting and purposeful tasks as they learn how to measure and how to interpret other people's measures. The earliest measurement activities involve matching and making direct comparisons, such as those young children do naturally as they build with blocks, play store, dress dolls, and sift sand. These types of activities are a necessary part of the introduction to various measurement units. Measurement tasks become more complicated as children gain experience.

Measurement is the source of many of the numbers that we use in everyday life. Measures, along with their units, tell "how much" of something there is. Arithmetic operations performed with measures

chapter 12

For more information, see Section 12.10.1: Measurement and Estimation.

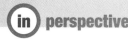

Measures in geography are a focus throughout *Fourth* through *Sixth Grade Everyday Mathematics.*

lead to results that make sense in real-life contexts. For example, a 6-pound cabbage weighs twice as much as a 3-pound cabbage, and someone who spends 30 minutes on homework spends twice as much time as someone who spends 15 minutes on homework. Quantifying and comparing are common quests of childhood as well as adulthood, and both are important when exploring measurement. Furthermore, because all measures are approximate, knowing how to measure means knowing how to deal with error.

This chapter begins with a discussion of measurement systems and units, including personal measures, the metric system, and U.S. customary measures. Then it turns to specific uses of measurement in one, two, and three dimensions (length, area, and volume), followed by discussions of weight and mass, angle measures, elapsed time, and money.

▶ 12.1 Personal Measures

Units for measures of length appeared relatively early in human history and were based on things familiar to people, namely, their bodies. Just as many early number systems were based on *ten,* probably because humans have 10 fingers, many early linear measures were based on the lengths of certain body parts. This is the origin of such measures as *foot, digit, span,* and *hand,* each of which was, or still is, a commonly used unit for measuring length.

The problem with a measurement system based on body parts is that bodies differ. Who is to say whose *cubit,* a measure based on the distance between the elbow and fingertips, is the cubit to measure by? Without agreement, how do buyers know that they are getting their money's worth when someone sells them 56 cubits of cloth? In ancient Egypt, this problem led to the creation of a *royal master cubit* made of black granite. The royal master cubit was the *standard* against which every cubit stick in the land was periodically matched for building projects. For example, the length of any side of the Great Pyramid of Cheops at Giza differs only 0.05% from the mean length of all four sides. This precision is evidence of the consistency of the thousands of cubit sticks used to build the monument. Eventually, individual nations established their measures by agreeing on standards against which all measurement implements were compared.

Another problem arose when members of two or more groups that had been isolated because of distance, geography, or politics came into contact with one another. In the medieval trade fairs of Europe, for example, merchants from many nations gathered to sell their wool cloth. Most agreed to measure cloth in *ells,* but the length of an ell differed among the various nations' merchants. Therefore, an *iron standard ell* of 2 feet, 6 inches was made and left with the Keeper of the Fair. Each participating merchant was required to use this ell in all business dealings at the fair.

In England, cheating and abuse of measures became so common that a few years after the Magna Carta was signed in 1215, the *Assize of*

Weights and Measures was drawn up. For almost 600 years, the Assize defined and standardized a broad list of units. One of these units, *The Iron Yard of Our Lord the King,* was divided into 3 feet of 12 inches each. Eventually, all kinds of measures became standardized in some way, and many national systems of measures came into being. Nearly all of these systems were replaced in Europe by the metric system during the 19th century. Britain and its former colonies in America kept to their old ways until well into the 20th century. The United States still uses the old system.

Several of the original common measures are still good for approximating lengths today. Some measures based on dimensions of an adult human body are listed below. For children, of course, these personal measurements are likely to be smaller than the standards.

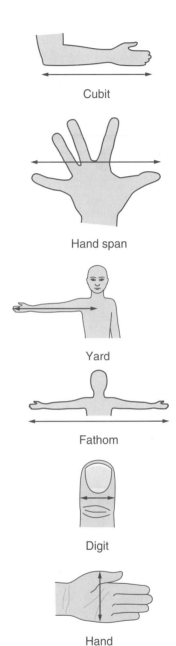

Cubit

Hand span

Yard

Fathom

Digit

Hand

- *Cubit* A very old unit of measure, based on the distance between the elbow and the extended fingertips. The Egyptians used the cubit as early as 3000 B.C. to build pyramids. The cubit has been standardized at various times at values between 18 and 22 inches.

- *Hand span* The distance from the end of the thumb to the end of the little finger in an outstretched hand; used to measure things smaller than a cubit. The span has been standardized at 9 inches.

- *Yard* The distance from the center of the chest to the tips of the fingers of an arm held out to the side of the body; often used to measure cloth. A yard has been standardized at 3 feet (36 inches).

- *Fathom* The distance from fingertip to fingertip of the outstretched arms; said to be derived from an Anglo-Saxon word meaning "embrace." Fathoms are often used to measure the depth of water. Perhaps this is because the "leadsman" on a boat or ship in the days before electronic depth finders would drop a lead weight on the end of a rope until it hit bottom and then count the number of fingertip-to-fingertip measures as he gathered in his line. A fathom has been standardized at 6 feet (2 yards).

- *Digit* The width of a finger. One twenty-fourth of the royal master cubit in ancient Egypt.

- *Hand* The width of a hand laid flat. Horses are said to be so many "hands" high. The hand has been standardized at 4 inches.

Units of length too long to be measured conveniently with body parts tended to vary widely from country to country before the adoption of the metric system. For example, for distances for which the United States used a *mile* (5,280 feet), the Russians used a *verst* (about 3,500 feet or about 1 kilometer).

Beginning in Kindergarten, children measure various items or parts of their classrooms with parts of themselves and discuss which body parts are more appropriate for which objects. This is a predecessor to choosing measurement tools and units that fit a given measuring task. These activities are expanded later in Kindergarten and in first grade as children learn techniques for measuring with their body-part units, such as putting the measuring device end to end to measure

NOTE: Originally, 4 *fingers* made a *palm,* 3 palms a *span,* and 2 spans a *cubit.* Later, a thumb was included with a palm to make a *hand,* presumably because it is easier to lay a hand flat than to tuck the thumb under.

chapter 12

larger objects. The most common measurement errors that children make are not lining up the zero end of the ruler with one end of the object being measured and not using a careful end-to-end technique when moving the measuring device.

Even young children are asked to record their measurements (often with drawings at first; later numbers and words may be included) and to make a habit of labeling their measures with appropriate "units." This practice is important not only for the act of measuring itself but as an important part of learning to solve number stories.

From second grade on, children continue to use personal reference measures, but the focus shifts to finding body parts that approximate customary or metric units. These parts can then be used to estimate measures without using a ruler, tape measure, or other standardized measuring device. For example, the width of a finger may be about 1 centimeter or a child's foot may be about 8 inches long.

▶ 12.2 Measurement Systems

This section discusses the two standardized measurement systems most commonly used today, the *U.S. customary system* and the *metric system*. By "customary" measures, we mean the ones commonly used in the United States. If you have children from other countries in your class, the metric system may be customary to them, so be sure the meaning of "customary" is clear in discussions.

There are also several commonly used measures that are neither metric nor U.S. customary: measures of angles, elapsed time, and monetary values, to name a few. *Everyday Mathematics* activities that engage children in understanding these measures are discussed later in this chapter.

12.2.1 U.S. Customary System

The *U.S. customary system* of measures is adapted from the English system, which was developed around the 13th century. Although most people in the United States are relatively comfortable with the U.S. customary system, it has definite drawbacks compared to the metric system. For one thing, because they evolved gradually out of specific, often local, needs, customary units of length, weight, and capacity are largely independent of one another. Another drawback is that the relationships among units are somewhat cumbersome. For example, a foot is $\frac{1}{3}$ of a yard, but an inch (the next-smaller standard unit) is $\frac{1}{12}$ of a foot. A quart is $\frac{1}{4}$ of a gallon, but a pint (the next-smaller standard unit) is $\frac{1}{2}$ of a quart.

12.2.2 Metric System

Scientifically minded people in France deliberately developed the metric system at the end of the 18th century. The basic unit of length in this system is the *meter*. Originally, the meter was defined as 1 ten-millionth of the distance from the North Pole to the equator along the global meridian through Paris. These days, the meter is defined as the distance light will travel in a vacuum in $\frac{1}{299,792,458}$ second.

in perspective

Body-part estimation activities continue in Grades 4 through 6; as children grow, they need to adjust their personal reference measures.

NOTE: The relationships among inches, feet, yards, and miles are based on a *duodecimal* (base-12) number system. An advantage to this is that many different whole numbers divide 12, including 2, 3, 4, and 6. In this way, the U.S. customary system is much like the ancient Egyptian system.

In the metric system, many units are defined relative to the meter. Next-smaller or next-larger units are ratio comparisons by a power of 10, so they are easily converted from one to another. For example, a *decimeter* is 1 tenth (0.1) of a meter, and a *centimeter* is 1 tenth (0.1) of a decimeter.

Metric units of length, area, volume, capacity, and weight are interrelated. For example, a *liter* is a measure of volume or capacity equal to 1 cubic decimeter, and a cubic decimeter is equal to the volume of 1 kilogram of distilled water at 4°C.

12.3 Length

Distances along 1-dimensional objects or along paths are measured with *linear* measures. Like all measures, a linear measure consists of a value and a *unit*. For example, *The edge of my desk is about 3.5 long* makes no sense. However, *The edge of my desk is about 3.5 feet long* provides both the approximate length and a unit of measure.

Two common linear measures are *length,* the distance between two points on a line or arc, and *perimeter,* the distance around an object. The perimeter of a circle is called the *circumference* of the circle.

12.4 Area

While length and perimeter are measures of a finite distance along a path, *area* is a measure of a finite amount of a 2-dimensional surface. This surface may lie in a single plane, such as the interior of a rectangle; or it may exist in 3-dimensional space, such as the curved surface of a cylinder or cone. This latter type of area is called *surface area.*

Like other numerical measures, a measure of area always includes both a value and a unit. Units of area are typically square units based on linear units such as square inches, square centimeters, square yards, and square meters. Some traditional units of area are not square units. For example, it is said that long ago an acre of land was the amount of land a farmer could plow in one day.

12.4.1 Discrete and Continuous Models of Area

This section discusses two different models for thinking about area. Each model has its strengths and weaknesses in helping children understand a concept that many people find difficult.

Discrete Model of Area

In most schoolbooks, the definition of area is based on the idea of *tiling,* or covering a surface with identical unit squares without gaps or overlaps and then counting those squares. This is a *discrete model of area* because it involves separate, countable parts. If the surface is bounded by a rectangle, you can arrange the tiles in an array and multiply the number of tiles per row by the number of rows. The formula $A = l \times w$ is then easily linked to array multiplication: area A is the number of square-unit tiles in one row (the length l of one side of the rectangle in some linear unit) times the number of rows (the width w of the rectangle in the same unit).

in **perspective**

Converting between units within a measurement system begins in *Third Grade Everyday Mathematics.* Converting between measurement systems is first addressed in *Fourth Grade Everyday Mathematics,* and students in Grades 5 and 6 continue to practice and apply this skill.

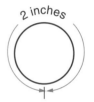

2 inches

2 inches

interior of a rectangle

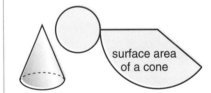

surface area of a cone

40 square units

chapter 12

About 21 square units

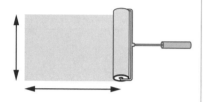

A discrete model of area

A continuous model of area

 perspective

Beginning in Grade 4, children use formulas to model area symbolically. In Grades 4 and 5, children estimate areas of land and research areas of states, countries, and continents in the World Tour and American Tour, respectively.

NOTE: Dry ingredients such as sugar are sometimes measured by weight.

For other surfaces, defined by regular or irregular boundaries, the tiling with square units can be thought of as, or actually done by, laying a grid of appropriate square units on the region and counting, estimating, or otherwise calculating how many squares or partial squares it takes to cover the region.

Continuous Model of Area

Tiling activities develop a discrete model of area, as described above. In later grades, children touch on a *continuous model of area.* Imagine rolling a paint roller 1 foot wide on the floor of a rectangular room. For every foot the roller travels, a square foot of the floor is painted.

Now imagine that the room is 20 feet wide and that you use a roller the width of the room (a 20-foot-wide roller). Then, for every foot the roller travels, 20 square feet of floor will be painted. When the roller reaches the other side of the room, the entire floor will be painted.

If you think of the floor as the interior of a rectangle, then the area of the rectangle is obtained not by counting squares (a discrete model) but by *sweeping* the width of the rectangle across the interior of the rectangle, parallel to its base (a continuous model). The area is simply the product of the length of the base and the width of the rectangle. This can be shown by rubbing the long part of a piece of chalk on the chalkboard to mark a rectangular region; the farther it is swept along, the larger the rectangle and the greater the area.

Children have experience with area throughout *Everyday Mathematics.* Younger children focus on manipulating discrete conceptions of area through tiling activities. Beginning in third grade, children are asked to estimate area measures, and sometimes they check them by actually measuring.

▶ 12.5 Volume (Capacity)

Volume, or *capacity,* is the measure of a finite amount of 3-dimensional space. As with measures in one and two dimensions, all measures of volume require a unit, and all are approximate. Volume units are often cubic units based on linear measures, such as cubic inches, cubic centimeters, cubic yards, and cubic meters. Other units for volume, such as milliliters, teaspoons, pints, quarts, and liters, are used to measure liquids or fine-grained materials such as sand and sugar.

As with all measures, it is possible to convert from one unit to another. For example, a *fluid ounce* is 1.804 cubic inches, and a *liter* is 1,000 cubic centimeters. You can see why the U.S. customary system is not as popular as the metric system when it comes to conversions.

12.5.1 Discrete and Continuous Models of Volume

Discrete and continuous models of volume are analogous to the corresponding models of area.

Discrete Model of Volume

In a *discrete model of volume,* imagine building 3-dimensional shapes with identical cubes, or filling shapes completely with such cubes, and then counting the cubes. If the shape is a rectangular prism, you can build one layer of cubes, count the cubes in that layer, and then multiply that number by the number of layers needed to fill the prism. Because the number of cubes in one layer corresponds to the area of the base, often represented by the formula $A = l \times w$, this process of counting cubes can be linked to two standard formulas for the volume V of rectangular prisms: $V = B \times h$ (the product of the area B of the rectangular base and the height h perpendicular to that base) and $V = l \times w \times h$ (the product of the length l and width w of the rectangular base and the height h perpendicular to that base).

Continuous Model of Volume

The formula $V = B \times h$ for volume of a rectangular prism captures a *continuous model of volume* similar to the "sweeping out" of area. For example, imagine the base of a box as a rectangular region. Then imagine sweeping this rectangular region through the height of the box, and so filling the space. Or imagine gradually filling the box with water. The surface of the water is rectangular, like the base of the box, so the higher the water level, the more space the water occupies and the greater is its volume.

This model for a rectangular prism leads to a general formula for the volume of prisms and cylinders—the area of the base multiplied by the height. Unlike $V = l \times w \times h$, the formula $V = B \times h$ works for any shape base.

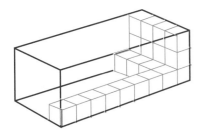

Filling a box with cubes is a discrete model of volume.

A continuous model of volume

Both models of volume are used throughout *Everyday Mathematics.* In Pre-Kindergarten and Kindergarten, children explore volume informally by pouring sand, water, and other materials between containers of different sizes and shapes. A discrete approach to volume dominates first and second grades as young children fill objects with cubes. In Grades 3 and 4, they experiment with a continuous approach by filling objects with water or sand.

▶ 12.6 Weight and Mass

Mass is a measure of the amount of matter in an object. *Weight* is the force of gravity on an object. If you weighed yourself on different planets on a trip around the solar system, your weight would vary drastically depending on the size of the planet. You would weigh more on large planets because their gravitational pull is stronger. You would weigh less on small planets because they don't exert as

In Grades 5 and 6, students focus on the use of variables in formulas to model volume symbolically.

chapter 12

NOTE: Your weight even varies slightly at different altitudes above sea level on Earth. Yet your mass remains the same.

For more information, see Section 12.10.3: Scales and Balances.

For more information, see Section 11.4.1: Angles and Rotations.

(in) **perspective**

Students in *Fourth Grade Everyday Mathematics* start using protractors to measure angles in degrees. A degree is $\frac{1}{360}$ of a full rotation and is the angle measure used in most practical situations. In Grades 5 and 6, angle measurement is often a part of contexts for problem-solving activities. In later mathematics courses, students will learn about other angle measures, especially the *radian* (2π radians $= 360°$).

For more information, see Section 13.2: Time.

much pull. Your mass, however, would be the same regardless of the planet you were on because the amount of matter in your body is not affected by gravity.

In *Everyday Mathematics,* children focus on measuring weight, not mass. It can be measured with a variety of scales. For example, a *balance scale* compares an object's weight to a standard set of weights, or it can simply compare relative weights of any two objects to see which is heavier without measuring. A *spring scale* measures the pull of gravity as evidenced by an object's push or pull on a spring.

The units of measure most common to your classroom will depend on the units defined by your scales. Some scales measure with U.S. customary units such as ounces and pounds, while others measure with metric units such as grams and kilograms.

▶ **12.7 Angle Measure**

Angular measures quantify turns or rotations. Although Pre-Kindergarten and Kindergarten children do not focus on angle measures, the topic may come up informally and in a qualitative way as they describe properties of different shapes. In the primary grades, children measure or describe angles as fractions of a circle; for example, a right angle is a quarter turn and a straight angle is a half turn.

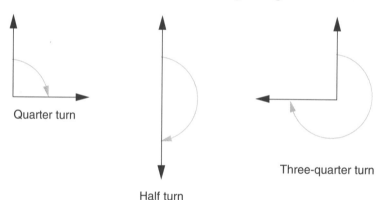

Quarter turn

Half turn

Three-quarter turn

▶ **12.8 Elapsed Time**

Numbers are used both to mark time and to measure it. We mark time by establishing reference frames, such as a calendar year and the number of days in a month. Events are then described by locations on one or more of these frames, such as *She was born August 15, 1989, at 2:00 A.M.* These numbers are not measures because they cannot be added or subtracted with any meaning. For example, 2:00 P.M. plus 3:00 P.M. is not 5:00 P.M., nor is April 12 plus April 15 equal to April 27. The reference labels *P.M.* and *April* are not units of measure.

Once reference frames have been established, however, there are reference units that can be used as measures. For example, *The play lasted 68 minutes. He finished the race in 3.9 seconds. The past 4 years have been warm.* The use of time units to measure the duration of an event or the time between events is called *elapsed time.*

Children use time measures frequently throughout *Everyday Mathematics,* most often in the context of number stories. As children learn new arithmetic skills, elapsed-time applications of these skills are developed. For example, in first and second grades, children use addition and subtraction to figure out elapsed times: *What time was it 2 hours ago? What time will it be in 3 hours?*

12.9 Money

Money may be viewed as a reference frame because it is an arbitrary scale used to establish the values of goods and services. Like the variations in the linear measure *foot* before standardization, however, different people place different values on the same goods or services. To make matters even more complicated, the differences are not just physical but emotional, spiritual, and intellectual in nature. Even an individual's perceived value of something changes with time and experience.

However, in everyday life, money is more a *measure of relative value* than a reference frame. We measure the value of one thing versus another or of one thing now versus that thing yesterday or last year. Statements such as *This TV costs $50 more now than it did 3 months ago* and *Bananas are up 17% this season* are examples of how we use arithmetic to compare monetary values. This is a sign that money behaves like a measure, so it is categorized as such in *Everyday Mathematics.*

Experience with money is important because of its inherent usefulness and, like most measures, because of the context it provides for number stories. Additionally, our base-ten monetary system is an excellent vehicle for the study of place value, fractions, and decimal notation. *Everyday Mathematics* provides children with early experiences to develop their knowledge about the details of money. Then the familiar context of money makes it easier for children to become acquainted with fractions and decimals at earlier ages than they would in a traditional mathematics curriculum.

In *Kindergarten* through *Third Grade Everyday Mathematics,* money is a focus of instruction. By fourth grade, it is assumed that most students have a good understanding of money and can use it in number stories without explicit coverage or review.

12.9.1 Money Facts

Talking about coins and bills also provides a unique opportunity to bridge various curriculum subjects. Money lore contains interesting facts about the history of our country, about the science of metals, and about symbols in our heritage. Use these facts liberally in your teaching about coins and bills in the *Everyday Mathematics* money activities and at other times during the year. Selected definitions follow.

- *Alloy* A mixture of two or more chemical elements, at least one of which is a metal.
- *Denomination* The official value of a coin.

 **perspective**

In Grades 4 through 6, time measurements are important parts of rate problems. For example, students figure out gallons per minute of water flow, an animal's speed in feet per second, or calculations per millisecond by a computer. Students also answer ratio-comparison questions about time, such as *What fraction of a year is 9 months?*

NOTE: In the wizard world of Harry Potter, there are 29 copper *knuts* in a silver *sickle* and 17 sickles in a gold *galleon.* This is certainly a context in which a calculator can help with conversions.

- *E Pluribus Unum* The original motto of the United States; translated from Latin as "From many, one." This motto is required by an 1873 law to appear on any coin that contains an eagle. In fact, it appears on all U.S. coins.

- *In God We Trust* A motto that was permitted, but not required, on coins by the 1873 law; a 1955 law required that the motto be placed on all coins and bills. In 1956, President Dwight D. Eisenhower signed a law making "In God We Trust" the official motto of the United States.

- *Intrinsic value* The actual worth of the metal in a coin.

- *Obverse* The face, or "front," of a coin; "HEADS."

- *Reverse* The back, or "rear," of a coin; "TAILS."

- *Rim* The edge of a coin, which is quite functional because it allows coins to be stacked and protects the design from damage. Most U.S. coins worth more than 5 cents have always had rims that are ornate, lettered, or *reeded,* that is, with parallel grooves that are perpendicular to the face of the coin, as in our dime and quarter. This is intended to discourage the scraping of the coin edges to steal some of its metal; it also makes it easier to identify coins by touch, which is necessary for people with visual impairments and useful for pulling a specific amount of change out of your pocket without looking.

New designs for coins and bills are adopted periodically, putting currency in the United States in a constant, albeit slow, state of flux. Recently, the U.S. Treasury Department has been producing a quarter commemorating each state and has minted a new American-bison nickel. A rewarding cross-curricular activity is to explore individual coins and their designs while touching upon history, metallurgy, and architecture. Some interesting facts about pennies, nickels, dimes, and quarters are given below.

Pennies

Pennies are made of copper and zinc. The composition of this alloy has been changed in recent years because of the increased price of copper. For some war years in the early 1940s, no copper was used in pennies and they were silver-colored rather than copper-colored.

Obverse The Lincoln bust was designed by Victor D. Brenner, whose initials, VDB, appear inconspicuously on Lincoln's sleeve cutoff.

> **NOTE:** To make it easier to distinguish it from a quarter, which is about the same size, the Sacagawea dollar coin is *not* reeded.

Obverse

Information about Abraham Lincoln	
Born	February 12, 1809; Hardin County, Kentucky
Died	April 15, 1865; Washington, D.C.
Occupations	Surveyor; lawyer; Illinois state congressman; U.S. Congressman; President
Important Dates	1861 elected 16th President 1863 issued Emancipation Proclamation, freeing all slaves 1864 reelected President 1865 April 14, assissinated by John Wilkes Booth while attending Ford's Theater, Washington, D.C.

Reverse The Lincoln Memorial image was designed by Frank Gasparro. His initials, FG, appear to the right of the base of the memorial.

Reverse

Information about the Lincoln Memorial	
Location	Washington, D.C.
Cornerstone Laid	1915
Dedicated	Memorial Day (May 30), 1922
Statue of Seated Lincoln	19 ft high
Scupltor	Daniel Chester French
Inscription	"In this temple, as in the hearts of the people for whom he saved the Union, the memory of Abraham Lincoln is enshrined forever."
Architect	Henry Bacon

Nickels

Until 1866, 5-cent pieces were called "half-dimes." The word *nickel* comes from the metal in the coin. Currently, nickels are made of an alloy of 75% copper and 25% nickel. The information that follows describes the "Monticello" nickel, not the nickels in the Westward Journey Nickel Series™ minted in 2004 and 2005, although those nickels feature Thomas Jefferson on the obverse also.

Obverse The Jefferson bust was designed by Felix O. Schlag, whose initials, FS, appear between the rim and the bottom of the bust on nickels produced after 1965.

Obverse

Information about Thomas Jefferson	
Born	April 13, 1743; Shadwell (now Albemarle County), Virginia
Died	July 4, 1826; at Monticello, his estate in Albemarle County, Virginia. Jefferson died on the 50th anniversary of the signing of the Declaration of Independence. The second President of the United States, John Adams, died on the same day.
Occupations	Lawyer; delegate to the Continental Congress; author of the Declaration of Independence; Governor of Virginia; ambassador to France; Vice President; President; founder of the University of Virginia; farmer; architect
Important Dates	1797 elected Vice President under President John Adams 1801 inaugurated as third President 1803 Louisiana Purchase 1804 reelected President

Reverse Monticello, Jefferson's home in Virginia, appears on the reverse, along with its name. President Franklin D. Roosevelt suggested this coinage design in 1938.

Reverse

Information about Monticello	
Location	Albemarle County, Virginia
Architect	Thomas Jefferson
Built	First version, 1769–1793 Second version, 1793–1809

chapter 12

Dimes

Dimes, like quarters and larger coins, are made of "clad" metal, which consists of a sandwich of a silver-colored coating and a copper-colored core. The word *dime* comes from the English word *disme,* which is derived from the French and Latin words for tenth.

Obverse

Obverse The bust of Franklin Delano Roosevelt was designed by John R. Sinnock, whose initials, JS, appear at the front of Roosevelt's neck.

Information about Franklin Delano Roosevelt	
Born	January 30, 1882; Hyde Park, New York
Died	April 12, 1945; Warm Springs, Georgia
Occupations	Lawyer; state senator; Assistant Secretary of Navy; Governor of New York; President
Important Dates	1933 March 4, inaugurated as President 1940 elected to an unprecedented third term as President 1944 elected to a fourth term as President

Reverse

Reverse A vertical flaming torch is flanked on the left by an olive branch and on the right by an oak branch.

Quarters

The quarter was first issued in 1932 to commemorate the 200th anniversary of George Washington's birth. The information that follows describes the "Eagle" quarter, not the 50 State Quarters in production from 1999 through 2008. The state quarter designs also provide opportunities for interesting cross-curricular learing.

Obverse

Obverse The Washington bust was designed by John Flanagan. His initials, JF, appear on the very bottom of the bust toward the rear of Washington's head.

Information about George Washington	
Born	February 22, 1732; Westmoreland County, Virginia
Died	December 14, 1799; Mount Vernon, Virginia
Occupations	Surveyor; colonel in the militia during the French and Indian War; tobacco and wheat farmer; legislator; President
Important Dates	1774 elected member of First Continental Congress 1775 named Commander-in-Chief of colonial army 1787 President of Constitutional Convention 1789 unanimously elected first President 1789 April 30, inaugurated as President (New York City) 1792 elected to second term as President

Reverse

Reverse An eagle with inverted wings standing on a fasces of arrows pointing to the left is pictured. The fasces, a bundle of arrows bound by a ribbon, is a stylized version of the Roman symbol of authority—a bundle of sticks with a battle-ax in the center, bound by a red ribbon. In this century, the fasces became the symbol for fascism. Two laurel branches appear under the eagle.

Resources on Money

Information about U.S. coins and bills and the history of money can be found in these books and Web site:

Barabas, K. (1997). *Let's Find Out About Money*. New York: Scholastic.

Doty, R. (1988). *America's Money, America's Story*. Iola, WI: Krause.

U.S. Treasury Web site: www.ustreas.gov/topics/currency

Yeoman, R. S. (Yearly). *Guide Book of United States Coins*. New York: Golden Books Adult.

12.10 Measurement Tools and Techniques

No matter which system or unit is being used, measuring tools provide ways to attach numbers to many common and uncommon things in everyone's life. Young children should have experiences with a wide range of measuring tools and should experience many real-life uses of measurement. Cooking is a wonderful, but often-overlooked opportunity for measurement!

The history of science is intertwined with the development of improved measuring instruments. New scientific discoveries often hinge on new and more precise measuring tools, and verification or rejection of theories often depends on increasingly precise measurements. Much of modern industry and technology depends on using very precise measures that are standardized throughout the world. Children learn that the measuring tools that we all use are based on mutually agreed-upon standards and that our own measurements are mere approximations, as the following section explains.

12.10.1 Measurement and Estimation

All measurements are approximate. Even measures that seem exact are actually estimates that are "close enough" for practical considerations. We can never line up the precise edge of an object with a precise point on a measuring tool. For example, this page is not exactly 11 inches long. If you look at its edge under a microscope you will see that it is not even straight. So, is the actual measure the straight-line path from one corner to the other, or is it the path following all the dips and curves of the paper's edge? No matter how careful the measurer, no physical measurement can be exact.

The measuring tool also affects how good a measurement can be. A ruler marked only with inches can be used only to give measures to the nearest inch. And no matter how small the subdivisions on a ruler, there are always unmarked spaces between the marked lines. In general, the *precision* of a measuring tool is the smallest interval on its scale.

So when children learn to measure, whether it be with inexact body measures in Kindergarten or to the nearest half-inch, quarter-inch, or centimeter in later grades, they also are learning to approximate and deal with error.

12.10.2 Rulers and Tape Measures

Along with weighing scales and balances, *rulers* and *tape measures* are among the first tools used for practical everyday measurements, both in human history and in the lives of children. In the early grades, children learn to give ballpark estimates of heights and lengths; then, over the years, they get progressively more sophisticated in their use of measuring instruments to find approximate lengths. In later grades, *carpenters' rules* are important tools for applying the "half" fractions—$\frac{1}{2}$, $\frac{1}{4}$, $\frac{1}{8}$, and so on, each fraction being half the previous one. Metersticks and centimeter rulers are instructive when teaching about decimals.

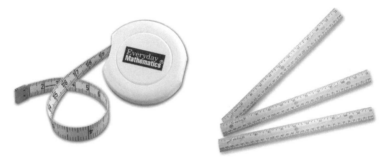

12.10.3 Scales and Balances

For more information, see Section 12.6: Weight and Mass.

A scale is another historically old measuring tool. *Scales* are used to measure how heavy things are according to a standard weight. There are many different kinds of scales, including *balance scales, beam scales, spring scales,* and *electronic scales.*

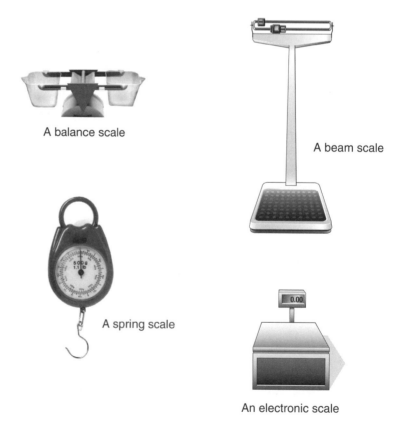

A balance scale

A beam scale

A spring scale

An electronic scale

chapter 12

Different scales are designed to measure different amounts of weight. There are scales with a variety of capacities and a variety of increments. High-precision scales can measure the weight of a piece of hair or a dose of medicine in increments as small as 0.001 gram or 0.000001 pound. Some platform scales can accommodate trucks weighing as much as 100 tons or railroad cars weighing 825 tons.

Scales have a variety of uses. In the kitchen, they are used to weigh food for cooking and for monitoring diets. Bathroom, nursery, and doctors' scales help monitor personal health. All kinds of scales are used by businesses that sell produce, meat, fish, and bakery items. The U.S. Post Office and other delivery services determine shipping prices based on package weight. Scales are used to weigh trucks to determine the amount of tax that drivers must pay for using the roads. Scales are also used to count pieces, such as the number of nails in a box or pennies in a bag. Scales may give the weight on a dial or digital display in U.S. customary units, metric units, or both.

Reference Frames

Reference frames are something of an oddity in mathematics. Unlike measurements or counts, numbers in reference frames locate things only within definite systems or contexts. Examples include dates, times, Celsius and Fahrenheit temperatures, and coordinates on maps. The numbers in reference frames are set to meet the needs of their creators. For example, the year 2000 in our calendar system is not the same as the year 2000 in the traditional Chinese calendar system, and the Celsius temperature scale is quite different from the Fahrenheit scale.

Most reference frames have a *zero point,* or *origin.* Positive and negative numbers may describe locations on one side of zero or the other. Zero in a reference frame means something different from zero as a count or a measure. A measure or count of zero means that there is none of whatever is being measured or counted. In contrast, the zero point in a reference frame is simply a starting point; it does not necessarily correspond with nothingness or a lowest bound for positive numbers. As a result, numbers in reference frames are not necessarily governed by the same mathematical rules as other numbers.

Doing arithmetic with numbers in reference frames often makes no sense. For example, adding the year 1950 to the year 2010 gives no meaningful result; 30°C is not 3 times as warm as 10°C; and 3:00 P.M. plus 2:00 P.M. does not equal 5:00 P.M. On the other hand, the numbers in reference frames can be used to find the distance from one point to another in the same reference frame. For example, 1950 was 60 years earlier than 2010, 30°C is 20 degrees warmer than 10°C, and 5:00 P.M. is 2 hours later than 3:00 P.M.

in perspective

Coordinate systems, including maps, are reference frames in which one or more numbers, called *coordinates,* are used to locate points. The simplest coordinate system is a number line. Number lines, number grids and number scrolls are discussed in Chapter 8: Number and Counting. More complicated coordinate systems are not discussed here because they are not a focus in *Everyday Mathematics* until Grade 4.

chapter 13

Frank and Ernest

In *Everyday Mathematics,* children learn about a variety of contemporary and historical reference frames. This chapter discusses reference frames for temperature and time.

▶ 13.1 Temperature

Temperature is the amount of heat something has relative to a reference frame usually called a *temperature scale.*

13.1.1 Temperature Scales

The two *temperature scales* with which most people are familiar are the Fahrenheit and Celsius scales. Each scale has a zero point based on when water freezes (but not the same kind of water) and each has a unit interval called a *degree* (but Fahrenheit degrees are smaller than Celsius degrees).

The Fahrenheit Scale

German physicist D. G. Fahrenheit developed the *Fahrenheit scale* in the early 1700s, although it may have been based on a similar scale invented by Danish astronomer Ole Christensen Romer. The zero point of this scale (0°F) was originally the freezing point of a saturated salt and water solution *(brine)* at sea level. The point at which pure water freezes at sea level was set at 32°F for reasons that are not clear. After Fahrenheit's death, the scale was recalibrated to the temperatures that pure water freezes (32°F) and boils (212°F), and brine was left out of it. The normal temperature for the human body is 98.6°F. The Fahrenheit scale is used primarily in the United States.

The Celsius Scale

Swedish astronomer Anders Celsius developed the *Celsius scale* in 1742. The zero point for this scale (0°C) is the freezing point of pure water at sea level. The boiling point of pure water at sea level was set at 100°C in order to divide the span of temperatures into a convenient 100 parts. For this reason, the Celsius scale is also called the *centigrade scale.* The normal temperature for the human body is 37°C. The Celsius scale is standard for most people living outside of the United States and for most scientists everywhere.

13.1.2 Thermometers

Thermometers have been evolving since the late 16th century. Galileo built the first known thermometer, an inaccurate device called a *thermoscope,* in about 1592. In 1709, D. G. Fahrenheit made an accurate thermometer using alcohol. In 1714, he built a mercury

NOTE: Both the Fahrenheit and Celsuis scales are examples of a reference frame that first defines where two points are on the scale and then arbitrarily divides the distance between the points into unit intervals, in this case, called *degrees.*

NOTE: A Fahrenheit degree is $\frac{1}{180}$ of the difference between the boiling and freezing temperatures of pure water, and a Celsius degree is $\frac{1}{100}$ of that difference. Once again, U.S. customary units are much more difficult to calculate with than metric units.

NOTE: The *Kelvin scale,* suggested in 1848 by British physicist Lord Kelvin, is used in science and engineering. Its zero point is a temperature at which the atoms and molecules in any substance have minimum energy. Thus there are no negative temperatures on the Kelvin scale. Pure water at sea level freezes at 273.15 K and boils at 373.15 K. The zero point of this scale (0 Kelvins or 0 K) is called *absolute zero.* The Kelvin unit interval is the same as the Celsius degree.

A thermometer with
a circular scale

thermometer like those still in use today. In 1954, U.S. Army Colonel George T. Perkins invented an electronic thermometer.

The designs of thermometers depend on the temperature scale(s) they intend to display and the range of temperatures of interest. Common thermometers include those used to measure cooking temperatures, (candy; deep-frying; oven), machine temperatures (automobile engine; climate control), body temperatures, and air temperatures. Some thermometers have circular scales, others are straight, and still others have digital readouts. The zero point and scale intervals are often not evident on the third type, making them less desirable as learning tools than the circular and straight-line designs.

In *Kindergarten Everyday Mathematics,* children keep daily temperature charts that are color-coded by temperature range for easier reading. Most air-temperature thermometers use mercury or colored alcohol and are based on straight-line, vertical, or circular number-line scales. In first grade, the Fahrenheit temperature scale is emphasized. In second and third grades, both Fahrenheit and Celsius scales should be available.

In all grades of *Everyday Mathematics,* temperature is the context for number stories, data exploration, and graphical displays.

Be careful about doing arithmetic with temperatures. Temperature changes can be calculated within one scale but not across different scales. For example, if it was 58°F this morning and the temperature rose 30°F to the high for the day, then the high was 58 + 30 = 88°F. Differences in Fahrenheit and Celsius temperatures are not meaningful; for example, 30°F minus 20°C does not equal 10° of anything.

The limitations of doing arithmetic with reference-frame numbers can be a difficult concept. Although some children will grasp it intuitively, others will need to work with many examples over time before they understand when reference-frame numbers cannot be manipulated like other numbers and when they can be meaningfully added and subtracted.

▶ 13.2 Time

As with many reference frames, locating an event or a point in time requires a zero, or starting, point and a unit interval. Both of these depend on the context in which time is being examined. This section begins with discussions of clocks to keep track of short-term time passage and calendars and timelines to keep track of broad expanses of time, from days to millennia.

As with units in other reference frames, it does not always make sense to compute with numbers pertaining to time. For example, June 8 plus June 13 is not June 21, and 8:30 P.M. minus 1:20 P.M. is not 7:10 P.M. Within one reference frame, however, you can calculate elapsed time as a difference, or distance, between two times.

In *Kindergarten* through *Third Grade Everyday Mathematics,* children engage in many everyday activities with clocks and calendars that help them develop a *time sense* and become familiar with the language of time. Older children are expected to be comfortable with clocks and calendar reference frames; they use them as a context for number stories, investigations, and other problem-solving situations.

13.2.1 Clocks

Clock time is a reference frame with second, minute, and hour intervals that, although logical to most adults, can seem quite arbitrary and confusing to children. Learning to tell time accurately on an analog clock is one of the objectives of *Kindergarten* through *Second Grade Everyday Mathematics.* For older children, elapsed time is a common context for number stories.

Clocks have been important in the development of many human enterprises, such as navigation, business, and science. Three important types of clocks are analog, digital, and atomic. In *Kindergarten* through *Third Grade Everyday Mathematics,* children practice telling time using both digital and analog clocks. In Kindergarten, children focus on estimating time on an analog clock using only the hour hand.

Analog Clocks

Analog clocks, which used to be called simply "clocks" before the invention of digital clocks, are clocks with hands. In general, *analog* refers to any system that measures a *continuously* changing quantity, such as time, with continuously varying markers of some kind. The first analog clocks may have been trees with markers showing where their shadows fell at different times during the day. These were precursors to sundials, which work on the same principle. For thousands of years, water clocks have been a standard for telling time. They work even when the sun is down or behind a cloud. In a water clock, the water flows from one vessel to another, the flow being the analog for the time. The first successful mechanical clocks were constructed late in the Middle Ages, a development that thoroughly transformed the world.

An analog clock

Nowadays, most people who say "analog clock" mean the type with hands on a round face. The first of these, with only an hour hand on it, is credited to the German inventor Henry de Vick in the 1300s. More advanced features came along in the 1700s, including minute and second hands and a pendulum. Electric analog clocks use an alternating current that vibrates 60 times per second to keep the clock on time.

Digital Clocks

Digital clocks are not analog because time is displayed in *discrete* units, not in a continuous manner. Every digital clock has a smallest unit of time that it displays without changing until an interval of that unit has gone by. Commonly, the smallest unit is a minute. For example, a display of 10:10 on a digital clock does not change until a minute has passed.

A digital clock

On some digital clocks, the colon in the time display blinks on and off once per second to indicate that time is still passing or perhaps just to let you know the clock is still working. Yet even the seconds are discrete. A "hand" does not sweep from one second to the next.

Instead, the time displayed on a digital clock jumps discretely from one minute or second to the next. Most digital clocks work on alternating current.

Atomic Clocks

Atomic clocks keep time according to the vibrations of atoms or molecules. The vibrations are so reliable that an atomic clock may lose or gain only a few seconds in 100,000 years. There are both analog and digital versions of atomic clocks.

13.2.2 Calendars

There are many different calendric systems, each one its own reference frame for marking the passage of time. The word *calendar* has roots in the Latin word *kalendae,* meaning "first of the month." *Kalendae,* in turn, is rooted in the word *calare,* which means "to call out solemnly." This etymology points to the importance that people have always placed on keeping track of months and marking their beginning and passing.

In the earliest times, the lunar month of 29.5 days was an important measure because of its close association with seasonal planting and harvesting schedules. Unfortunately, no whole number of lunar months coincides with a solar year of 365 days, 5 hours, 48 minutes, and 46 seconds (about 365 and 1 fourth days). Twelve lunar months are 354 days; 13 lunar months are 383.5 days. The fact that these important, naturally occurring cycles can't easily be reconciled has led to the peculiar natures of the calendar systems used throughout history. According to *The World Book Encyclopedia,* some noteworthy calendars include the following:

- *Babylonian Calendar* This ancient Middle-Eastern calendar was based on a now-unknown zero point and a lunar month interval. The calendar had alternating 29- and 30-day months, with an extra month added three times every 8 years to make up for error.

- *Egyptian Calendar* This ancient calendar had a zero point at the annual flooding of the Nile when the Dog Star, Sirius, first appeared. The year was broken into twelve 30-day months, with 5 days added at the end of the year. Because the extra 1 fourth of a day per year wasn't accounted for, the calendar slowly became inaccurate over the years. It has been calculated that the earliest recorded date on this calendar corresponds to 4236 B.C. on our current Gregorian calendar.

- *Roman Calendar* According to legend, Romulus, the founder of Rome, introduced the earliest Roman calendar in the eighth century B.C. It came from the Greeks and was made up of 10 months and a 304-day year. The zero point was March 1 by our current calendar. It is not clear how the other 61-odd days were accounted for.

  The names of eight of our current months came from the names for the ten Roman months: *Martius, Aprilis, Maius, Junius, Quintilis, Sextilis, September, October, November,* and *December.* Quintilis through December came from the numbers 5 through 10.

The name *Martius* came from Mars, a Roman god; *Junius* from Juno, a Roman goddess; and *Maius* from Maia, a Greek goddess. It is thought that *Aprilis* may derive from the Latin word *aperire,* "to open," referring to the unfolding of buds and blossoms during this month. Another possibility is that it may derive from Aphrodite, the Greek goddess of love and beauty.

Every two years, a 22- or 23-day month was added to account for error with the solar year. Later, two more months, *Januarius* and *Februarius,* were added to the end of the year. *Januarius* was likely named after Janus, the Roman god of gates and doorways, and Februarius took its name from Februa, a Roman festival of purification held on the 15th day of this month.

- *Julian Calendar* In 46 B.C., Julius Caesar acted on suggestions from his astronomer Sosigenes to upgrade the Roman calendar. A system close to our own was implemented, including what we now know as a *leap day* in February every fourth year. To accommodate the fact that the Roman calendar was three months out of line with the seasons, Caesar made the year 46 B.C. 445 days long. Later, *Quintilis* was renamed July for Julius Caesar and *Sextilis* was named August to honor Emperor Augustus Caesar.

  The Christian version of the Julian calendar was invented in A.D. 532 by an abbot named Dionysius Exiguus, or Dennis the Short. In his plan, the Christian era began January 1 of the year after Christ was born. He called the beginning year the Year of Our Lord, or Anno Domini (A.D.) 1. The Christian version of the calendar was not taken up immediately by church authorities but became widely used in Western Europe beginning in the 11th century. The abbreviation B.C. for "Before Christ" was introduced later. However, Dennis got the year of Christ's birth wrong. It now seems likely that Christ was born in 4 B.C., if not earlier. The abbreviations C.E. (Common Era) and B.C.E. (Before the Common Era) are sometimes used instead of A.D. and B.C.

- *Gregorian Calendar* By 1582, the Julian calendar was off by about 10 days because of the slight difference between $365\frac{1}{4}$ days and 365 days, 5 hours, 48 minutes, and 46 seconds. So Pope Gregory XIII dropped 10 days from October. He then decreed that February should continue to get an extra day every four years, as in the Julian calendar, except in century years that were not divisible by 400. This calendar is so accurate that, more than 400 years later, the time is only about 26 seconds off. Most of the Western World uses the Gregorian calendar.

- *Hebrew Calendar* The zero point for the Hebrew calendar is Creation, which has been calculated at 3,760 years and 3 months before the Christian era began. To find a year on the Hebrew calendar, add 3,760 or 3,761 to the year in the Gregorian calendar. The Hebrew year is based on the phases of the moon and usually has 12 months, each 29 or 30 days long. Seven times every 19 years, an extra 29-day month is added.

NOTE: 46 B.C. is known as the "year of confusion" because of calendar reform.

NOTE: There is no year 0 in the Christian versions of the Julian and Gregorian calendars, but just a "zero moment" at which Christ was born, that was labeled as year "1". So this is a reference frame without a real zero point; that is, from 1 B.C. to A.D. 1 is only 1 year, not 2.

chapter 13

- *Islamic Calendar* The zero point for the Islamic calendar is Muhammad's flight from Mecca to Medina in A.D. 622 on the Gregorian calendar. This calendar is also lunar, with 12 months alternating between 29 and 30 days long. The months do not keep to the same seasons relative to the sun each year, and so the Islamic New Year moves backward through the seasons. Nineteen of every 30 years have 354 days each, and the other 11 years have an extra day each.

There are groups that advocate standardizing all calendars around the world. Three such calendars have been proposed: the Thirteen-Month calendar, with 13 months each 4 weeks long; the World calendar; and the Perpetual calendar. The latter two propose variations on a 12-month, 30- or 31-day-per-month design. And, according to *Star Trek* creator Gene Roddenberry, the calendar will be metric by the 24th century.

13.2.3 Timelines

Timelines, which are number lines labeled with time units, are also reference frames. As with all reference frames, a timeline's zero point and unit interval vary according to its intended use. For example, a timeline designed to track the development of Earth may have "The Big Bang" as its zero point and use a large interval (millions or perhaps billions of years) to allow for a display over billions of years. A family-history timeline might use generational intervals and mark its zero point with the most distant, known relative.

A timeline of someone's life might use the person's birth date as its zero point and a 1-year unit interval corresponding to the person's age. For example, a timeline of a young child's landmarks might include such events as rolling over at about $\frac{1}{2}$ year, learning to walk at age 1, having a sibling when she was 3, and going to Kindergarten shortly after her fifth birthday. A timeline such as this could also include numbers that refer to the Gregorian dates for the above events, for example, birth (1999), walking (2000), sibling (2002), and Kindergarten (2004), but it would not need to include these dates if birth were established as the zero point and age intervals were the specified unit. Keep in mind that in each instance above, times before the chosen zero point exist. This is true with most reference frames.

You may have timelines associated with social studies or science units, or your colleagues teaching different grades may have them. If they are available and appropriate, it would be instructive to review them with children from a reference-frame point of view. Ask *What is the zero point? What is the unit interval? Why did they choose this zero point and these intervals for this timeline?* Children can make their own timelines to demonstrate or reinforce knowledge in other content areas, especially social studies. Because timelines are visual, they are very useful tools for many children as they learn about history.

Estimation, Mental Arithmetic, and Number Sense

Contents

chapter 14

If you list everyday situations that involve arithmetic and identify the kind of answer and method of calculation that is likely in each situation, you may end up with something like the table below.

Situation	Kind of Answer	Likely Method
doubling a recipe	exact	mental arithmetic
making change	exact	mental arithmetic
deciding if you have enough money for a purchase	estimated	mental arithmetic
planning a daily schedule	estimated	mental arithmetic
balancing a checkbook	exact	calculator
computing gas mileage	estimated	mental arithmetic
comparing prices	estimated	mental arithmetic
calculating a discount percent	estimated	mental arithmetic
figuring income tax	exact	calculator
tipping	estimated	mental arithmetic

Of course, in certain situations you may seek a different kind of answer or use a method different from that listed above; but, in any case, your list is likely to reveal how common and valuable estimates and mental arithmetic are in everyday life. The practical importance of paper-and-pencil computation for daily living, which was never very great, is even further diminished in today's highly technological society. Sensible use of calculators and proficiency at mental arithmetic are more important than ever.

This diagram displays six ways to find answers to arithmetic problems. The traditional school mathematics curriculum focuses almost exclusively on just one of these—obtaining exact answers with paper-and-pencil algorithms. The authors of *Everyday Mathematics* believe that children deserve to be proficient in all six.

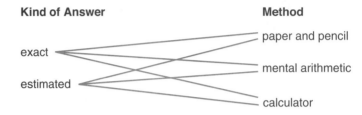

Paper-and-pencil algorithms for finding exact answers are discussed in Chapter 9. This chapter examines some of the other varieties of computation shown in the diagram above. The first part discusses why estimates may be necessary or desirable and how estimates may be obtained. The second part describes the *Everyday Mathematics* approach to mental arithmetic for exact and estimated answers. The last part is about basic facts, which must eventually be mastered (although not in Pre-Kindergarten or Kindergarten) if facility at mental arithmetic and paper-and-pencil algorithms is to be achieved.

▶ 14.1 Estimation

Estimation is a major thread in *Everyday Mathematics* because of its importance in mathematics and everyday life. We estimate counts, measures, and results of calculations. In practical matters, ballpark estimates are often as important as exact answers.

Being able to make educated guesses about counts or measures is a powerful tool, even for young children. Young children need help distinguishing between a wild guess and a ballpark estimate. You might ask *We have only 30 children in the class and not all of them drink milk, so how could we have a million milk cartons?* Many children like to make guesses and then verify how close they have come. Opportunities to estimate occur naturally during the course of the school day. You might ask *About how many steps to the door? About how many cartons of milk do we drink in a day? In a week?* In addition, *Kindergarten Everyday Mathematics* includes many estimation activities that you can do with your class, such as setting up an Estimation Jar or Estimation Station to be used regularly in the classroom.

Despite its utility, many children and some adults feel that estimation is like cheating or lying. In reality, estimation is not a shoddy alternative to doing things right. Estimation requires good intuition about numbers, good understanding of problem situations, and a flexible repertoire of techniques. Good estimation skills take years to develop but are worth striving for. Focusing on estimation can help children develop mental flexibility, good number sense, and confidence that mathematics makes sense.

The next section of this chapter outlines the principal reasons for estimating. Later sections address estimates in calculations, number sense, and mathematical connections.

14.1.1 Why Estimate?

Sometimes we use estimates because we have no choice; other times, because they are easier to understand than exact quantities; and still other times to help us solve problems or to check answers given by machines.

Estimates May Be Necessary

Estimates are necessary in many situations because exact values are unobtainable for a variety of reasons:

- *A number may simply be unknown.* Predictions about the future, guesses about the past, measurements of economic conditions, and even educated guesses about what groceries will cost are all examples of estimates necessitated by lack of precise knowledge.

- *A quantity may be different each time it is measured.* Temperatures, populations, air pressures, and keyboarding speeds are examples of this type of estimate, as are situations involving random processes such as the number of HEADS to come up in 100 tosses of a coin.

- *Physical measurements are never exact.* Even measures that seem exact are approximate, although they may be close enough to exact for all practical purposes. For example, no sheet of paper is exactly 11 inches long; if you look at the edge under a microscope, it will appear quite rough and uneven.

- *Getting an exact value may be too expensive.* In many situations, the numbers are so large that exact counts cannot be easily obtained. More often than not, large counts are estimated by taking samples and using statistics. To estimate how many people saw a particular TV program, pollsters interview just a sample of the viewing public, not the entire viewing public.

- *Decimal or fractional results may not make sense.* For example, if the price of items is 3 for $1, you do not pay $33\frac{1}{3}$¢ for each item because there are no longer coins for fractions of pennies. Instead, you pay 34¢ for the first item and 33¢ for each of the other two items.

- *Some situations require a built-in margin of error, so quantities are overestimated.* For example, you overestimate the costs of items you are buying to make sure you have enough money to pay the cashier. Safety factors in new buildings are overestimated to more than meet minimal requirements.

- *Numbers may not be in a form suitable for computation.* For example, to compute with irrational numbers like $\sqrt{2}$ or π, you need to replace them with rational approximations.

In the situations above, there is no choice about whether to estimate. People who believe that estimates are inferior to exact answers are thus ignoring many situations in which it is necessary to estimate.

NOTE: Many ideas and examples in this chapter come from "Reasons for Estimating and Approximating" in *Applying Arithmetic* by Max Bell and Zalman Usiskin. A full reference is available on page 127.

NOTE: Working with very large and very small numbers—such as the populations or areas of countries, stars in galaxies, hairs on a head, the national debt, or years since the dinosaurs—illustrates the need for estimating and approximating. Extreme numbers may need to be estimated if the things with which they are associated cannot be accurately counted, if they are measurements, or if the number is a large product or a small quotient.

chapter 14

Estimates Are Easy to Understand

Estimates help us communicate by making numbers easier to understand.

- *Estimates may be clearer than exact values.* A school budget of $148,309,563 for a school population of 62,772 children might be reported as "about $150 million for 63,000 children." A house on a lot with a surveyed width of 40.13 feet is likely to be described as being on a 40-foot lot. In such cases, estimates are easier to understand than more precise numbers are.

  Sometimes estimates themselves are approximated to make them easier to understand. For example, an almanac estimates the area of Canada to be 3,849,674 square miles. Approximating this estimate to 3.8 million or 4 million square miles makes the measure easier to understand and communicate.

  Children in *Everyday Mathematics* encounter many examples of estimates made for clarity. Many are found in data-analysis activities throughout the program.

- *Estimates provide consistency.* Estimates for consistency are often prompted by a desire to show data uniformly in tables, charts, and graphs. For example, government unemployment reports often give a percent rounded to the nearest tenth. So, if 8.5 million of 99 million potential workers are unemployed, the government reports 8.6% unemployed rather than 8.59% or any closer approximation to 8.5858 . . .%. Here an estimate is necessary because the original data are inexact, but the particular choice to report in tenths is done both to be consistent from month to month and to reflect the 2-digit precision of the original data.

  Sometimes the desire for consistency comes from tradition. For example, the batting average of a baseball player is found by dividing the number of hits by the number of times at bat. The answer is rounded to the nearest thousandth and is usually referred to as a percent in tables, even though it is shown as a 3-place decimal. A batting average is usually cited as if the decimal point were not there. For example, in 1941 Ted Williams made a hit in over 40 percent of his times at bat when he hit *406*, usually pronounced "four-oh-six."

Estimates Can Help in Problem Solving

Estimation can be useful in solving problems both before and after an answer is obtained. During the early phases of the problem-solving process, estimating may help you better understand the problem. Estimating helps clarify what is known and what is unknown and helps guide your search for a solution. Even if an estimate made early in the problem-solving process turns out to be very inaccurate, simply having made one may help you get insight into a particularly difficult problem.

For more information on precision, see Section 14.2: Approximation and Rounding.

Once an answer is obtained, an estimate can be used to check its reasonableness. Looking back over the problem-solving process is valuable, and estimating to verify the accuracy of a result is a good activity to encourage such reflection. Estimating to check answers also emphasizes that results obtained in different ways should agree and, more generally, that mathematics makes sense.

In *Kindergarten* through *Third Grade Everyday Mathematics,* children are often asked to make estimates to check their answers obtained from manipulatives, mental arithmetic, paper-and-pencil, or calculator methods. Sometimes they are asked to estimate before calculating in order to let the calculated answer verify their estimating skills. More often, they estimate after calculation in order to check the reasonableness of the answer.

Children should be encouraged to estimate answers in problem situations in which exact answers are unnecessary or not justified. Because many people are uncomfortable with estimates, it is important to discuss the differences between exact and estimated answers and to identify situations in which an estimate is good enough or even makes more sense than an exact answer. For example, *I have 75¢. I want to buy an eraser for 29¢ and a notebook for 39¢. Do I have enough money?* Sharing strategies can help children develop their estimation skills. Children should become aware that there is no single "correct" estimate; the purpose of estimation is to find a reasonable answer, not the exact answer.

14.1.2 Estimates in Calculations

Ballpark estimates make calculations easier when exact answers are not needed. For example, when you plan a trip, estimates of the costs of driving and flying are easier to compare than are exact values. Your thinking might be as follows: *The trip will be about 800 miles, my automobile gets about 25 miles per gallon, and gasoline costs about $3.10 per gallon; but there will be two days' extra driving and the motel will cost $120 and meals on the road about $60. On the other hand, the cheapest way to fly costs about $350, and I'll need to rent a car at the destination for five days at $80 per day . . ..*

Even with calculators and computers taking much of the work out of computation, estimating may make things a lot easier with no important loss in the quality of the answers. In fact, answers derived using estimates may be more reasonable and more realistic than exact answers, as in planning a car trip.

For situations in which exact answers are required and a calculator is used to find them, estimation can help check the results. Most of us have heard the story about the cashier at the fast-food restaurant who entered the price for an item incorrectly but couldn't tell that the total was incorrect. This story is often used to support the argument that people depend too much on machines and, therefore, that calculators should be banned from the classroom and children should master the traditional paper-and-pencil algorithms.

This argument misses the point entirely. Few people would want the cashier to stop using a machine and do the work on paper. What the cashier needs are estimation skills to check whether the machine total is reasonable. If it isn't, then it should be recalculated. In the cashier's defense, many traditional mathematics curricula don't teach estimation skills in conjunction with arithmetic operations. In fact, such skills are sometimes reviled as being merely trial and error. *Everyday Mathematics,* on the other hand, sees these skills as an integral component of a comprehensive and balanced approach to computation. As they move through the grades, children are encouraged to compute either exactly or approximately, working mentally, with paper and pencil, or with a calculator, depending on what is most appropriate for each situation.

▶ ## 14.2 Approximation and Rounding

Although rounding is not taught in Pre-Kindergarten or Kindergarten, it is useful to recognize the difference between rounding and estimation. Estimation is a reasoned guess at an unknown or unknowable value. *Rounding* is a technique to approximate *known* numbers. Often numbers are rounded to make them easier to work with. Usually, you round either up or down to a number that is close to a known number but easier to work with, where "close" and "easier" are determined by the context of a problem. In the following example, rounding makes estimation easier.

Example:	You want to buy 4 cans of tennis balls that cost $4.57 a can. Estimate the least number of dollar bills you need in order to pay for your purchase.
Solution 1:	Rounding up to $5 per can, a reasonable estimate for the cost of 4 cans is $4 \times \$5 = \$20$. However, because you rounded up, you will definitely not need more than $20. So 20 $1 bills will be enough.
Solution 2:	Rounding down to $4.50 per can, a closer estimate to the cost of 4 cans is $18, because $4 \times \$4.50 = \$18$. However, $4 \times \$4.57$ is a bit more than $18, so you will need at least 19 $1 bills.

Both solutions are good applications of rounding. Which solution is right? Although the second solution of $19 is closer to the exact cost of $18.28 than the first solution of $20, it is not necessarily a better estimate.

All calculators round decimals to fit the display screen. Some 4-function calculators use the round-to-the-nearest algorithm, but most round down. Most scientific calculators round to the nearest value of the place at the far right of the display. Almost all calculators hold more digits accurately in memory than they display. Understanding the principles and effects of rounding is important when using a calculator.

NOTE: Both the Texas Instruments TI-108 and Casio SL-450 that the authors used while writing this edition of *Everyday Mathematics* round down.

▶ 14.3 Mental Arithmetic

Although people frequently associate mental arithmetic with estimation, it is also useful for finding exact answers. In many situations, an exact answer is required but a calculator is not available and *mental arithmetic* is a convenient alternative. Even most paper-and-pencil algorithms for finding exact answers involve mental arithmetic. Paper-and-pencil division, for instance, is likely to require mental addition, multiplication, and subtraction.

In *Everyday Mathematics,* children practice mental arithmetic to learn useful techniques; to develop flexible thinking; and to gain *fact power,* or the automatic recall of basic addition/subtraction and multiplication/division facts. These skills contribute to children's *number sense,* which includes a flexible understanding both of numbers and of operations on those numbers. *Everyday Mathematics* also emphasizes number sense because calculators and computers have actually increased the importance of estimation and mental arithmetic in daily life. Complicated paper-and-pencil computation has become relatively less important in everyday life and in the curriculum, while mental arithmetic and skillful use of calculators have become relatively more important.

For more information, see Section 14.3.2: Basic Facts and Fact Power and Section 14.4: Number Sense and Mathematical Connections.

An important part of being a flexible problem solver is to add continually to a personal tool kit of mental-arithmetic skills. As children move through the grades, some of these mental-arithmetic skills should become automatic so they can be used reflexively, almost without thinking.

Mental-arithmetic skills are developed throughout the *Everyday Mathematics* curriculum as an integral part of the program. Each lesson in first through sixth grades begins with a brief set of oral or slate exercises called Mental Math and Reflexes. In Pre-Kindergarten through Grade 3, *Minute Math* and *Minute Math+* provide many activities for practicing mental arithmetic and problem-solving skills.

Strategy sharing is vitally important throughout *Everyday Mathematics.* Perhaps the most important part of learning mental-arithmetic skills is to have children share their solution strategies after they solve a problem. Sharing strategies requires children to verbalize their thinking, thus making them conscious of a process that is often intuitive. Children also get insights into alternative approaches from their classmates and develop creative and flexible thinking processes. Importantly, children learn that common sense applies to mathematics and that they can solve difficult problems by themselves.

For more information, see Section 1.3: Encouraging Problem Solving: Sharing Strategies and Solutions.

14.3.1 Mental-Calculation Strategies

There are many strategies and techniques for mental arithmetic. Some are formally introduced in *Everyday Mathematics,* and children develop others on their own. Gradually, children are exposed to many techniques, learn how they work, master a few, and build some into reflexes. The following examples emerge from older students, but through repeated problem-solving and strategy-sharing experiences, even Pre-Kindergarten and Kindergarten children begin to figure out expedient ways to solve the types of problems they encounter. Children's experiences with flexible thinking and problem solving in younger grades lays the groundwork for developing the types of strategies that are described below in later grades.

- *Round* Techniques include rounding, as appropriate, to the nearest ten, hundred, thousand, and so on, and computing with rounded numbers. For example, 647 + 284 is approximately 600 + 300 = 900, or perhaps 650 + 280 = 930.

- *Adjust the numbers* A sum is unchanged if one addend is increased by a given amount and the other addend is decreased by the same amount. For example, in 86 + 37, think *86 + 4 = 90 and 37 − 4 = 33, so 90 + 33 = 123.* This is called the *opposite-change rule for addition.*

  A similar rule is the *same-change rule for subtraction:* a difference is unchanged if the same amount is added to or subtracted from both the minuend and the subtrahend. For example, in 54 − 37, think *37 + 3 = 40 and 54 + 3 = 57, so 57 − 40 = 17.*

- *Look for easy combinations* For example, in 17 + 25 + 3 + 15, add 17 and 3 *(20)* and 25 and 15 *(40)*. So 17 + 25 + 3 + 15 = 20 + 40 = 60.

- *Estimate, then adjust* An approximate answer is obtained first and then adjusted to make it more accurate. For example, 647 + 284 is approximately 640 + 280 *(920);* then add 7 + 4 *(11)* to that sum *(920 + 11 = 931).*

- *Estimate magnitude* As a useful check for answers found another way, ask *Is a reasonable answer in the tens? hundreds? thousands?*

14.3.2 Basic Facts and Fact Power

Automatically knowing basic number facts is as important to learning mathematics as knowing words by sight is to reading. This has not gone unnoticed among educational researchers. Benjamin Bloom (1986) has written at length on the importance of *automaticity* as part of any complex talent and *Everyday Mathematics* co-creator Max Bell has long emphasized the importance of number-fact reflexes. Children are often told that habits, good and bad, come from doing something over and over until they do it without thinking. Developing basic number-fact reflexes can be likened to developing good habits.

In *Everyday Mathematics,* good fact habits are called *fact power.* In Grades 1 through 3, children keep fact power tables of the facts they know. The grades in which *Everyday Mathematics* activities help children gain fact power for each of the four basic arithmetic operations are shown in the table on the next page. For each operation, easier facts are introduced, explored using a variety of strategies, and practiced before harder facts are introduced, usually in the next grade.

Grade-Level Development of Children's Fact Power					
	K	1	2	3	4
Addition					
Easy facts	░	░	░		
Hard facts		░	░	░	
Subtraction					
Easy facts	░	░	░		
Hard facts		░	░		
Multiplication					
Easy facts			░	░	░
Hard facts			░	░	░
Division					
Easy facts			░	░	░
Hard facts				░	░

Each bar in this table represents the *Everyday Mathematics* grade levels during which children continuously gain a higher degree of fact power, from introduction and exploration of new facts with manipulatives to automatic recall (automaticity) in which facts are easily recalled from long-term memory. In the middle of this process, children develop their own strategies and learn new strategies for calculating mentally. The goal is to increase children's proficiency using favorite strategies that can help them gain automaticity. For example, easier facts are made more automatic through their application to learning the harder facts; that is, 8 + 7 may be seen as 1 less than the "easier" double 8 + 8.

As children share their strategies, encourage them to articulate what they are doing and to learn new ways of thinking about facts from you and their classmates.

14.3.3 Fact Practice

Practicing the facts traditionally involves pages and pages of drills. This can be tedious and can lead children to dislike mathematics. In *Everyday Mathematics,* playing games is perhaps the most successful approach to practicing skills and is discussed in the following paragraphs.

Games for Fact Practice

Frequent practice is necessary in order for children to build and maintain strong mental-arithmetic skills and reflexes. Although drill has its place, much of the practice in *Everyday Mathematics* is in game format. Games are not attractive add-ons but essential parts of the complete *Everyday Mathematics* program.

in perspective

By the end of the school year, most second graders should know the addition and subtraction facts automatically. In third and fourth grades, the emphasis shifts to learning the multiplication and division facts. Although some children may not know all these facts, they should be well on their way to achieving this goal by the end of fourth grade.

chapter 14

NOTE: Cognitive and educational psychologists have long supported children's playing games in school. For a concise summary, see *Theories of Childhood: An Introduction to Dewey, Montessori, Erickson, Piaget and Vygotsky* by C. G. Mooney. A full reference can be found on page 127.

NOTE: The federal and some state education departments advocate children playing mathematics games in school and at home. The U.S. Department of Education (2004) places high value on games in *Helping Your Child Learn Mathematics.* A full reference can be found on page 127. The New York State Department of Education has recommended games along with concrete objects, number lines, and other approaches for more than 25 years. For more information on New York's position, see this Web site: www.emsc.nysed.gov/ciai/mst/math.html

In "Playing games and real mathematics," Ainley (1988) writes,

> The most effective mathematical games are those in which the structure and rules of the game are based on mathematical ideas, and where winning the game is directly related to understanding this mathematics. (p. 241)

All grades of *Everyday Mathematics* include games that have been developed to help children learn specific arithmetic and other skills at an appropriate developmental level. Some, in fact, are so targeted to the development of certain skills that once a child becomes proficient, the game is no longer necessary.

Drill and games should not be viewed as competitors for class time, nor should games be thought of as time-killers or rewards. In fact, games satisfy many, if not most, standard drill objectives, with many built-in options. Drill tends to become tedious and, therefore, gradually loses its effectiveness. Games relieve the tedium because children enjoy them. Indeed, children often wish to continue to play games during their free time, lunch, and even recess.

Arithmetic practice through games is also recommended to help you deal with individual differences in children's motivations and abilities. Seckinger, Mitchel, and Lemire (1989) found that games improve children's attitudes about mathematics as well as improve achievement among low-achievers. Alternatively, Johnson (2000) advocates using mathematical games with gifted children, who tend to invent new rules or increase difficulty of games on their own. Researchers such as Wolpert (1996) also support games or other play to encourage automaticity of arithmetic skills by learning-disabled children.

Drill exercises aim primarily at building fact and operation skills. Practice through games shares these objectives, but at the same time, games often reinforce calculator skills, logical thinking, geometric intuition, and intuition about probability and chance because many games involve randomly generated numbers.

Using games to practice number skills also greatly reduces the need for worksheets. Because the numbers in most games are generated randomly, the games can be played over and over without repeating the same problems. Many of the *Everyday Mathematics* games come with variations that allow players to progress from easy to more challenging versions. Games, therefore, offer an almost unlimited source of practice material.

Other Approaches to Fact Practice

In addition to using games to provide fact practice, teachers in *First* through *Third Grade Everyday Mathematics* have also reported great success using alternative approaches that involve choral drills, "labels for the day," double-9 dominoes, fact triangles, and fact extensions. Some of these approaches are described briefly on the next page for your information, although fact practice should not be a focus in Pre-Kindergarten and Kindergarten. Rather, young children should focus on exploring facts with manipulatives and games.

Double-9 dominoes are wonderful concrete models of the addition/ subtraction facts through 9 + 9 and 18 − 9. Dominoes help children visualize the facts as well as develop an understanding of the meanings of addition and subtraction and the relationship between the two operations.

A *fact family* is a collection of four related facts linking two inverse operations. For example, the following four equations symbolize the fact family relating 8, 9, and 17 by addition and subtraction.

$$8 + 9 = 17 \qquad 9 + 8 = 17$$
$$17 - 9 = 8 \qquad 17 - 8 = 9$$

You may recognize that the two addition facts in this family taken together are an instance of the Commutative Property of Addition. Although *Everyday Mathematics* does not require children to learn mathematical names for properties, sometimes it is handy to have a name for occasional use. The *turn-around rule for addition* is the name used in *Everyday Mathematics* for the Commutative Property of Addition.

Everyday Mathematics calls properties of arithmetic *shortcuts,* and the four facts in a fact family are all related by shortcuts. A major reason for teaching fact families is to give children different options when solving problems that are new or difficult. By recalling a shortcut, a child can reword or rewrite the problem in a more meaningful way. For example, faced with 7 − 3 = ?, a first grader may think *Hmm, lemme think. What plus 3 is 7? Ah, that's easy, it's 4.*

Fact Triangles are the *Everyday Mathematics* version of flash cards. Fact Triangles are more effective than traditional flash cards because they emphasize fact families. An addition/subtraction Fact Triangle has two addends and a sum; a multiplication/division Fact Triangle has two factors and a product. A Fact Triangle for the 8 + 9 = 17 fact family is shown in the margin.

Fact extensions are powerful mental-arithmetic strategies for all operations with larger numbers. For example:

- If you know 3 + 4 = 7, you also know 30 + 40 = 70, 70 − 30 = 40, and 300 + 400 = 700.
- If you know 6 × 5 = 30, you also know 60 × 5 = 300, 600 × 5 = 3,000, and 3,000 ÷ 600 = 5.

Fact extensions are introduced in first grade and are extended throughout the program.

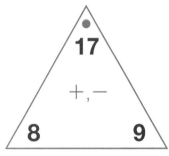

An addition/subtraction Fact Triangle

in perspective

First Grade Everyday Mathematics uses Fact Triangles to establish and emphasize addition/ subtraction fact families through 9 + 9. In second grade, the addition/ subtraction fact families are developed, and multiplication/division Fact Triangles are introduced. In third grade, children get both addition/subtraction and multiplication/division Fact Triangles. By fifth grade, *Everyday Mathematics* fact families are extended further as children learn equivalent values for decimals, fractions, and percents.

chapter 14

▶ 14.4 Number Sense and Mathematical Connections

It is perhaps the single greatest goal of *Everyday Mathematics* that children completing the program acquire number sense. People with *number sense:*

- Have good mental-arithmetic skills as well as reliable algorithms and procedures for finding results they can't produce mentally;
- Are flexible in thinking about numbers and arithmetic and will look for shortcuts to make their efforts as efficient as possible;
- Can use their number and arithmetic skills to solve problems in everyday situations;
- Are familiar with a variety of ways to communicate their strategies and results;
- Can recognize unreasonable results when they see them in their own work, in everyday situations, or in the media.

Number sense develops only with wide mathematical experience, including instruction and practice in specific techniques. But good number sense also depends on attitudes and beliefs, especially the belief that mathematics makes sense. People with good number sense expect their mathematical knowledge to connect with the rest of what they know, including their common sense and whatever they know about the situation at hand. Number sense thus depends on making connections between various kinds of mathematical knowledge and between mathematics and other subjects.

Everyday Mathematics helps children develop number sense in the contexts of data analysis, geometry, and elementary explorations of functions and sequences. In *Everyday Mathematics,* children make connections across mathematical topics and come to view mathematics as a coherent, consistent discipline rather than a hodgepodge of disconnected procedures and skills.

Number sense also involves making connections between mathematics and other subjects in the curriculum. Many activities in *Everyday Mathematics* are designed to show how number sense applies to science, social studies, and geography. Throughout *Everyday Mathematics* there are connections between mathematics and history, including both the history of mathematics and how mathematics has shaped human endeavors.

Everyday Mathematics also connects mathematics to the community through efforts to share the authors' commitment to number sense with children's families and other caregivers. Family Letters explain how *Everyday Mathematics* introduces children not only to the traditional mathematics people expect but also to a richer mathematics curriculum that older family members may not have experienced. Home Links enable parents or guardians to see the kinds of mathematics their children do in school and pass along some interesting ideas for family involvement as well.

References and Resources on Estimation, Mental Arithmetic, and Number Sense

Ainley, J. (1988). "Playing games and real mathematics." In Pimm, D. (Ed.) *Mathematics, Teachers and Children.* London: Hodder and Stoughton.

Bell, M., and Usiskin, Z. (1983). *Applying Arithmetic.* Chicago: University of Chicago. Available in three parts from Educational Resources Information Center (ERIC): ED 264087, ED 264088, and ED 264089.

Bloom, B. (1986). "Automaticity: The Hands and Feet of Genius." *Educational Leadership (43)5,* pp. 70–77.

Kamii, C., and DeVries, R. (1980). *Group games in early education: Implications of Piaget's theory.* Washington, DC: National Association for the Education of Young Children.

Mooney, C. G. (2000). *Theories of Childhood: An Introduction to Dewey, Montessori, Erickson, Piaget and Vygotsky.* St. Paul, MN: Redleaf.

Office of Intergovernmental and Interagency Affairs. (2004). *Helping Your Child Learn Mathematics.* Washington, DC: U.S. Department of Education.

Peters, S. (1998). "Playing games and learning mathematics: The results of two intervention studies." *International Journal of Early Years Education (6)1,* pp. 49–58.

Schoen, H. L., and Zweng, M. J. (1986). *Estimation and Mental Computation: 1986 Yearbook.* Reston, VA: National Council of Teachers of Mathematics.

Steen, L. (Ed.) (1997). *Why Numbers Count: Quantitative Literacy for Tomorrow's America.* New York: College Entrance Examination Board.

Wolpert, G. (1996). *The Educational Challenges Inclusion Study.* New York: National Down Syndrome Society.

Patterns, Sequences, Functions, and Algebra

Contents

Patterns can be found in sounds, in movements, in shapes, in numbers, in graphs, and in data. Indeed, patterns can be found almost anywhere. Patterns are especially important in mathematics. Some people even define mathematics as the science of patterns.

Most of mathematics deals with patterns that are predictable. This means that objects, colors, or numbers are arranged so that you can predict what comes next. You can "see" or continue such patterns; and in many cases, it is possible to find a rule that underlies a given pattern. The first part of this chapter deals with such patterns, including sequences and functions.

The second part of the chapter discusses uses of variables and how to read and write open number sentences. It closes with a brief description of some informal ways to solve open sentences.

Patterns and algebra are closely related. Pattern activities involve many mathematical processes that are fundamental in algebra. Among these are looking for patterns; making, testing, and proving conjectures about patterns; and representing patterns in several ways. Looking for patterns helps children develop modeling skills, which are crucial to many applications of algebra. By making and justifying conjectures about patterns, children develop habits of generalization and verification that will serve them well in algebra and beyond. Finally, working with multiple representations for functions, such as function machines, tables, rules, graphs, words, and symbols, helps children to build the conceptual understanding that will eventually support the symbol-manipulation skills so necessary for success in algebra.

15.1 Patterns, Sequences, and Functions

Most of the patterns in *Everyday Mathematics* are either *visual patterns,* such as those found in colored manipulatives, geometric shapes, and data or coordinate graphs, or *number patterns,* such as those found in sequences and functions. In Pre-Kindergarten and Kindergarten, children also practice with sound and movement patterns to help them understand the concept of repeating patterns through multisensory experiences.

15.1.1 Visual Patterns

A major aim of *Everyday Mathematics* is for children to become aware of patterns of shapes and colors in their environment. Many pattern-recognition activities help children focus on geometric properties of shapes. Three examples follow.

- Make a pattern with craft sticks and ask your partner what comes next.

This type of sequence involves an understanding of the beauty and symmetry of parallel line segments and right-angle turns. What comes next, a horizontal triplet or a repetition of the first five triplets?

- Look at this pattern and describe what comes next.

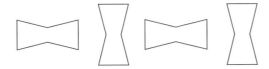

This puzzle introduces children to a sequence of concave hexagons, each of which is a 90° turn of the previous one. Or is it a slide of the first two repeated over and over? Or is it one sequence of horizontally oriented shapes with another sequence of vertically oriented ones spliced in? Without the need for formal names of the shapes or definitions of the slides and turns involved, this kind of activity helps children become aware of relationships of 2-dimensional objects and how those relationships can be described.

For more information, see Section 11.7: Transformations.

- Color the diamond pattern with three colors.

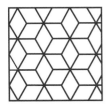 

This pattern is a *tessellation.* Without knowing any of the names of the shapes, young children can explore some rather sophisticated relations of polygons in the plane. In this example, the result suggests a pattern of stacked 3-dimensional cubes.

Everyday Mathematics engages children in many other activities with visual patterns. Patterns around the classroom or school include covers on fluorescent lights, panes in windows, wires or slats in fences, milk cartons in crates, floor and ceiling tiles, and patterns in magazine and newspaper pictures and advertisements. Home Links encourage children to find patterns at home and bring in examples.

15.1.2 Odd and Even Number Patterns

For centuries people have studied number patterns in a branch of mathematics called *number theory*. This section discusses perhaps the simplest of these patterns, *odd* and *even* numbers.

Children do informal explorations with odd and even numbers in *Kindergarten Everyday Mathematics*. In Grade 1, this topic becomes more of a focus. Odd and even numbers are simple, but exploring them can lead children to generalizations that are of fundamental importance in number theory. For example, it is easy to observe that pairing odd numbers of things always leaves one left over. Building on this simple observation, some children discover relationships such as the following:

- The sum of any two even numbers is even (there are no leftover pieces).
- The sum of an even number and an odd number is odd (the leftover piece remains).
- The sum of any two odd numbers is even (the leftovers pair up).
- The statements are still true if *positive difference* is substituted for *sum*. For example, the positive difference of any two even numbers is even.

Odd numbers of people or things are often seen as a nuisance. An odd number of people cannot be assigned equally to two different teams. Similarly, two people cannot equally share an odd number of unbreakable objects, such as marbles. On the other hand, it is easier to find the middle value, or median, of an odd number of data values because an even number of values has no single middle value.

Making generalizations based on observations of patterns is fundamental to mathematics and science. When children discover and "prove" simple relationships about odd and even numbers, they are learning powerful ways of thinking that will serve them throughout their mathematical careers.

15.1.3 Sequences

A *number sequence* is a list of numbers. Many sequences are important enough to have names:

- Whole numbers: 0, 1, 2, 3, 4, 5, 6, . . .
- Odd numbers: 1, 3, 5, 7, 9, 11, . . .
- Even numbers: 2, 4, 6, 8, 10, 12, . . .
- Prime numbers: 2, 3, 5, 7, 11, 13, . . .
- Square numbers: 1, 4, 9, 16, 25, 36, . . .

KEVIN: Odd numbers are neat. They always have a middle.

FATHER: What?

KEVIN: See (pointing to the third of five sticks in a row), always something in the middle. But with even numbers (removing the third stick from the row), there is just a space in the middle.

Sequences of numbers are similar to visual patterns in that both number sequences and shape or color sequences often have a *rule* that governs what the next number or object in the sequence is. For number sequences, the rule may involve one or more arithmetic operations. For example, the counting numbers can be generated by starting with 1 and then repeatedly applying the rule "Add 1." The even numbers can be generated by starting with 2 and then applying the rule "Add 2."

Many number sequences can be linked to visual patterns. The square numbers, for example, can be modeled by a sequence of square arrays. The even numbers and triangular numbers can also be modeled by sequences of dot patterns. The interplay of number sequences and visual patterns is fertile ground for investigations in elementary school mathematics.

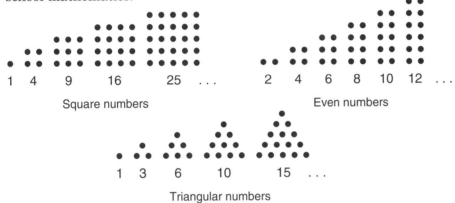

Patterns in many number sequences are accessible to children of any age. In Kindergarten, children may notice such patterns as they learn to skip count by 2s, 5s, and 10s and as they work with number lines and the Class Number Grid. Starting in *First Grade Everyday Mathematics,* children use Frames-and-Arrows diagrams and incomplete number lines to explore number sequences. Although Frames and Arrows and incomplete number lines are not part of the Pre-Kindergarten and Kindergarten programs, a brief description of these types of activities follows to give you a sense of how children will begin their more formal work with number sequences after Kindergarten.

Frames and Arrows

Frames-and-Arrows diagrams consist of a sequence of frames connected by arrows. Each frame contains a number; each arrow represents a rule that determines which number goes in the next frame. The numbers in a Frames-and-Arrows diagram form a sequence; the arrow rule(s) represent the mathematical structure that generates the sequence. Frames-and-Arrows diagrams are also called *chains.* A simple example of a Frames-and-Arrows diagram for the rule "Add 1" is shown below.

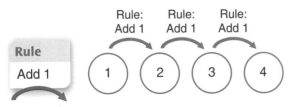

In Frames-and-Arrows problems, some information (either the rule or the numbers in some of the frames, or some combination of both) is missing. This allows children to invent or extend sequences or to find a rule or rules for a given sequence.

A chain can also have more than one arrow rule. If it does, the arrows for the rules must look different. For example, you might use a color arrow for one rule and a black arrow for the other rule.

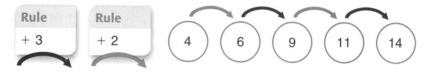

Incomplete Number Lines

Beginning in *First Grade Everyday Mathematics,* number lines are also used in a variation of Frames and Arrows. Children are given a number line with a sequence of blanks to fill in or tick marks to label. Like Frames-and-Arrows diagrams, *incomplete number lines* involve sequences in a different format. The scale of the number line, that is, the distance between tick marks, corresponds to the rule that governs the sequence. Examples of two general types of problems are given below.

- Given two boundary points on a number line with scale 1, fill in the blanks.

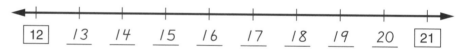

Note that the rule does not actually need to be stated in this type of problem because the number of intervals between the boundary points determines the scale.

- Given one or two numbers on a number line with scale 1, fill in the blanks in either direction. This encourages practice with both counting up and counting down.

Note that in the second type of problem, children could use a scale other than 1. For example, they could decide to count by 10s, which would lead to the values 749 through 819. This provides practice with more sophisticated counting techniques. Eventually, incomplete-number-line problems can include fractions, decimals, and negative numbers.

As they work with number lines over time, children may discover the amazing fact that between any two points or numbers, there is always another point or number. The number line is thus doubly infinite. The entire number line contains infinitely many numbers, but even the smallest interval between two numbers also contains infinitely many numbers.

15.1.4 Functions

Function is one of those everyday words that mathematicians use in a special way. This section begins with descriptions of how *Everyday Mathematics* approaches this powerful idea in ways that even Kindergarteners can understand. The mathematical definition of function follows that idea, along with a discussion of the many ways functions can be represented or modeled.

Function Machines

A *function machine* is an imaginary device that receives inputs and generates outputs. For example, the function machine in the margin takes an *input* number and *outputs* its double.

Children can imagine putting a number into this machine, waiting a moment, and then getting its double out. If a 1 is put in, then a 2 comes out. If a 5 is put in, then a 10 comes out. Whatever number goes in, twice that number comes out.

The inputs and outputs from a function machine can be recorded in a *function table*. Each row in the table holds an *ordered pair* in which the first number is the input and the second number is the output. Here is a table for the doubling function machine.

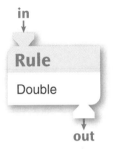

A doubling machine

in	out
1	2
2	4
3	6
5	10
638	1,276

A doubling function

In Kindergarten, a simpler format is used to display the inputs and outputs from a function machine. Rather than a table, the *in* and *out* numbers are shown in boxes, with the rule connecting each *in* and *out* box, as shown below.

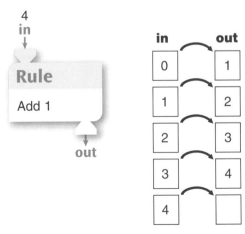

A Kindergarten function machine and *in/out* table

An important feature of a function machine is that it *always* gives the same output for a given input number. If two rows in an input-output table have the same number in the input column, then they must also have the same number in the output column.

Often, every input number has a different output number as in the doubling machine, but this is not required. For example, a function machine might always output the same number, no matter what is put in. Such functions are called *constant functions* and are perfectly legitimate, if a bit dull.

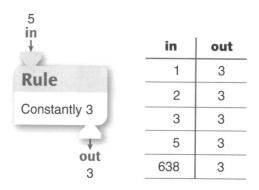

A constant function

A function machine captures the key features of most of the functions that are studied in pre-college mathematics, in which there are a set of inputs, a set of outputs, and a rule associating each input with exactly one output.

In *Kindergarten* through *Third Grade Everyday Mathematics,* function machines and function tables help children visualize how a rule associates each input value with an output value. A principal activity for developing this concept further is called "What's My Rule?"

"What's My Rule?"

Simple "What's My Rule?" games begin in *Pre-Kindergarten* and *Kindergarten Everyday Mathematics*. The first games are attribute or rule activities that sort children into a specified group. For example, children with hook-and-loop fasteners on their shoes belong to the group while children with other types of fasteners do not. You sort the children without revealing your rule, and the children have to guess what the sorting rule is.

In first through third grades, this idea is extended to sorting numbers. For example, you might draw a circle on the board and begin writing even numbers in the circle and odd numbers outside the circle. The children say numbers and try to guess where they go. Once they can reliably predict which numbers belong in the circle, they propose rules for the sorting. This can be repeated for other rules such as 1-digit numbers, numbers with zero in the ones place, and numbers between 20 and 30.

"What's My Rule?" activities are eventually extended to include problems in which pairs of numbers are given and the task is to find a rule that relates the numbers in each pair. The same rule has to

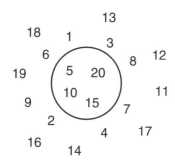

"What's My Rule?"

work for every pair. If the first number is input to a function machine, the second number is output. The problem is to identify a function machine's rule. The pairings can be displayed in a table of values.

Generally, in a "What's My Rule?" problem, two of the three parts of a function (input, output, and rule) are known. The goal is to find the unknown part. There are three basic types of problems:

- The rule and some input numbers are known. Give the corresponding output numbers.

in	out
3	
5	
12	

3
in
↓
Rule
+ 2

out
?

- The rule and some output numbers are known. Give the corresponding input numbers.

in	out
	6
	10
	20

?
in
↓
Rule
– 1

out
6

- Some input and output numbers are known. Give a rule.

in	out
0	5
5	10
6	11

0
in
↓
Rule
?

out
5

Eventually, more than one type of problem can be combined in a single table. For example, consider the following partially completed table with an unknown rule. There are enough input and output clues to allow someone to figure out a rule and fill in the blanks. This would be too difficult for most Kindergarteners, but many first graders could figure it out.

in	out
15	25
4	14
7	
	63

in
↓
Rule
?

out

What Is a Function?

Like many ideas in mathematics, the concept of a function is simple, yet powerful. Also like many ideas in mathematics, the definition of function seems at first to be rather odd. According to a dictionary of mathematics, "A *function* is a set of ordered pairs (x, y) in which each value of x is paired with exactly one value of y." A few examples may help clarify what this means:

- Doubling: {(1,2), (2,4), (3,6), (4,8), . . .}
- Squaring: {(1,1), (2,4), (3,9), (4,16), . . .}
- Adding 1: {(1,2), (2,3), (3,4), (4,5), . . .}

In each of these sets of ordered pairs, the first number is paired with exactly one second number. According to the definition, then, each of these sets is a function.

This definition applies to all the functions discussed so far in this chapter, but you will note that there is no mention of a rule. *The pairings in a function don't have to follow any rule.* The only requirement is that *each* first value has to be paired with *exactly one* second value. For example, you have a function if you pair each whole number less than 100 with any other whole number less than 100.

Along with no mention of rules, the mathematical definition of a function does not mention numbers. In fact, *functions do not have to involve numbers at all*—just a set of paired inputs and outputs. A function might take polygons in and output a name based on number of sides (triangle, quadrangle, pentagon, and so on). Another function might take triangles in and output a name based on angles (acute, right, or obtuse). All that is required for a function is a set of ordered pairs—(*input, output*)—in which every input has exactly one output.

In *Everyday Mathematics,* children do not explore functions without rules. Most interesting functions are interesting because they have rules. So all the functions in the program are associated with rules that are either given or may be deduced. To keep the rules interesting to children, the authors based many of them in real-life situations.

Many real-world situations may remind you of functions. A bathroom scale is a function machine; when you stand on it, it outputs your weight. A gasoline pump has a built-in function machine, in which the input is an amount of gasoline pumped and the output is a total cost including tax. One way to think about science is as a search for functions that relate real-world variables.

Sequences can also be considered to be functions. Some sequences are *iterative* functions, in which an output comes from applying a rule to the previous output, that is, to the previous number, or *term,* in the sequence, rather than to an independent input value. For example, to get the next even number, just add 2 to the previous even number. Other sequences are not iterative because there is no rule that gives the next term from the previous terms.

Another way to think of sequences as functions is to number, or *index*, the terms. For example, indexing a sequence of even numbers beginning with 2 led to the table in the margin. The indices can be thought of as input values and the even numbers in the sequence as the output. Thinking of a sequence in this way can sometimes lead you to a rule that will give any term in the sequence without having to find all the previous terms. From the table, it appears that a rule to find the *n*th even number is to simply double *n*.

In *Everyday Mathematics,* sequences are not treated as functions. It's easier to think of sequences as lists of numbers, often with a rule for generating the next term, as in Frames-and-Arrows diagrams. However, activities with sequences are quite helpful for developing children's understanding of functions.

in	out
1	2
2	4
3	6
4	8
5	10

> **NOTE:** Functions are not restricted to a single input variable and a single output variable. For example, a function with two input variables and one output variable is a *set of ordered triples*—perhaps the number of gallons of gasoline and the price per gallon as the inputs and total cost as the output. *Everyday Mathematics* is restricted to functions with only two variables.

Representing Functions

In *Everyday Mathematics,* children approach functions *concretely, pictorially, verbally,* and *symbolically.* Children see concrete representations in activities such as sorting objects according to some measure or attribute, lining up by height, or ordering pattern blocks by shape. All of these concrete activities include patterns that lead to functions.

For more information about these four representations, see Section 16.3: Problem Representations.

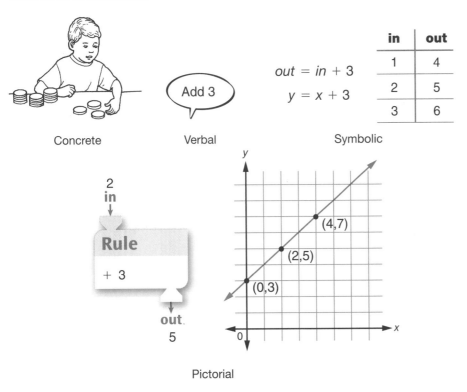

Four representations of functions

Verbal representations of functions include rules like "Double" or "Add 5." Verbal representations can often be made more concise by using *symbolic* representations like + 3 or *out = in* + 3 or *y = x* + 3, where *x* is input and *y* is output. The symbolic representation of functions as equations is explored extensively in fourth through sixth grades.

chapter 15

Frames-and-Arrows problems, incomplete number lines, and function machines are *pictorial* representations of functions and sequences. In Grade 3, children get their first exposure to graph models when they plot ordered pairs on a coordinate grid. Graphs are particularly important pictorial representations that are investigated extensively in *Fourth* through *Sixth Grade Everyday Mathematics.*

Function tables, or *in/out* charts, are an important kind of representation of functions in *Kindergarten* through *Third Grade Everyday Mathematics* and beyond. A table is sort of a cross between a pictorial and a symbolic representation. Many functions in real life are given as tables, such as those that fill the sports and business sections of a newspaper. For example, the input could be the name of a baseball team and the output the team batting average on the date of the newspaper. Many sports standings, financial tables, weather tables, and the like may represent functions. A great deal of the tabular information in almanacs and other reference books may also represent functions.

▶ 15.2 Algebra and Uses of Variables

Most adults in the United States probably remember algebra as a junior or senior high school course devoted to learning how to manipulate equations containing variables. But algebra is actually far more than just symbol manipulation. Algebra can be thought of as generalized arithmetic, as a set of powerful problem-solving procedures, as a study of numeric relations, or as a study of the structure of mathematics. The authors of *Everyday Mathematics* believe these are all valid descriptions of algebra. Accordingly, although the formal study of algebraic syntax is not appropriate for most elementary school children, *Everyday Mathematics* includes many activities involving algebra.

Algebra is a branch of mathematics that deals with variables and operations on variables. As soon as Kindergarteners or first graders encounter problems like $8 + \_\_ = 12$ they are thinking algebraically because the blank is a kind of variable. The same is true when young children try to solve missing-addend-type "pocket problems." Later in *Everyday Mathematics,* children experience variables as *unknowns* $(5 + x = 8)$, in formulas $(A = lw)$, in statements of mathematical *properties* $(a + b = b + a)$, and in functions $(y = x + 5)$. All of these experiences with variables prepare children for eventual success in algebra.

Algebra has important links to the patterns, sequences, and functions strand, as well as to the problem-solving thread in *Everyday Mathematics.* The diagram at left identifies the four representations that are featured in the program to model problems: concrete, verbal, pictorial, and symbolic. To represent problems symbolically, children need to understand the usefulness of algebraic notation and variables.

NOTE: For more on the place of algebra in the elementary school curriculum, see *The Ideas of Algebra, K–12,* edited by Art Coxford and Al Shulte. A full reference can be found on page 140.

For more information, see Section 16.3: Problem Representations and Section 15.1.4: Functions.

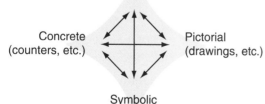

Four problem-solving representations

15.2.1 Uses of Variables

A *variable* is a letter or other symbol that stands for a number. In *Kindergarten* through *Third Grade Everyday Mathematics*, variables are primarily *unknowns* in open number sentences as described in the next section. In later grades, variables are also used in formulas, to express mathematical properties, to write functions, and in computer programs, but those uses are not discussed here.

Variables as Unknowns

As children write number sentences to fit problem situations, they often find that they need to represent numbers that are *unknown*. For example, the problem *There are 24 children in our class, but today only 18 are here. How many are not here?* might be modeled using any of these three equations using ? as the variable:

$$24 - ? = 18 \qquad 18 + ? = 24 \qquad 24 - 18 = ?$$

Alternatively, a *letter,* a *blank,* or a *box* can be used to indicate the unknown number:

$$24 - n = 18 \qquad 18 + \_\_ = 24 \qquad 24 - 18 = \boxed{}$$

All four of the symbols ?, n, ___, and $\boxed{}$ are variables.

Introducing the term *variable* in *Kindergarten* through *Third Grade Everyday Mathematics* is unnecessary because variables are used primarily as unknowns in open sentences. Also, in sentences such as $5 + n = 13$, the unknown is a single number that doesn't vary, so explaining the root of the word variable (*vary*) is not helpful.

15.2.2 Reading and Writing Open Sentences

Just as English words are more meaningful when they are in sentences, mathematical symbols are more meaningful in number sentences. And just as proper punctuation and grammar make written English easy to read, rules and conventions for reading and writing number sentences ease mathematical communication.

Number sentences such as $10 = 7 + 3$, $12 \div n = 6$, and $14 > 3$ have a left-hand side, a relation symbol, and a right-hand side. Symbols for numbers, unknowns, and operations can appear on either side of the relation symbol. Each side of a number sentence is a *numerical expression*. In the sentences above, 10, $7 + 3$, $12 \div n$, 6, 14, and 3 are expressions. In practice, however, single numbers are usually just called "numbers" and expressions usually include one or more operations.

Equations are number sentences in which the relation symbol is $=$, meaning *equals* or *is equal to*.

Inequalities are number sentences in which the relation symbol is one of the following:

$<$ (*is less than*)	$\leq$ (*is less than or equal to*)
$>$ (*is greater than*)	$\geq$ (*is greater than or equal to*)
$\neq$ (*is not equal to*)	$\approx$ (*is approximately equal to*)

---

in perspective

Besides being used to represent single unknown numbers, variables can represent more than a single unknown number in certain situations. For example, *I'm thinking of a number less than 10* can be modeled as $x < 10$. There can also be more than one unknown in situations modeled by equations. For example, *What pairs of whole numbers have 8 as their sum?* can be modeled as $m + n = 8$. Students in Grades 4 through 6 use more than one unknown when they write and interpret open sentences for "What's My Rule?" problems or geometric formulas.

A number phrase with a variable but no relation symbol, such as $3 + y$, is called an *algebraic expression* or simply an *expression*. A single number, called a *constant,* or a product of a constant and one or more variables is a *term* of an expression. Terms are operated on in expressions, if they are not the whole expression itself. For example, in the expression $75 + 3x$, the terms are 75 and $3x$. In $y = 3x$, the expression $3x$ is also a term.

An *open sentence* is a number sentence that is neither true nor false because it contains a variable or unknown. Examples are $14 = t - 9$ and $81 + c < 100$. Any number can replace the variable. A number that makes an open sentence *true* is called a *solution* of the sentence. The process of determining a value or values for a variable that make a number sentence true is called *solving the sentence.*

15.2.3 Solving Open Sentences

In *Pre-Kindergarten* and *Kindergarten Everyday Mathematics,* children begin by modeling number stories with manipulatives and pictoral representations or by solving them mentally. As the Kindergarten year progresses, children are also introduced to the concept of modeling number stories with number sentences. It is important that children develop a solid understanding of the underlying concepts before trying to translate their thoughts and concrete representations to symbolic representations.

In *Kindergarten* through *Third Grade Everyday Mathematics,* number models are used primarily to represent quantities and relationships in number stories and to help children understand them. For example, before solving a number story like *Marie has $5. She wants to go to a movie that costs $8. How much more does she need?* a child might think about finding the answer by counting up. Later, the child might write the number model $5 + ? = 8$. The model shows the relationships between the quantities in the story and suggests finding the answer by counting up or thinking of an addition fact. After solving the story, the child might write $5 + 3 = 8$ to summarize his work. Learning to use number models to represent number stories helps children learn the mathematical symbol system that is the foundation of algebra.

References and Resources for Patterns, Sequences, Functions, and Algebra

Coxford, A. F., and Shulte, A. P. (1988). *The Ideas of Algebra, K–12: 1988 Yearbook.* Reston, VA: National Council of Teachers of Mathematics.

Friedlander, A., and Tabach, M. (2001). "Promoting Multiple Representations in Algebra." In Cuoco, A. A., and Curcio, F. R. (Eds.) *The Roles of Representation in School Mathematics: 2001 Yearbook.* Reston, VA: National Council of Teachers of Mathematics.

Kalchman, M., and Koedinger, K. R. (2005). "Teaching and Learning Functions." In Donovan, M., and Bransford, J. (Eds.) *How Students Learn: History, Mathematics, and Science in the Classroom.* Washington, DC: The National Academies Press.

(in) perspective

Open sentences with inequalities are introduced in fourth grade. The terms *expression* and *equation* are introduced in fifth grade. In fifth and sixth grades, students begin to solve open number sentences using algebraic manipulations.

16 Problem Solving

Contents

In 1977, the National Council of Supervisors of Mathematics issued a position paper on basic skills. The first basic skill listed was *problem solving:* "Learning to solve problems is the principal reason for studying mathematics" (NCSM, 1977, p. 20). Ever since, problem solving has remained at the top of the school mathematics agenda.

This chapter is about problem solving and how *Everyday Mathematics* teaches it. It begins by discussing *mathematical sense,* which is integral to being a good problem solver. Next, it examines different definitions of problem solving and explains what problem solving means in *Everyday Mathematics.* This is followed by a discussion of ways mathematical ideas can be represented (concretely, pictorially, verbally, and symbolically) and what such representations have to do with problem solving. Next is an explanation of what mathematical modeling is and its relationship to problem solving. The chapter closes with details about teaching problem solving in *Everyday Mathematics* and a list of resources to help you learn more about this important mathematical thread.

▶ 16.1 Mathematical Sense

The range of experiences provided by *Everyday Mathematics* is designed to help children develop *mathematical sense,* which includes both an understanding of the body of mathematical knowledge and children's abilities to do mathematics to solve problems. Mathematical sense has the following principal components:

- *Number sense* is a feeling for where numbers come from and what they mean. Children need a great deal of experience using numbers of various kinds and sizes in order to understand which numbers make sense in a given situation. Number sense leads them to continually ask *What is a reasonable answer?* It helps children check the accuracy of answers whether they were obtained mentally, with pencil and paper, with a calculator, or by other means.

- *Operations sense* is a feeling for what addition, subtraction, multiplication, and division mean. For example, *why is it that products of whole numbers greater than zero are greater than one or both factors, but products of fractions or decimals can be less than the factors?*

- *Measure sense* is a feeling for what measurement means, what kinds of measures and units are appropriate in different situations, and what range of results are reasonable to accept. *Is 20 square feet a sensible measure of the area of the backyard? Might my dog really weigh 800 kilograms?*

- *Data sense* is an appreciation of a collection of numbers as a whole. *How reliable are the numbers? How might they be used? What are the "spread" and "landmarks" of a collection, such as the range and middle value?*

- *Spatial sense* comes from extensive experience with 2-dimensional and 3-dimensional geometric objects and from hands-on constructions that apply geometric principles. *How many grocery bags will fit in the trunk of my car? Can I cover all the walls in my bedroom with a quart of paint?*

- *Function sense,* or *pattern sense,* comes from looking for visual and number patterns and predicting outcomes from applying a rule. It helps children develop multiple perspectives by relating pictorial, symbolic, verbal, and concrete representations of a pattern. *Which is better, doubling $2 every year or adding $50 every year?*

In addition to mathematical sense, *Everyday Mathematics* is committed to helping children recognize and develop their own common sense. By *common sense,* the authors mean an understanding of one's own basic ideas and how they are useful for judging between reasonable alternatives in everyday situations. Children make use of all of these sensibilities as they solve problems throughout *Everyday Mathematics.*

▶ 16.2 What Is Problem Solving?

In elementary school mathematics books, *problem solving* often refers only to finding answers to printed "word problems." But problem solving is much more than that. In the NCSM position paper cited on the previous page, problem solving is defined as "the process of applying previously acquired knowledge to new and unfamiliar situations." In *Principles and Standards for School Mathematics,* the National Council of Teachers of Mathematics (NCTM) states that problem solving "is finding a way to reach a goal that is not immediately attainable" (NCTM, 2000, p. 116). In his classic book *How to Solve It,* George Polya wrote, "Solving a problem is finding the unknown means to a distinctly conceived end" (1988, p. 1).

These broader definitions of problem solving are not restricted to arithmetic and certainly not to arithmetic "word problems." Central to all of them is the idea that solution methods are not known in advance. A problem is not a problem if the problem solver knows exactly what to do right away. "Problems" for which the solution method is known ahead of time are simply exercises.

In *Everyday Mathematics,* problem solving is broadly conceived. Number stories, the program's version of word problems, have their place, but problem solving permeates the entire curriculum. Children solve problems both in purely mathematical contexts, such as "What's My Rule?" tables, and in real situations from the classroom and everyday life. Children also create and solve problems using information from the materials, from you, and from their own experiences and imaginations.

Everyday Mathematics defines problem solving as "the process of modeling everyday situations to find solutions using tools from mathematics." Mathematical modeling is discussed in detail in Section 16.4, but, in a nutshell, it means that expert problem solvers generally do one or more of these things:

- Identify what the problem is;
- Analyze what is known and seek out further data as necessary;
- Play with the data to discover patterns and meaning;
- Identify and apply mathematical techniques to find a solution;
- Look back after finding a solution to ask whether it makes sense and whether the method can be applied to other problems.

▶ ### 16.3 Problem Representations

Often a key step in solving a problem is simply looking at it in the right way. Consider the problem *How many handshakes are there when five people shake hands with one another?* Some ways to solve this problem are listed here.

- Find five people and have them shake hands, being careful to count each handshake. This approach is, to say the least, not very convenient.
- Make a list. If the people are represented by the letters A, B, C, D, and E, the handshakes could be listed as follows: A-B, A-C, A-D, A-E, B-C, B-D, B-E, C-D, C-E, and D-E. Although this is practical for five people, it could be troublesome for larger numbers, as you might make a mistake in listing all the handshakes.
- Draw a picture of a pentagon with all its diagonals. Each corner stands for a person, and each line connecting two people stands for a handshake. Finding a mistake in such a figure may be easier than finding one in a long list, although it might be a nuisance to draw the figure for a large number of people.

Each of these solutions to the handshake problem depends on a different way of approaching, or representing, the problem. One way

NOTE: A comprehensive curriculum like *Everyday Mathematics* must include many exercises so children can practice essential skills. But they are not genuine problems in the sense implied here.

in	out
55	60
85	90
103	108

A "What's My Rule?" problem

NOTE: In mathematics, the word *solution* has two related meanings. One meaning is *the answer.* The other is *how the answer was obtained.* Usually the context makes clear which meaning is intended, but you may find it useful to call a final result an "answer" and the method used to get the result the "solution."

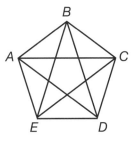

chapter 16

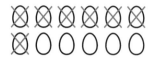

For examples of four representations of functions, see Section 15.1.4: Functions.

For more information on problem representations, see *The Roles of Representation in School Mathematics* edited by Cuoco and Curcio (2001). A full reference is on page 152.

NOTE: Individual differences are likely to lead some children, and even teachers, to favor some representations over others. For example, ELL or hearing-impaired children may be less likely to favor verbal representations. Be careful not to over-emphasize the need for all children to explore all the representations.

used real people; another involved a list; the third made use of a drawing. Different ways of approaching a problem are called *problem representations.*

Everyday Mathematics focuses on four problem representations: *concrete, verbal, pictorial,* and *symbolic.* Suppose, for example, you need a dozen eggs to make egg salad, but when you take the eggs out of the refrigerator, you drop the carton on the floor. That's a *concrete* situation. A *verbal* description might make certain details explicit, such as *Oh no! I broke 7 of them!* A *pictorial* representation like the one in the margin could show the unfortunate eggs, and symbolically, you could write this number model $12 - 7 = 5$.

These varieties of problem representations are diagrammed below. Note that double-headed arrows connect each kind of representation with each of the other kinds. Children and adults are likely to use all of these representations at one time or another, depending on the situation at hand.

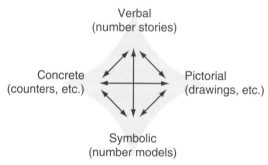

Four problem-solving representations

Representations are used both to give problems and to model solutions. Different children have different talents for, and preferences among, the representations, so all children benefit from repeated exposures to all four types. One of the aims of *Everyday Mathematics* is to increase children's facility with a variety of representations.

Another objective in *Everyday Mathematics* is to help children make easy translations among various ways of representing problems. Representations are closely related to solution strategies; translating a problem into another representation is often a key to solving it. Discussion of different representations and solutions exposes children to methods they may like to try and reinforces the important message that there are many ways to solve problems.

As you discuss problems and solutions with children, compare various representations and ask for translations from one to another. For example:

- Ask children to draw a picture for a problem given in words.
- If a child solves $21 + 6$ by counting up on a number grid, ask her to solve $25 + 4$ by just thinking about the grid rather than by using an actual grid.
- Ask children to translate a situation diagram into an open number sentence with a ? or __ for the unknown.

By encouraging multiple representations and translations among representations, you can help children develop into more powerful problem solvers.

As you observe children working with various representations, you can also determine their problem-solving strengths and weaknesses. In turn, this can help you tailor activities to meet individual needs. For example, you might observe that a certain child always uses counters to solve problems. This might lead you to suggest drawing a simple picture of the counters. Or a child who is adept at drawing pictures might benefit from a suggestion to try using a number grid.

16.4 Mathematical Modeling

A *mathematical model* is something mathematical that corresponds to something in the real or imaginary world. A sphere is a model for a basketball. The number sentence $22 + 1 = 23$ is a model for the number of children in a classroom when a new student arrives. The equation $d = (5 \text{ hours}) \times (50 \text{ miles/hour})$ is a model for the distance a car travels in 5 hours at 50 mph; and the formula $d = rt$ is a model linking distance, rate (speed), and time more generally. Specialists in science and industry spend much of their time building and testing mathematical models of real-world systems. Some people do mathematical modeling whenever they use mathematics to solve a problem.

Put another way, *mathematical modeling* is a process of translating a real or hypothetical situation into mathematical language. After the translation, a solution is found using mathematical techniques. Then the result is translated back into the real or hypothetical world as the answer to the original problem. This process is illustrated in the margin.

Yet the figure in the margin probably oversimplifies the process. Mathematical modeling is often more complicated and is likely to involve some or all of the following stages:

- Formulate or confront a problem. Try to understand your problem. What do you want to find out? Imagine what the answer would look like if you had one.
- Study the information that is given and seek additional data as necessary. Discard unnecessary information. Sort the data you have.
- Explore the data. Represent the data in various ways, perhaps by drawing a picture, making a graph, or writing a number model. Play with the data.
- Do the math. Do the arithmetic, algebra, geometry, data analysis, or whatever else is necessary to find an answer.
- Check the answer to see if it makes sense. Compare your answer to someone else's or to an answer you obtain in another way. Think about the method you used. Can the same method be used to solve other problems? Is there another method that would work for this problem? Compare various solutions and methods.

NOTE: Using pictures to represent problems and solutions can be especially helpful for children who are having difficulty with other representations. Use simple pictures and diagrams to illustrate classroom discussions as much as possible.

NOTE: The word *model* can also refer to something in the real world that illustrates something mathematical. In this sense, a basketball is a model of a sphere. When people speak of mathematical modeling, however, the model is the mathematical object and the thing that is modeled is something in the real or hypothetical world.

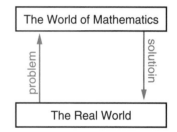

Mathematical modeling

These stages of the mathematical-modeling process are summarized in the diagram below.

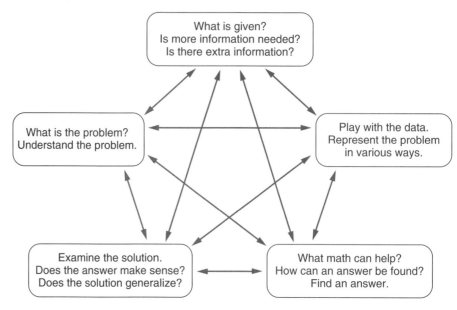

Stages in the mathematical-modeling process

chapter 16

NOTE: In *Pre-Kindergarten* and *Kindergarten Everyday Mathematics,* children often use class-generated data (from surveys, voting, attendance, or aspects of everyday classroom life) to make up and solve problems. Later in *Everyday Mathematics,* data or information that children can use to make up and solve problems is often given on a journal or *Student Reference Book* page.

The process of mathematical modeling can actually begin anywhere and go anywhere. The arrows in the figure above illustrate this. For example, mathematical modeling often begins with data. Suppose you are a baseball fan and are studying tables of baseball statistics. As you explore the data, you might notice that it appears that in inter-league games, National League teams win more often than American League teams. This might lead you to ask whether this is actually true. By finding the total number of wins for each league, you might find that the National League does win more often. If you wished, you could test your conclusion by making a prediction about the next set of inter-league games.

This baseball situation involves all five stages of the mathematical-modeling process. Sometimes, only a few of the stages are involved. An expert problem solver, or a child for that matter, might see a solution to a problem instantly and simply have to check that it's correct. Sometimes it may be necessary to cycle repeatedly among the stages—play with the data, find more data, play with the new data, and so on—before finding a solution.

Mathematical modeling involves *abstraction.* For example, the number model $100 - 79 = 21$ is an abstraction of buying a 79¢ granola bar with a dollar bill. The modeling process involves both a real situation and an abstract mathematical model of that situation. Even a mathematical model that uses concrete physical objects, such as base-10 blocks, is abstract in the sense that it omits many details of the original situation. Because it is abstract, a single mathematical model can fit many different real-world situations. For example, the formula for the area of a rectangle, $A = lw$ (area A equals length l times width w), applies to all real-world rectangles. This versatility is part of what makes mathematics such a powerful problem-solving tool.

However, because they are abstract, mathematical models can become disconnected from the situation they are meant to model. Sometimes, children work their way through a mathematical process, arrive at an answer that makes no sense, and are completely unconcerned that they have produced nonsense. Making frequent connections between the real situation and the abstract model can help keep the process on track. Encourage children to ask themselves questions to keep the modeling process grounded: *What does this number refer to? What does this graph say about the problem situation? Does this solution make sense?*

One reason for making ballpark estimates is to keep the problem-solving process on track. If a solution doesn't agree with the estimate, then something is wrong either with the estimate or with the solution. Making ballpark estimates helps reinforce connections between mathematical abstractions and real-world situations.

16.5 Teaching Problem Solving

Often when you are trying to learn something complicated, it is a good idea to focus on just one part of the whole. A pianist might play a difficult passage over and over again; a chef might practice making a *roux* until it's just right; a golfer might spend hours working on 8-foot putts. Practicing just one part at a time helps develop component skills that are essential for mastery of the entire complex activity, whether it's piano playing, cooking, or golfing.

As the mathematical-modeling-process diagram illustrates, problem solving is a complicated activity that can be broken down into parts, such as formulating problems and playing with data, each of which children can practice separately. Many of the exercises in *Everyday Mathematics* aim to provide practice in specific parts of the problem-solving process. For example, children become skilled at counting, measuring, calculating, estimating, looking up information, and many other skills that are useful in solving problems. During their years in school, children thus learn how to be effective in each separate stage of the mathematical-modeling process.

Such instruction is effective in teaching children how to manage each individual stage of the process, but successful problem solving in real life requires experience in navigating among the stages, just as cooking a fine meal requires successfully orchestrating many separate steps. It may take years of experience to become proficient at navigating among the stages. Knowing when to abandon an approach that's not working and go back to playing with the data, for example, is a skill that develops with experience.

As children progress through *Everyday Mathematics,* they confront or pose problems that are more interesting and less routine, that make use of more sophisticated skills and concepts, and that require more complicated navigation through the mathematical-modeling process.

16.5.1 Number Stories

Everyday Mathematics aims to help children deal with real, age-appropriate problems. The authors' research shows that young children have impressive but largely untapped problem-solving abilities. One way *Everyday Mathematics* works to expand these abilities is through the use of number stories.

Number stories are stories that involve numbers and one or more explicit or implicit questions. For example:

- *I have 7 crayons in my desk. Carrie gave me 8 more crayons. How many crayons do I have in all? There are 15 crayons in all.*

- *I have 7 crayons in my desk. Carrie gave me 8 more crayons. Now I have 15 crayons in all.*

Number stories may be written, oral, pictorial, or even dramatic. They may be created by you or by the children. Stories may arise spontaneously from classroom situations or be designed to practice specific problem-solving techniques.

Starting with *Pre-Kindergarten* and *Kindergarten Everyday Mathematics,* children create number stories based on everyday experiences. The children's stories are based on real situations—getting lollipops, inviting friends, losing toys, sharing snacks, and so on. In Grades 1 through 3, many of the children's stories are based on journal pages that present a range of numerical data related to real situations such as animal measures, shopping for groceries, and vending machines.

Problem posing, that is, making up problems, is a part of the problem-solving process that is often ignored in school mathematics; yet identifying and defining the problem is often the crucial first step toward a solution. Problem posing also leads to a high level of enthusiasm and involvement because children feel they have ownership of the problems they themselves create. Because the information presented tends to cover a wide range of difficulty, all members of the class have opportunities to participate.

Children enjoy hearing and telling number stories. You might consider devoting an occasional language arts lesson to working with number stories. Creating, sharing, and discussing number stories can help develop children's communication and listening skills as well as their problem-solving abilities. The careful reading required for solving number stories helps children develop skills that will serve them well when they deal with technical text in later years.

Number stories provide a bridge from natural to symbolic language. In Pre-Kindergarten, most children will and should remain at the natural language stage. Children in Kindergarten and Grade 1 can be helped across the bridge from natural to symbolic language if you follow these steps:

- Introduce number stories using a situation that is familiar to the children. Keep the stories short and the language simple. Be aware that when children tell their own stories, this is not always easy to do. Draw pictures or diagrams whenever possible to illustrate the stories. Modeling with concrete objects is effective with all ages and essential with younger children.

- Begin to include occasional mathematical terms in your comments on children's stories. For example, *You told an addition story. You had 5 candies and then you added 3 more.*

- Begin writing number models beneath your illustrations as you discuss the stories. Connect the numbers and relation symbols in the number models to quantities and actions in the stories. For example, *This 5 is for the candies you started with, + 3 means you got 3 more, 8 tells how many you ended up with, and = means that 8 is the same as 5 and 3 more.* Help children understand how the symbols fit the problem situation. Explain that symbols let them write a number story quickly and easily. *If you write it in words, it takes a long time and might fill the board.*

- Children may begin writing number models to fit stories. Often more than one number model can fit a given number story. Some first-grade children may begin to use diagrams for parts-and-total, change, and comparison stories, although this is not expected until second grade.

Many first-grade teachers report that children enjoy trying to put their stories into words. For many children, it appears that skill at writing stories develops later than the ability to write number models using +, −, and =. But by second grade, most children are able to write number stories. Younger children can tell or dictate stories before they can write them, or they can draw pictures and write a few words or numbers for their stories.

Children use a variety of methods to solve one another's number stories, but *Everyday Mathematics* encourages using mental arithmetic whenever possible. This does not mean restricting children to doing the arithmetic entirely in their heads. Instead, children should develop a variety of flexible solution strategies that use whatever means are familiar and comfortable, such as manipulatives, fingers, jumps on a number line, doodles, diagrams, and calculators. The emphasis is on solving problems in the children's own ways, on being open to a variety of approaches, and on choosing the approach that is most appropriate for a particular problem situation.

16.5.2 Sharing Children's Strategies and Solutions

Research indicates that children develop a variety of problem-solving strategies if they are given the opportunity to share their ideas with their peers. If this sharing takes place in an open, receptive environment, children will learn that inventing creative, innovative ways of solving problems is acceptable in mathematics. The practice of gathering together to share solutions after individual or group problem solving continues throughout *Everyday Mathematics*.

Number stories are an excellent context for developing habits of sharing. Children can share their strategies, both correct and incorrect. They can record their solutions on the board, illustrating with pictures

 perspective

By fourth grade, students consistently use variables in number models for number stories.

For more information, see "Exploring Mathematics through Talking and Writing" by Whitin and Whitin (2000). A full reference is on page 152.

chapter 16

NOTE: See Section 1.3: Encouraging Problem Solving: Sharing Strategies and Solutions for a discussion of ways to promote children's problem-solving abilities through strategy sharing.

Guide to Solving Number Stories

1. What do you know from reading the story?

2. What do you want to find out?

3. What do you need to do? Do it, and then record what you did.

4. If you can, write a number model that fits the problem.

5. Answer the question.

6. Check. Ask *Does my answer make sense? How do I know?*

---

and number models. Children develop a better understanding of various mathematical processes when asked to think and strategize rather than when they are merely asked to repeat the steps of a standard written algorithm.

16.5.3 Problem-Solving Strategies for Beginners

The diagram of the mathematical-modeling process shown on page 146 fits what experts actually do when they solve problems but is too complicated to be of much help for beginners. On the other hand, many elementary school mathematics textbooks include long lists of strategies and tips; but these lists are often little help even with simple real-life problems and are essentially useless for dealing with complicated problems on public policy and the workplace.

Children need a guide that is more useful than a list of tips but simpler than a diagram of expert behavior. To this end, *Everyday Mathematics* outlines general guidelines for managing problem solving, such as those in the margin. These guidelines need not be formally discussed with Pre-Kindergarteners and Kindergarteners, but they are useful to keep in mind as you support children in developing their problem-solving abilities.

Because problems from everyday life are usually complicated, the first need is often to simplify the situation and figure out exactly what is known and what is to be found out. For example, problem situations in daily life often contain many irrelevant numbers. Sometimes relevant numbers are missing and must be inferred or derived from what is known. Often, the problem solver must deal not only with just a few counts or measures but also with large sets of data. Considerable effort may be required to make the data consistent in format and to devise a display that suggests useful patterns or interesting questions. The process seldom follows one predictable step after another.

16.5.4 Results from *Everyday Mathematics* Teachers

Teachers who have used the approach to problem solving that is integrated into *Everyday Mathematics* report very positive results, as have researchers and program evaluators who have studied problem solving in the program. These teachers and researchers find that children develop strong, flexible, and independent calculation skills and problem-solving strategies. After using mental arithmetic with interesting number stories and relatively small numbers, children become able to operate with much larger numbers than they would typically have been able to handle. Children also develop an understanding of various mathematical processes that many children do not attain when using standard written algorithms.

Blair Chewning, an *Everyday Mathematics* teacher from Virginia, provides an example of the powerful results that this approach can yield. Ms. Chewning read an article in the *Richmond Times-Dispatch* with the headline "State, national math scores add up to poor report card." The picture painted was bleak, charging that on a recent national mathematics test, 40% of eighth-grade students failed to perform at even a basic level. The following problem was given as an example of a "basic" problem for grade 8:

> Jill needs to earn $45 for a class trip. She earns $2 each day on Mondays, Tuesdays, and Wednesdays. She earns $3 each day on Thursdays, Fridays, and Saturdays. She does not work on Sundays. How many weeks will it take her to earn $45?

Ms. Chewning was teaching second grade at the time, using *Everyday Mathematics,* and decided to see how her children would handle this problem. This is what she reported:

Every single student attempted the problem, which was presented as optional. Such risk-takers they have become! Two children, using mental math only, presented me with the correct answer by the time I had completed writing the number story on the board. A total of 82% of the children, using a variety of strategies (see below), successfully solved the problem in less than five minutes. Of the three children who struggled, two were right on track, making only minor computational errors, and the third achieved success after extensive trial and error.

Needless to say, I was astounded. While I had expected them to be successful to some extent, I had not anticipated the speed and comfort with which they approached the task.

Thank you, *Everyday Mathematics.* The skills your program fosters empowered my second graders to soar higher than they or their teacher thought possible. They wore the "hats" of eighth graders quite proudly that day and would seem to suggest that our math future is anything but bleak.

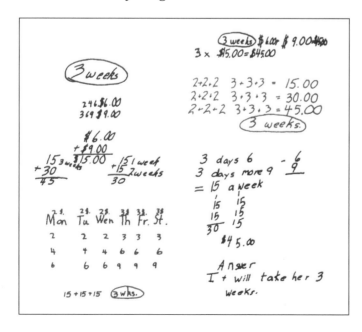

References and Resources on Problem Solving

Cuoco, A. A., and Curcio, F. R. (2001). *The Roles of Representation in School Mathematics: 2001 Yearbook*. Reston, VA: National Council of Teachers of Mathematics.

National Council of Supervisors of Mathematics. (1977). Position paper on basic skills. *Arithmetic Teacher 25 (1)*, pp. 19–22.

National Council of Supervisors of Mathematics. (1988). *Essential mathematics for the 21st century: The position of the National Council of Supervisors of Mathematics*. Minneapolis, MN: Author.

National Council of Teachers of Mathematics. (1980). *An Agenda for Action: Recommendations for School Mathematics of the 1980s*. Reston, VA: Author.

National Council of Teachers of Mathematics. (1989). *Curriculum and Evaluation Standards for School Mathematics*. Reston, VA: Author.

National Council of Teachers of Mathematics. (2000). *Principles and Standards for School Mathematics*. Reston, VA: Author.

Polya, George. (1988). *How to Solve It*. Princeton, NJ: Princeton University Press.

Whitin, D.J., and Whitin, P. (2000). "Exploring Mathematics through Talking and Writing." In Burke, M., and Curcio, F.R. (Eds.) *Learning Mathematics for a New Century: 2000 Yearbook*. Reston, VA: National Council of Teachers of Mathematics.

Glossary

This glossary contains words and phrases from *Pre-Kindergarten* through *Third Grade Everyday Mathematics*. To place the definitions in broader mathematical contexts, most entries also refer to sections in this *Teacher's Reference Manual*. In a definition, terms in italics are defined elsewhere in the glossary.

accurate As correct as possible according to an accepted standard. For example, an accurate measure or count is one with little or no error. See *precise* and Section 14.2: Approximation and Rounding.

acre A U.S. customary unit of *area* equal to 43,560 square feet. An acre is roughly the size of a football field. A square mile is 640 acres. See the Tables of Measures and Section 12.4: Area.

acute angle An *angle* with a measure less than 90°. See Section 11.4.1: Angles and Rotations.

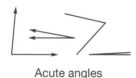

Acute angles

acute triangle A *triangle* with three acute angles. See Section 11.4.2: Polygons (*n*-gons).

An acute triangle

addend Any one of a set of numbers that are added. For example, in $5 + 3 + 1$, the addends are 5, 3, and 1.

addition fact Two 1-digit numbers and their sum, such as $9 + 7 = 16$. See *arithmetic facts* and Section 14.3.3: Fact Practice.

addition/subtraction use class In *Everyday Mathematics,* situations in which addition or subtraction is used. These include *parts-and-total, change*, and *comparison* situations. See Section 9.3.1: Addition and Subtraction Use Classes.

adjacent angles Two *angles* with a common *side* and *vertex* that do not otherwise overlap.

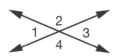

Angles 1 and 2, 2 and 3, 3 and 4, and 4 and 1 are pairs of adjacent angles.

adjacent sides Same as *consecutive sides*.

algebra (1) The use of letters of the alphabet to represent numbers in *equations, formulas,* and rules. (2) A set of rules and properties for a number system. (3) A school subject, usually first studied in eighth or ninth grade. See Section 15.2: Algebra and Uses of Variables.

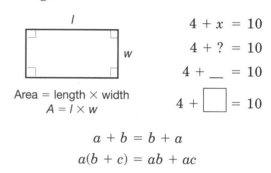

$$4 + x = 10$$
$$4 + ? = 10$$
$$4 + \_\_ = 10$$
$$4 + \boxed{} = 10$$

Area = length × width
$A = l \times w$

$$a + b = b + a$$
$$a(b + c) = ab + ac$$

Formulas, equations, and properties using algebra

algebraic expression An *expression* that contains a *variable*. For example, if Maria is 2 inches taller than Joe and if the variable M represents Maria's height, then the algebraic expression $M - 2$ represents Joe's height. See *algebra* and Section 15.2: Algebra and Uses of Variables.

algebraic order of operations Same as *order of operations*.

algorithm A set of step-by-step instructions for doing something, such as carrying out a computation or solving a problem. The most common algorithms are those for basic arithmetic computation, but there are many others. Some mathematicians and many computer scientists spend a great deal of time trying to find more efficient algorithms for solving problems. See Section 9.4: Algorithms.

Glossary

altitude (1) In *Everyday Mathematics,* same as *height* of a figure. (2) Distance above sea level. Same as *elevation.*

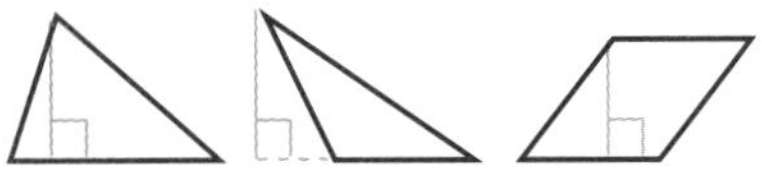

Heights/altitudes of 2-D figures are shown in blue.

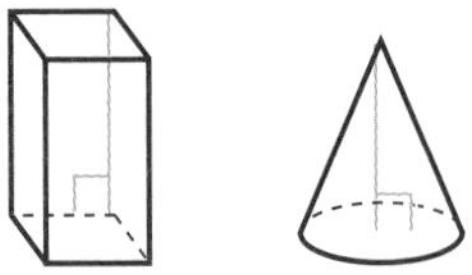

Heights/altitudes of 3-D figures are shown in blue.

A.M. The abbreviation for *ante meridiem,* meaning "before the middle of the day" in Latin. From midnight to noon.

analog clock (1) A clock that shows the time by the positions of the hour and minute hands. (2) Any device that shows time passing in a continuous manner, such as a sundial. Compare to *digital clock.* See Section 13.2.1: Clocks.

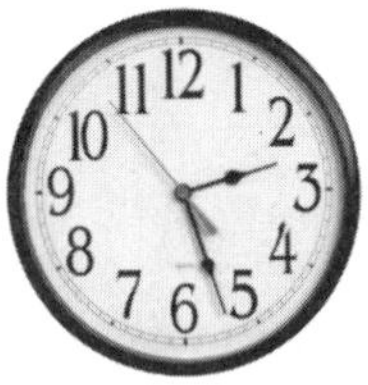

An analog clock

-angle A suffix meaning *angle,* or corner.

angle A figure formed by two *rays* or two *line segments* with a common *endpoint* called the *vertex* of the angle. The rays or segments are called the *sides* of the angle. An angle is measured in degrees between 0 and 360. One side of an angle is the *rotation* image of the other side through a number of degrees. Angles are named after their vertex point alone as in $\angle A$ below; or by three points, one on each side and the vertex in the middle as in $\angle BCD$ below. See *acute angle, obtuse angle, reflex angle, right angle, straight angle,* and Section 11.4.1: Angles and Rotations.

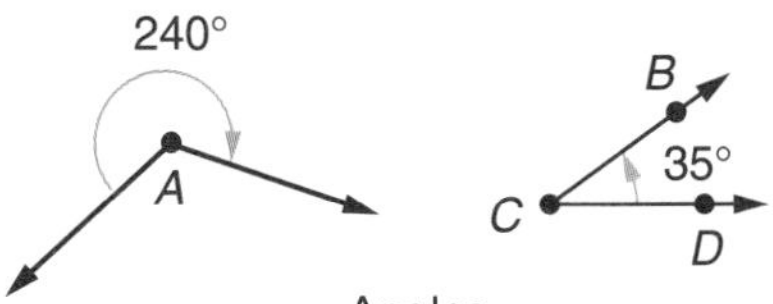

Angles

apex In a *pyramid* or *cone,* the *vertex* opposite the *base.* In a pyramid, all the nonbase faces meet at the apex. See Section 11.5.2: Polyhedrons and Section 11.5.3: Solids with Curved Surfaces.

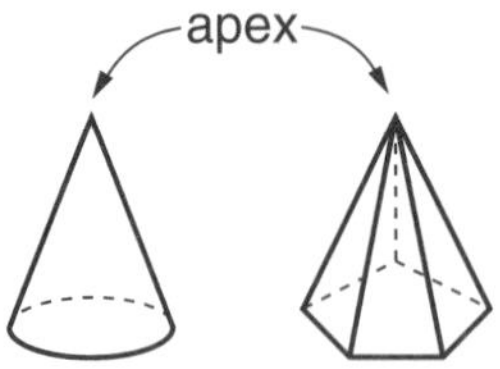

approximately equal to (≈) A symbol indicating an *estimate* or approximation to an exact value. For example, $\pi \approx 3.14$. See Section 14.2: Approximation and Rounding.

arc of a circle A part of a *circle* between and including two *endpoints* on the circle. For example, the endpoints of the *diameter* of a circle define an arc called a *semicircle.* An arc is named by its endpoints.

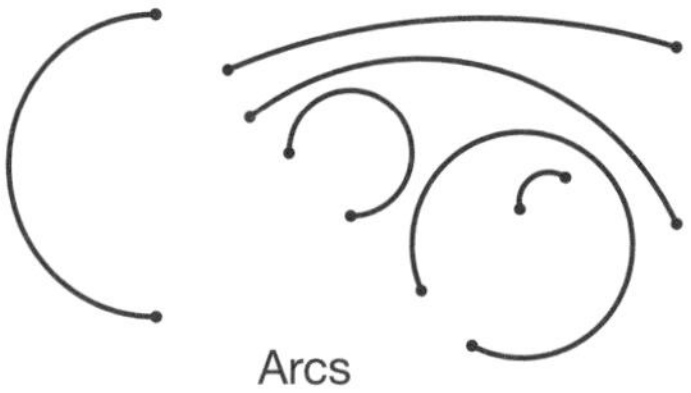

Arcs

area The amount of *surface* inside a *2-dimensional figure.* The figure might be a triangle or rectangle in a plane, the curved surface of a cylinder, or a state or country on Earth's surface. Commonly, area is measured in *square units* such as square miles, square inches, or square centimeters. See Section 12.4: Area.

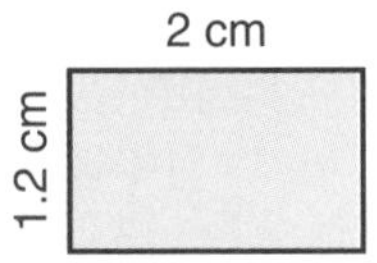

A rectangle with area
$1.2 \text{ cm} \times 2 \text{ cm} = 2.4 \text{ cm}^2$

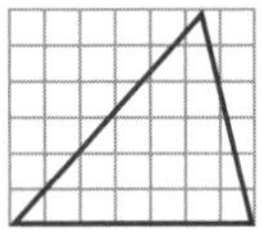

A triangle with area
21 square units

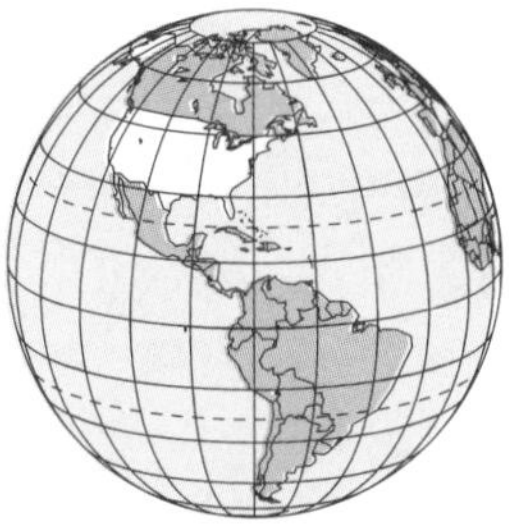

The area of the United States
is about 3,800,000 square miles.

arithmetic facts The addition facts (whole-number *addends* 9 or less); their inverse subtraction facts; multiplication facts (whole-number *factors* 9 or less); and their inverse division facts, except there is no division by zero. There are

100 addition facts: $0 + 0 = 0$ through $9 + 9 = 18$
100 subtraction facts: $0 - 0 = 0$ through $18 - 9 = 9$
100 multiplication facts: $0 \times 0 = 0$ through $9 \times 9 = 81$
90 division facts: $0 \div 1 = 0$ through $81 \div 9 = 9$

See *extended facts, fact extensions, fact power,* and Section 14.3.2: Basic Facts and Fact Power.

arm span Same as *fathom.*

array (1) An arrangement of objects in a regular *pattern,* usually rows and columns. (2) A *rectangular array.* In *Everyday Mathematics,* an array is a rectangular array unless specified otherwise. See Section 9.3.2: Multiplication and Division Use Classes and Section 12.4: Area.

arrow rule In *Everyday Mathematics,* an operation that determines the number that goes into the next frame in a *Frames-and-Arrows* diagram. There may be more than one arrow rule per diagram. See Section 15.1.4: Functions.

arrows In *Everyday Mathematics,* the links representing the *arrow rule(s)* in a *Frames-and-Arrows* diagram. See Section 15.1.4: Functions.

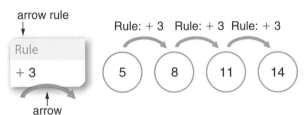

Associative Property of Addition A property of addition that three numbers can be added in any order without changing the sum. For example, $(4 + 3) + 7 = 4 + (3 + 7)$ because $7 + 7 = 4 + 10$.

In symbols:
For any numbers $a, b,$ and $c,$
$(a + b) + c = a + (b + c).$

Subtraction is not associative. For example, $(4 - 3) + 7 \neq 4 - (3 + 7)$ because $8 \neq -6.$

attribute A feature of an object or common feature of a set of objects. Examples of attributes include size, shape, color, and number of sides. Same as *property.*

attribute blocks A set of blocks in which each block has one each of four *attributes* including color, size, thickness, and shape. The blocks are used for attribute identification and sorting activities. Compare to *pattern blocks.*

average A typical value for a set of numbers. In everyday life, average usually refers to the *mean* of the set, found by adding all the numbers and dividing the sum by the number of numbers. In statistics, several different averages, or *landmarks,* are defined, including *mean, median,* and *mode.* See Section 10.2.4: Data Analysis.

axis of rotation A line about which a solid figure rotates.

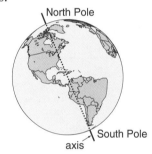

B

ballpark estimate A rough *estimate;* "in the ballpark." A ballpark estimate can serve as a check of the reasonableness of an answer obtained through some other procedure, or it can be made when an exact value is unnecessary or impossible to obtain. See Section 14.1: Estimation.

bank draft A written order for the exchange of money. For example, $1,000 bills are no longer printed so $1,000 bank drafts are issued. People can exchange $1,000 bank drafts for smaller bills, perhaps ten $100 bills.

bar graph A graph with horizontal or vertical bars that represent data. See Section 10.2.3: Organizing and Displaying Data.

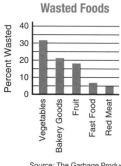

Wasted Foods

Source: The Garbage Product

Fat Content of Foods

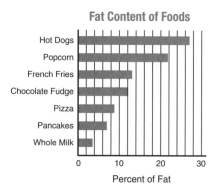

Source: The New York Public Library Desk Reference

base (in exponential notation) A number that is raised to a *power*. For example, the base in 5^3 is 5. See Section 9.2.1: Arithmetic Symbols.

base of a parallelogram (1) The side of a *parallelogram* to which an *altitude* is drawn. (2) The length of this side. The area of a parallelogram is the base times the *altitude* or height perpendicular to it. See *height of a parallelogram* and Section 11.4.2: Polygons (*n*-gons).

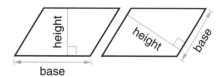

base of a prism or cylinder Either of the two parallel and congruent *faces* that define the shape of a *prism* or *cylinder*. In a cylinder, the base is a circle. See *height of a prism or cylinder,* Section 11.5.2: Polyhedrons, and Section 11.5.3: Solids with Curved Surfaces.

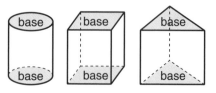

base of a pyramid or cone The *face* of a pyramid or cone that is opposite its *apex*. The base of a cone is a circle. See *height of a pyramid or cone,* Section 11.5.2: Polyhedrons, and Section 11.5.3: Solids with Curved Surfaces.

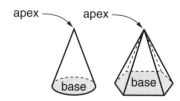

base of a rectangle (1) One of the sides of a *rectangle*. (2) The length of this side. The area of a rectangle is the base times the *altitude* or height. See *height of a rectangle* and Section 11.4.2: Polygons (*n*-gons).

base of a triangle (1) Any side of a *triangle* to which an *altitude* is drawn. (2) The length of this side. The area of a triangle is half the base times the altitude or height. See *height of a triangle* and Section 11.4.2: Polygons (*n*-gons).

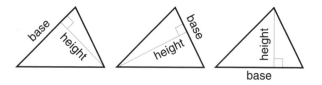

base ten Our system for writing numbers that uses only the 10 symbols 0, 1, 2, 3, 4, 5, 6, 7, 8, and 9, called *digits*. You can write any number using one or more of these 10 digits, and each digit has a value that depends on its place in the number (its *place value*). In the base-ten system, each place has a value 10 times that of the place to its right, and 1 tenth the value of the place to its left. See Section 8.2.1: Numeration and Place Value.

Glossary

base-10 blocks A set of blocks to represent ones, tens, hundreds, and thousands in the *base-ten place-value* system. In *Everyday Mathematics*, the unit block, or *cube*, has 1-cm edges; the ten block, or *long*, is 10 unit blocks in length; the hundred block, or *flat*, is 10 longs in width; and the thousand block, or *big cube*, is 10 flats high. See *long*, *flat*, and *big cube* for photos of the blocks. See *base-10 shorthand* and Section 8.6.1: Base-10 Blocks.

base-10 shorthand In *Everyday Mathematics*, a written notation for *base-10 blocks*. See Section 8.6.1: Base-10 Blocks.

Base-10-Block Shorthand		
Name	**Block**	**Shorthand**
cube	▫	▪
long	▯	│
flat	▦	☐
big cube	▨	◱

benchmark A count or measure that can be used to evaluate the reasonableness of other counts, measures, or estimates. A benchmark for land area is that a football field is about one acre. A benchmark for length is that the width of an adult's thumb is about one inch. See Section 12.1: Personal Measures.

big cube In *Everyday Mathematics*, a *base-10 block* cube that measures 10-cm by 10-cm by 10-cm. A big cube consists of one thousand 1-cm cubes. See Section 8.6.1: Base-10 Blocks.

A big cube

bisect To divide a segment, angle, or figure into two parts of equal measure. See *bisector*.

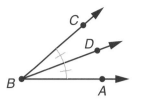

Ray *BD* bisects angle *ABC*.

bisector A *line, segment,* or *ray* that divides a segment, an angle, or a figure into two parts of equal measure. See *bisect*.

braces See *grouping symbols*.

brackets See *grouping symbols*.

broken-line graph Same as *line graph*.

C

calendar (1) A *reference frame* to keep track of the passage of time. Many different calendars exist, including the Gregorian calendar currently used by most of the Western world, the Hebrew calendar, and the Islamic calendar. See Section 13.2.2: Calendars. (2) A practical model of the reference frame, such as the large, reusable Class Calendar in *Everyday Mathematics*. (3) A schedule or listing of events.

August 2007

Sunday	Monday	Tuesday	Wednesday	Thursday	Friday	Saturday
			1 Dr's appt, 3:00	2	3	4
5	6	7	8	9	10	11
12	13 Mom's b-day	14	15	16	17	18
19	20	21	22	23	24	25
26	27	28	29	30	31	

calibrate (1) To divide or mark a measuring tool with gradations such as the degree marks on a *thermometer*. (2) To test and adjust the accuracy of a measuring tool.

capacity (1) The amount of space occupied by a *3-dimensional figure*. Same as *volume*. (2) Less formally, the amount a container can hold. Capacity is often measured in units such as quarts, gallons, cups, or liters. See Section 12.5: Volume (Capacity). (3) The maximum weight a scale can measure. See Section 12.10.3: Scales and Balances.

Celsius A *temperature scale* on which pure water at sea level freezes at 0° and boils at 100°. The Celsius scale is used in the metric system. A less common name for this scale is centigrade because there are 100 units between the freezing and boiling points of water. Compare to *Fahrenheit*. See Section 13.1.1: Temperature Scales.

cent A penny; $\frac{1}{100}$ of a dollar. From the Latin word *centesimus,* which means "a hundredth part." See Section 12.9: Money.

cent- A prefix meaning 100, as in *century* or centennial.

center of a circle The point in the plane of a *circle* equally distant from all points on the circle. See Section 11.4.3: Circles and Pi (π).

center

center of a sphere The point equally distant from all points on a *sphere*. See Section 11.5.3: Solids with Curved Surfaces.

center

centi- A prefix meaning 1 hundredth.

centimeter (cm) A metric unit of *length* equivalent to 10 millimeters, $\frac{1}{10}$ of a decimeter, and $\frac{1}{100}$ of a meter. See the Tables of Measures and Section 12.2.2: Metric System.

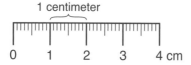
1 centimeter
0   1   2   3   4 cm

century One hundred years.

chance The possibility that an *outcome* will occur in an uncertain *event*. For example, in flipping a coin there is an equal chance of getting HEADS or TAILS. See Section 10.1.2: The Language of Chance.

change diagram A diagram used in *Everyday Mathematics* to model situations in which quantities are either increased or decreased by addition or subtraction. The diagram includes a starting quantity, an ending quantity, and an amount of change. See *situation diagram* and Section 9.3.1: Addition and Subtraction Use Classes.

| Change |
| Start | | End |
| 14 | − 5 | 9 |

A change diagram for 14 − 5 = 9

change-to-less story A *number story* about a change situation in which the ending quantity is less than the starting quantity. For example, a story about spending money is a change-to-less story. Compare to *change-to-more story*. See Section 9.3.1: Addition and Subtraction Use Classes.

change-to-more story A *number story* about a change situation in which the ending quantity is more than the starting quantity. For example, a story about earning money is a change-to-more story. Compare to *change-to-less story*. See Section 9.3.1: Addition and Subtraction Use Classes.

circle The set of all points in a *plane* that are equally distant from a fixed point in the plane called the *center* of the circle. The distance from the center to the circle is the *radius* of the circle. The *diameter* of a circle is twice its radius. Points inside a circle are not part of the circle. A circle together with its interior is called a disk or a circular region. See Section 11.4.3: Circles and Pi (π).

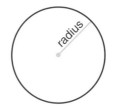
radius

A disk

Glossary

circle graph A graph in which a *circle* and its interior are divided into *sectors* corresponding to parts of a set of data. The whole circle represents the whole set of data. Same as *pie graph* and sometimes called a pie chart. See Section 10.2.3: Organizing and Displaying Data.

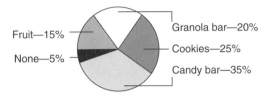

Fruit—15%
None—5%
Granola bar—20%
Cookies—25%
Candy bar—35%

circumference The distance around a circle; its *perimeter.* The circumference of a sphere is the circumference of a circle on the sphere with the same center as the sphere. See Section 11.4.3: Circles and Pi (π) and Section 11.5.3: Solids with Curved Surfaces.

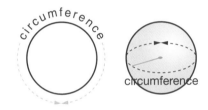

clockwise rotation The direction in which the hands move on a typical *analog clock;* a turn to the right.

column A vertical arrangement of objects or numbers in an *array* or a table.

column

Commutative Property of Addition A property of addition that two numbers can be added in either order without changing the sum. For example, $5 + 10 = 10 + 5$. In *Everyday Mathematics,* this is called a *turn-around fact,* and the two Commutative Properties are called *turn-around rules.*

In symbols:

For any numbers a and b, $a + b = b + a$.

Subtraction is not commutative. For example, $8 - 5 \neq 5 - 8$ because $3 \neq -3$. See Section 14.3.3: Fact Practice.

comparison diagram A diagram used in *Everyday Mathematics* to model situations in which two quantities are compared by addition or subtraction. The diagram contains two quantities and their difference. See *situation diagram* and Section 9.3.1: Addition and Subtraction Use Classes.

Quantity
12

Quantity	
9	?
	Difference

A comparison diagram for $12 = 9 + ?$

comparison story A *number story* about the difference between two quantities. Comparison situations can lead to either addition or subtraction depending on whether one of the compared quantities or the difference between them is unknown. See Section 9.3.1: Addition and Subtraction Use Classes.

complementary angles Two *angles* whose measures add to 90°. Complementary angles do not need to be *adjacent*. Compare to *supplementary angles.*

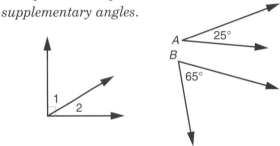

1
2
A 25°
B 65°

∠1 and ∠2 and ∠A and ∠B are pairs of complementary angles.

concave polygon A *polygon* on which there are at least two points that can be connected with a line segment that passes outside the polygon. For example, segment AD is outside the hexagon between B and C. Informally, at least one vertex appears to be "pushed inward." At least one interior angle has measure greater than 180°. Same as *nonconvex polygon.* Compare to *convex polygon.* See Section 11.4.2: Polygons (*n*-gons).

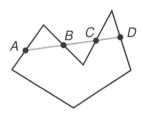

A
B C D

A concave polygon

Glossary

concentric circles *Circles* that have the same center but radii of different lengths.

Concentric circles

cone A *geometric solid* with a circular *base*, a vertex *(apex)* not in the *plane* of the base, and all of the line segments with one endpoint at the apex and the other endpoint on the circumference of the base. See Section 11.5.3: Solids with Curved Surfaces.

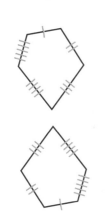
Cones

congruent figures (≅) Figures having the same size and shape. Two figures are congruent if they match exactly when one is placed on top of the other after a combination of slides, flips, and/or turns. In diagrams of congruent figures, the corresponding congruent sides may be marked with the same number of hash marks. The symbol ≅ means "is congruent to." See Section 11.6.2: Congruence and Similarity.

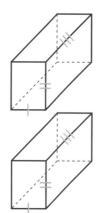
Congruent pentagons   Congruent prisms

consecutive Following one after another in an uninterrupted order. For example, A, B, C, and D are four consecutive letters of the alphabet; 6, 7, 8, 9, and 10 are five consecutive whole numbers.

consecutive angles Two *angles* in a *polygon* with a common side.

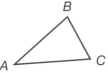
Angles *A* and *B*, *B* and *C*, and *C* and *A* are pairs of consecutive angles.

consecutive sides (1) Two *sides* of a *polygon* with a common *vertex*. (2) Two sides of a *polyhedron* with a common *edge*. Same as *adjacent sides*.

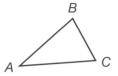
Sides *AB* and *BC*, *BC* and *CA*, and *CA* and *AB* are pairs of consecutive sides.

consecutive vertices The vertices of *consecutive angles* in a polygon.

constant A quantity that does not change. For example, the ratio of the circumference of a circle to its diameter is the famous constant π. In $x + 3 = y$, 3 is a constant.

conversion fact A fixed relationship such as 1 yard = 3 feet or 1 inch = 2.54 centimeters that can be used to convert measurements within or between systems of measurement. See Section 12.2.3: Converting between Measures.

convex polygon A *polygon* on which no two points can be connected with a line segment that passes outside the polygon. Informally, all vertices appear to be "pushed outward." Each angle in the polygon measures less than 180°. Compare to *concave polygon*. See Section 11.4.2: Polygons (*n*-gons).

A convex polygon

coordinate (1) A number used to locate a point on a *number line;* a point's distance from an *origin*. (2) One of the numbers in an *ordered pair* or triple that locates a point on a *coordinate grid* or in coordinate space, respectively. See Section 8.6.2: Number Grids, Scrolls, and Lines.

coordinate grid (rectangular coordinate grid) A *reference frame* for locating points in a plane by means of *ordered pairs* of numbers. A rectangular coordinate grid is formed by two number lines that intersect at *right angles* at their *zero points*.

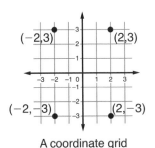

A coordinate grid

corner Same as *vertex*.

counterclockwise rotation Opposite the direction in which the hands move on a typical *analog clock;* a turn to the left.

counting numbers The numbers used to count things. The set of counting numbers is {1, 2, 3, 4, . . .}. Sometimes 0 is included, but not in *Everyday Mathematics.* Counting numbers are in the sets of *whole numbers, integers, rational numbers,* and *real numbers,* but each of these sets includes numbers that are not counting numbers. See Section 8.2.2: Plain and Fancy Counting.

cross section A shape formed by the intersection of a *plane* and a *geometric solid.*

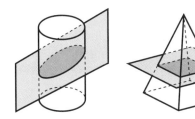

Cross sections of a cylinder
and a pyramid

cube (1) A *regular polyhedron* with 6 square faces. A cube has 8 *vertices* and 12 *edges.* See Section 11.5.2: Polyhedrons.

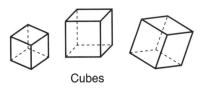

Cubes

(2) In *Everyday Mathematics,* the smaller cube of the *base-10 blocks,* measuring 1 cm on each edge. See Section 8.6.1: Base-10 Blocks.

cubic centimeter (cc or cm³) A metric unit of *volume* or *capacity* equal to the volume of a cube with 1-cm edges. 1 cm³ = 1 milliliter (mL). See the Tables of Measures and Section 12.5: Volume (Capacity).

cubic unit A unit such as cubic centimeters, cubic inches, cubic feet, and cubic meters used to measure *volume* or *capacity.* See Section 12.5: Volume (Capacity).

cubit An ancient unit of *length,* measured from the point of the elbow to the end of the middle finger. The cubit has been standardized at various times between 18 and 22 inches. The Latin word *cubitum* means "elbow." See Section 12.1: Personal Measures.

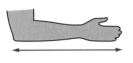

A cubit

cup (c) A U.S. customary unit of *volume* or *capacity* equal to 8 fluid ounces or $\frac{1}{2}$ pint. See the Tables of Measures and Section 12.5: Volume (Capacity).

curved surface A 2-dimensional surface that does not lie in a plane. *Spheres, cylinders,* and *cones* each have one curved surface. See Section 11.5.3: Solids with Curved Surfaces.

customary system of measurement In *Everyday Mathematics,* same as *U.S. customary system of measurement.*

cylinder A *geometric solid* with two congruent, parallel circular regions for *bases* and a curved *face* formed by all the segments with an endpoint on each circle that are parallel to a segment with endpoints at the centers of the circles. Also called a circular cylinder. See Section 11.5.3: Solids with Curved Surfaces.

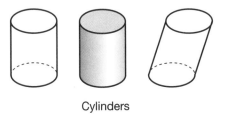

Cylinders

D

data Information that is gathered by counting, measuring, questioning, or observing. Strictly, data is the plural of *datum,* but data is often used as a singular word. See Section 10.2: Data Collection, Organization, and Analysis.

deca- A prefix meaning ten.

decade Ten years.

decagon A 10-sided polygon. See Section 11.4.2: Polygons (*n*-gons).

deci- A prefix meaning 1 tenth.

decimal (1) In *Everyday Mathematics,* a number written in standard *base-ten* notation containing a decimal point, such as 2.54. (2) Any number written in standard base-ten notation. See *repeating decimal, terminating decimal,* and Section 8.3 Rational Numbers: Fractions, Decimals, and Percents.

decimal notation In *Everyday Mathematics,* same as *standard notation.*

decimal point A mark used to separate the ones and tenths places in *decimals.* A decimal point separates dollars from cents in *dollars-and-cents notation.* The mark is a dot in the U.S. customary system and a comma in Europe and some other countries.

decimeter (dm) A metric unit of *length* equivalent to $\frac{1}{10}$ meter, or 10 centimeters.

degree (°) (1) A unit of measure for *angles* based on dividing a *circle* into 360 equal parts. Lines of latitude and longitude are measured in degrees, and these degrees are based on angle measures. See Section 11.4.1: Angles and Rotations. (2) A unit for measuring *temperature.* See *degree Celsius, degree Fahrenheit,* and Section 13.1.1: Temperature Scales.
The symbol ° means degrees of any type.

degree Celsius (°C) The *unit interval* on *Celsius* thermometers and a metric unit for measuring *temperatures.* Pure water at sea level freezes at 0°C and boils at 100°C. See Section 13.1.1: Temperature Scales.

degree Fahrenheit (°F) The *unit interval* on *Fahrenheit* thermometers and a U.S. customary unit for measuring *temperatures.* Pure water at sea level freezes at 32°F and boils at 212°F. A saturated salt solution freezes at 0°F. See Section 13.1.1: Temperature Scales.

denominator The nonzero divisor *b* in a fraction $\frac{a}{b}$ and *a/b*. In a part-whole fraction, the denominator is the number of equal parts into which the *whole,* or *ONE,* has been divided. Compare to *numerator.*

diagonal (1) A *line segment* joining two nonconsecutive vertices of a *polygon.* See Section 11.4.2: Polygons (*n*-gons).
(2) A segment joining two nonconsecutive vertices on different faces of a *polyhedron.*

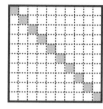

(3) A line of objects or numbers from upper left to lower right or from lower left to upper right, in an *array* or a table.

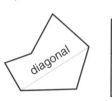

A diagonal of an array

diameter (1) A *line segment* that passes through the center of a *circle* or *sphere* and has endpoints on the circle or sphere. (2) The length of such a segment. The diameter of a circle or sphere is twice the *radius.* See Section 11.4.3: Circles and Pi (π) and Section 11.5.3: Solids with Curved Surfaces.

difference The result of subtracting one number from another. For example, the difference of 12 and 5 is $12 - 5 = 7$.

digit (1) Any one of the symbols 0, 1, 2, 3, 4, 5, 6, 7, 8, and 9 in the *base-ten* numeration system. For example, the numeral 145 is made up of the digits 1, 4, and 5. (2) Any one of the symbols in any number system. For example, A, B, C, D, E, and F are digits along with 0 through 9 in the base-16 notation used in some computer programming.

digital clock A clock that shows the time with numbers of hours and minutes, usually separated by a colon. This display is discrete, not continuous, meaning that the display jumps to a new time after a minute delay. Compare to *analog clock.* See Section 13.2.1: Clocks.

A digital clock

dimension (1) A measure along one direction of an object, typically length, width, or height. For example, the dimensions of a box might be 24-cm by 20-cm by 10-cm. (2) The number of *coordinates* necessary to locate a point in a geometric space. For example, a line has one dimension because one coordinate uniquely locates any point on the line. A plane has two dimensions because an *ordered pair* of two coordinates uniquely locates any point in the plane. See Section 11.1: Dimension.

division symbols The number *a* divided by the number *b* is written in a variety of ways. In *Everyday Mathematics*, $a \div b$; a/b and $\frac{a}{b}$ are the most common notations, while $b\overline{)a}$ is used to set up the traditional long-division algorithm. *a:b* is sometimes used in Europe, $\boxed{\div}$ is common on calculators, and $\boxed{/}$ is common on computer keyboards. See Section 9.2.1: Arithmetic Symbols.

dodecahedron A *polyhedron* with 12 faces. If each face is a regular pentagon, it is one of the five *regular polyhedrons*. See Section 11.5.2: Polyhedrons.

A decagonal prism

An irregular dodecahedron　　A regular dodecahedron

dollar The basic unit in the U.S. monetary system, equal to 100 *cents*.

dollars-and-cents notation The U.S. customary notation for writing amounts of money as a number of dollars and hundredths of dollars *(cents)*. The decimal is preceded by the $ symbol, as in $8.98, meaning "eight dollars and 98 cents." See Section 12.9: Money.

double Two times an amount; an amount added to itself.

doubles fact The sum (or product) of a 1-digit number added to (or multiplied by) itself, such as $4 + 4 = 8$ or $3 \times 3 = 9$. A doubles fact does not have a *turn-around fact* partner.

edge (1) Any *side* of a polyhedron's *faces*. (2) A line segment or curve where two surfaces of a *geometric solid* meet. See Section 11.5.2: Polyhedrons and Section 11.5.3: Solids with Curved Surfaces.

edges

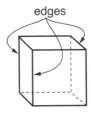

edge

elapsed time The difference in two times. For example, between 12:45 P.M. and 1:30 P.M., 45 minutes have elapsed.

elevation A height above sea level. Same as *altitude (2)*.

embedded figure A figure entirely enclosed within another figure.

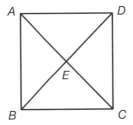

Triangle *ADE* is embedded in square *ADCB*.

endpoint A point at the end of a *line segment, ray,* or *arc*. These shapes are usually named using their endpoints. For example, the segment shown is "segment *TL*" or "segment *LT*."

endpoints

T　　*L*

enlarge To increase the size of an object or a figure without changing its shape. Same as *stretch*. See *scale factor*.

equal Same as *equivalent*.

equal-grouping story A *number story* in which a quantity is divided into equal groups. The total and size of each group are known. For example, *How many tables seating 4 people each are needed to seat 52 people?* is an equal-grouping story. Often division can be used to solve equal-grouping stories. Compare to *measurement division* and *equal-sharing story* and see Section 9.3.2: Multiplication and Division Use Classes.

equal groups Sets with the same number of elements, such as cars with 5 passengers each, rows with 6 chairs each, and boxes containing 100 paper clips each. See Section 9.3.2: Multiplication and Division Use Classes.

equal parts Equivalent parts of a *whole*. For example, dividing a pizza into 4 equal parts means each part is $\frac{1}{4}$ of the pizza and is equal in size to the other 3 parts.

4 equal parts, each $\frac{1}{4}$ of a pizza

equal-sharing story A *number story* in which a quantity is shared equally. The total quantity and the number of groups are known. For example, *There are 10 toys to share equally among 4 children; how many toys will each child get?* is an equal-sharing story. Often division can be used to solve equal-sharing stories. Compare to *partitive division* and *equal-grouping story*. See Section 9.3.2: Multiplication and Division Use Classes.

equally likely outcomes *Outcomes* of a chance experiment or situation that have the same *probability* of happening. If all the possible outcomes are equally likely, then the probability of an *event* is equal to:

$$\frac{\text{number of favorable outcomes}}{\text{number of possible outcomes}}$$

See *random experiment* and Section 10.1.2: The Language of Chance.

equation A *number sentence* that contains an equal sign. For example, $5 + 10 = 15$ and $P = 2l + 2w$ are equations. See Section 9.2.2: Reading and Writing Number Sentences and Section 15.2.2: Reading and Writing Open Sentences.

equilateral polygon A polygon in which all sides are the same length. See Section 11.4.2: Polygons (*n*-gons).

Equilateral polygons

equilateral triangle A *triangle* with all three sides equal in length. Each angle of an equilateral triangle measures 60°, so it is also called an equiangular triangle. See Section 11.4.2: Polygons (*n*-gons).

An equilateral triangle

equivalent Equal in value but possibly in a different form. For example, $\frac{1}{2}$, 0.5, and 50% are all equivalent. See Section 8.5.1: Equality.

equivalent names Different ways of naming the same number. For example, $2 + 6$, $4 + 4$, $12 - 4$, $18 - 10$, $100 - 92$, $5 + 1 + 2$, eight, VIII, and 卌 /// are all equivalent names for 8. See *name-collection box*.

estimate (1) An answer close to, or approximating, an exact answer. (2) To make an estimate. See Section 14.1: Estimation.

even number (1) A *counting number* that is divisible by 2. (2) An *integer* that is divisible by 2. Compare to *odd number* and see Section 15.1.2: Odd and Even Number Patterns.

event A set of possible *outcomes* to an experiment. For example, in an experiment flipping two coins, getting 2 HEADS is an event, as is getting 1 HEAD and 1 TAIL. The *probability* of an event is the chance that the event will happen. For example, the probability that a fair coin will land HEADS up is $\frac{1}{2}$. If the probability of an event is 0, the event is impossible. If the probability is 1, the event is certain. See Section 10.1: Probability.

expanded notation A way of writing a number as the sum of the values of each *digit*. For example, 356 is $300 + 50 + 6$ in expanded notation. Compare to *standard notation, scientific notation,* and *number-and-word notation*.

exponent A small raised number used in exponential notation to tell how many times the *base* is used as a *factor*. For example, in 5^3, the base is 5, the exponent is 3, and $5^3 = 5 \times 5 \times 5 = 125$. Same as *power*.

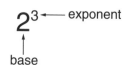

expression (1) A mathematical phrase made up of numbers, *variables, operation symbols,* and/or *grouping symbols.* An expression does not contain *relation symbols* such as =, >, and ≤. (2) Either side of an *equation* or *inequality.* See Section 9.2.2: Reading and Writing Number Sentences and Section 15.2.2: Reading and Writing Open Sentences.

$$2 + 3$$
$$\sqrt{2ab}$$
$$\pi r^2$$
$$9x - 2$$

Expressions

extended facts Variations of basic *arithmetic facts* involving multiples of 10, 100, and so on. For example, $30 + 70 = 100$, $40 \times 5 = 200$, and $560 \div 7 = 80$ are extended facts. See *fact extensions* and Section 14.3: Mental Arithmetic.

face (1) In *Everyday Mathematics,* a flat *surface* on a *3-dimensional figure.* Some special faces are called *bases.* (2) More generally, any 2-dimensional surface on a 3-dimensional figure. See Section 11.5: Space and 3-D Figures.

a flat face   a curved face

fact extensions Calculations with larger numbers using knowledge of basic *arithmetic facts.* For example, knowing the addition fact $5 + 8 = 13$ makes it easier to solve problems such as $50 + 80 = ?$ and $65 + ? = 73$. Fact extensions apply to all four basic arithmetic operations. See *extended facts* and Section 14.3.3: Fact Practice.

fact family A set of related *arithmetic facts* linking two inverse operations. For example,

$5 + 6 = 11$	$6 + 5 = 11$
$11 - 5 = 6$	$11 - 6 = 5$

are an addition/subtraction fact family. Similarly,

$5 \times 7 = 35$	$7 \times 5 = 35$
$35 \div 7 = 5$	$35 \div 5 = 7$

are a multiplication/division fact family. Same as *number family.* See Section 14.3.3: Fact Practice.

fact habits Same as *fact power.*

fact power In *Everyday Mathematics,* the ability to automatically recall basic *arithmetic facts.* Automatically knowing the facts is as important to arithmetic as knowing words by sight is to reading. Same as *fact habits.* See Section 14.3.2: Basic Facts and Fact Power.

Fact Triangle In *Everyday Mathematics,* a triangular flash card labeled with the numbers of a *fact family* that students can use to practice addition/subtraction and multiplication/division facts. The two 1-digit numbers and their sum or product (marked with a dot) appear in the corners of each triangle.

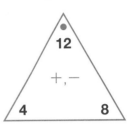

factor (1) Each of the two or more numbers in a *product.* For example, in 6×0.5, 6 and 0.5 are factors. (2) To represent a number as a product of factors. For example, factor 21 by rewriting as 7×3.

facts table A chart showing *arithmetic facts.* An addition/subtraction facts table shows addition and subtraction facts. A multiplication/division facts table shows multiplication and division facts.

Fahrenheit A *temperature scale* on which pure water at sea level freezes at 32° and boils at 212°. The Fahrenheit scale is widely used in the U.S. but in few other places. Compare to *Celsius.* See *degree Fahrenheit* and Section 13.1.1: Temperature Scales.

fair Free from bias. Each side of a fair die or coin will land up about equally often. Each region of a fair spinner will be landed on in proportion to its area.

fair game A game in which every player has the same chance of winning. See Section 10.1.2: The Language of Chance.

false number sentence A *number sentence* that is not true. For example, $8 = 5 + 5$ is a false number sentence. Compare to *true number sentence.* See Section 9.2.2: Reading and Writing Number Sentences.

fathom A unit of *length* equal to 6 feet, or 2 yards. It is used mainly by people who work with boats and ships to measure depths underwater and lengths of cables. Same as *arm span*. See Section 12.1: Personal Measures.

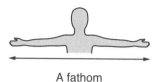

A fathom

figurate numbers Numbers that can be illustrated by specific geometric *patterns*. *Square numbers* and *triangular numbers* are figurate numbers. See Section 15.1.3: Sequences.

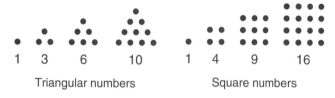

| Triangular numbers | Square numbers |

flat In *Everyday Mathematics,* the *base-10 block* consisting of one hundred 1-cm cubes. See Section 8.6.1: Base-10 Blocks.

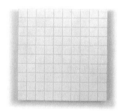

A flat

flat surface A *surface* contained entirely in one *plane*. See Section 11.4: Planes and Plane Figures and Section 11.5: Space and 3-D Figures.

flip An informal name for a *reflection* transformation. See Section 11.7: Transformations.

fluid ounce (fl oz) A U.S. customary unit of *volume* or *capacity* equal to $\frac{1}{16}$ of a pint, or about 29.573730 milliliters. Compare to *ounce*. See the Tables of Measures and Section 12.5: Volume (Capacity).

foot (ft) A U.S. customary unit of *length* equivalent to 12 inches, or $\frac{1}{3}$ of a yard. See the Tables of Measures and Section 12.3: Length.

formula A general rule for finding the value of something. A formula is usually an *equation* with quantities represented by letter *variables*. For example, a formula for distance traveled d at a rate r over a time t is $d = r \times t$. The area of a triangle A with base length b and height h is given below. See Section 15.2.1: Uses of Variables.

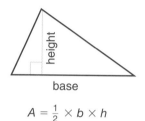

$$A = \tfrac{1}{2} \times b \times h$$

fraction (primary definition) A number in the form $\frac{a}{b}$ or a/b, where a and b are *whole numbers* and b is not 0. A fraction may be used to name part of an object or part of a collection of objects, to compare two quantities, or to represent division. For example, $\frac{12}{6}$ might mean 12 eggs divided into 6 groups of 2 eggs each, a ratio of 12 to 6, or 12 divided by 6. See Section 8.3: Rational Numbers: Fractions, Decimals, and Percents.

fraction (other definitions) (1) A fraction that satisfies the previous definition and includes a *unit* in both the *numerator* and *denominator*. For example, the *rates*

$$\frac{50 \text{ miles}}{1 \text{ gallon}} \text{ and } \frac{40 \text{ pages}}{10 \text{ minutes}}$$

are fractions. (2) A number written using a fraction bar, where the fraction bar is used to indicate division. For example,

$$\frac{2.3}{6.5}, \quad \frac{1\frac{4}{5}}{12}, \text{ and } \frac{\frac{3}{4}}{\frac{5}{8}}.$$

fractional part Part of a *whole*. *Fractions* represent fractional parts of numbers, sets, or objects.

frames In *Everyday Mathematics,* the empty shapes in which numbers are written in a *Frames-and-Arrows* diagram. See Section 15.1.4: Functions.

Frames and Arrows In *Everyday Mathematics,* diagrams consisting of frames connected by arrows used to represent number *sequences.* Each frame contains a number, and each arrow represents a rule that determines which number goes in the next frame. There may be more than one rule, represented by different-color arrows. Frames-and-Arrows diagrams are also called chains. See Section 15.1.3: Sequences.

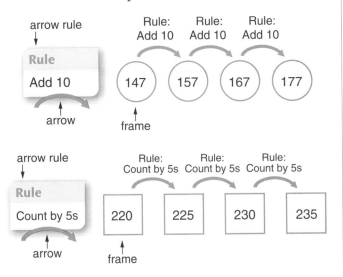

frequency (1) The number of times a value occurs in a set of data. See Section 10.2.3: Organizing and Displaying Data. (2) A number of repetitions per unit of time. For example, the vibrations per second in a sound wave.

frequency graph A graph showing how often each value occurs in a data set. See Section 10.2.3: Organizing and Displaying Data.

Colors in a Bag of Gumdrops

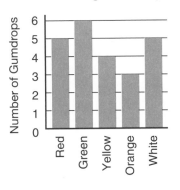

frequency table A table in which data are *tallied* and organized, often as a first step toward making a *frequency graph.* See Section 10.2.3: Organizing and Displaying Data.

Color	Number of Gumdrops
red	⳾⳾⳾
green	⳾⳾⳾ I
yellow	////
orange	///
white	⳾⳾⳾

fulcrum (1) The point on a mobile at which a rod is suspended. (2) The point or place around which a lever pivots. (3) The center support of a *pan balance.*

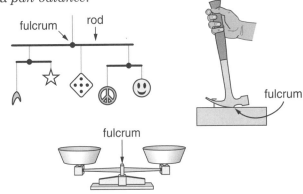

function A set of *ordered pairs* (x, y) in which each value of x is paired with exactly one value of y. A function is typically represented in a table, by points on a coordinate graph, or by a rule such as an *equation.* For example, for a function with the rule "Double," 1 is paired with 2, 2 is paired with 4, 3 is paired with 6, and so on. In symbols, $y = 2 \times x$ or $y = 2x$. See Section 15.1.4: Functions.

function machine In *Everyday Mathematics,* an imaginary device that receives *inputs* and pairs them with *outputs.* For example, the function machine below pairs an input number with its double. See *function* and Section 15.1.4: Functions.

A function machine and function table

in

Rule
Double

out

in	out
1	2
2	4
3	6
5	10
20	40
300	600

furlong A unit of *length* equal to 1 eighth of a mile. Furlongs are commonly used in horse racing.

gallon (gal) A U.S. customary unit of *volume* or *capacity* equal to 4 quarts. See the Tables of Measures and Section 12.5: Volume (Capacity).

generate a random number To produce a *random number* by such methods as drawing a card without looking from a shuffled deck, rolling a fair die, and flicking a fair spinner. In *Everyday Mathematics,* random numbers are commonly generated in games. See Section 10.4.1: Random-Number Generators.

geoboard A manipulative *2-dimensional coordinate system* made with nails or other posts at equally-spaced intervals relative to both axes. Children loop rubber bands around the posts to make polygons and other shapes.

geometric solid The *surface* or surfaces that make up a *3-dimensional figure* such as a prism, pyramid, cylinder, cone, or sphere. Despite its name, a geometric solid is hollow; that is, it does not include the points in its interior. Informally, and in some dictionaries, a solid is defined as both the surface and its interior. See Section 11.5.1: "Solid" Figures.

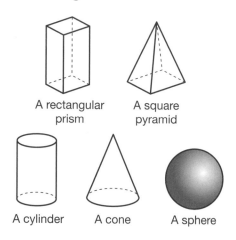

A rectangular prism   A square pyramid

A cylinder   A cone   A sphere

Geometric solids

girth The distance around a 3-dimensional object.

-gon A suffix meaning *angle*. For example, a *hexagon* is a plane figure with six angles.

gram (g) A metric unit of *mass* equal to $\frac{1}{1,000}$ of a kilogram. See the Tables of Measures and Section 12.6: Weight and Mass.

graph key An annotated list of the symbols used in a graph explaining how to read the graph.

great span The distance from the tip of the thumb to the tip of the little finger (pinkie), when the hand is stretched as far as possible. The great span averages about 9 inches for adults. Same as *hand span*. Compare to *normal span* and see Section 12.1: Personal Measures.

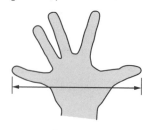

Great span

grouping symbols Parentheses ( ), brackets [ ], braces { }, and similar symbols that define the order in which operations in an *expression* are to be done. Nested grouping symbols are groupings within groupings, and the innermost grouping is done first. For example, in $(3 + 4) \times [(8 + 2) \div 5]$, the group $(8 + 2)$ is nested within $[(8 + 2) \div 5]$ and is done first. So $(3 + 4) \times [(8 + 2) \div 5]$ simplifies as follows:

$$(3 + 4) \times [(8 + 2) \div 5]$$
$$(3 + 4) \times [10 \div 5]$$
$$7 \times 2$$
$$14$$

See Section 9.2.2: Reading and Writing Number Sentences.

half One of two *equal parts.*

hand span Same as *great span.*

height (1) A perpendicular segment from one *side* of a geometric figure to a parallel side or from a *vertex* to the *opposite side.* (2) The length of this segment. In *Everyday Mathematics,* same as *altitude.* See *height of a parallelogram, height of a rectangle, height of a prism or cylinder, height of a pyramid or cone, height of a triangle,* Section 11.4.2: Polygons (*n*-gons), Section 11.5.2: Polyhedrons, and Section 11.5.3: Solids with Curved Surfaces.

Heights/altitudes of 2-D figures are shown in blue.

Heights/altitudes of 3-D figures are shown in blue.

Glossary

height of a parallelogram (1) The *length* of the shortest line segment between a *base of a parallelogram* and the line containing the *opposite side*. The height is perpendicular to the base. (2) The line segment itself. See *altitude, base of a parallelogram*, and Section 11.4.2: Polygons (*n*-gons).

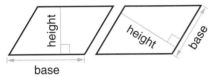

height of a prism or cylinder The *length* of the shortest line segment from a *base of a prism or cylinder* to the plane containing the opposite base. The height is perpendicular to the bases. (2) The line segment itself. See *altitude, base of a prism or cylinder,* and Section 11.5.2: Polyhedrons.

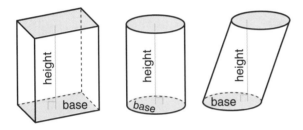

height of a pyramid or cone The *length* of the shortest line segment from the *apex* of a pyramid or cone to the plane containing the *base*. The height is perpendicular to the base. (2) The line segment itself. See *altitude, base of a pyramid or cone,* and Section 11.5.2: Polyhedrons.

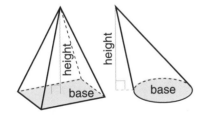

height of a rectangle The *length* of a side perpendicular to a *base of a rectangle*. Same as *altitude* of a rectangle. See Section 11.4.2: Polygons (*n*-gons).

height of a triangle The *length* of the shortest segment from a *vertex* of a triangle to the line containing the opposite *side*. The height is perpendicular to the base. (2) The line segment itself. See *altitude, base of a triangle,* and Section 11.4.2: Polygons (*n*-gons).

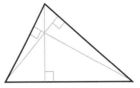

The heights of the triangle are shown in blue.

hemisphere (1) Half of Earth's surface. (2) Half of a *sphere*.

hepta- A prefix meaning seven.

heptagon A 7-sided *polygon*. See Section 11.4.2: Polygons (*n*-gons).

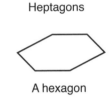

Heptagons

hexa- A prefix meaning six.

hexagon A 6-sided *polygon*. See Section 11.4.2: Polygons (*n*-gons).

A hexagon

Home Link In *Pre-Kindergarten* through *Third Grade Everyday Mathematics,* a suggested follow-up or enrichment activity to be done at home. See Section 2.3: Home Links.

horizontal In a left-to-right orientation. Parallel to the horizon.

hypotenuse In a *right triangle,* the *side* opposite the *right angle*. See Section 11.4.2: Polygons (*n*-gons).

icon A small picture or diagram sometimes used to represent quantities. For example, an icon of a stadium might be used to represent 100,000 people on a *pictograph*. Icons are also used to represent functions or objects in computer operating systems and applications.

icosahedron A *polyhedron* with 20 faces. An icosahedron with equilateral triangle faces is one of the five *regular polyhedrons*. See Section 11.5.2: Polyhedrons.

A regular icosahedron

image A figure that is produced by a *transformation* of another figure called the *preimage*. See Section 11.7: Transformations.

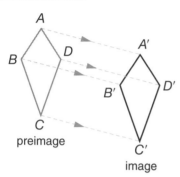

inch (in.) A U.S. customary unit of *length* equal to $\frac{1}{12}$ of a foot and 2.54 centimeters. See the Tables of Measures and Section 12.3: Length.

indirect measurement The determination of heights, distances, and other quantities that cannot be measured directly.

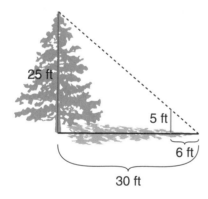

Indirect measurement lets you calculate the height of the tree from the other measures.

inequality A *number sentence* with a *relation symbol* other than =, such as >, <, ≥, ≤, ≠, or ≈. See Section 8.5: Numeric Relations.

input (1) A number inserted into an imaginary *function machine,* which applies a rule to pair the input with an *output.* (2) The values for *x* in a *function* consisting of *ordered pairs* (*x,y*). See Section 15.1.4: Functions. (3) Numbers or other information entered into a calculator or computer.

inscribed polygon A *polygon* whose vertices are all on the same *circle.*

An inscribed square

integer A number in the set {. . ., −4, −3, −2, −1, 0, 1, 2, 3, 4, . . .}. A *whole number* or its opposite, where 0 is its own opposite. Compare to *rational number, irrational number,* and *real number.* See Section 8.4: Positive and Negative Numbers.

interior of a figure (1) The set of all points in a *plane* bounded by a closed *2-dimensional figure* such as a *polygon* or *circle.* (2) The set of all points in space bounded by a closed *3-dimensional figure* such as a *polyhedron* or *sphere.* The interior is usually not considered to be part of the figure. See Section 11.4: Planes and Plane Figures and Section 11.5: Space and 3-D Figures.

intersect To share a common point or points.

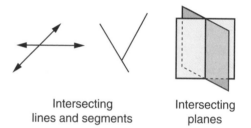

Intersecting lines and segments   Intersecting planes

interval (1) The set of all numbers between two numbers *a* and *b,* which may include one or both of *a* and *b.* (2) The points and their coordinates on a segment of a number line. The interval between 0 and 1 on a number line is the *unit interval.*

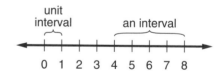

irrational numbers Numbers that cannot be written as *fractions* where both the *numerator* and *denominator* are *integers* and the denominator is not zero. For example, $\sqrt{2}$ and π are irrational numbers. An irrational number can be written as a nonterminating, nonrepeating decimal. For example, $\pi = 3.141592653\ldots$ continues forever without any known pattern. The number $1.10100100010000\ldots$ is irrational because its pattern does not repeat.

isometry transformation A *transformation* in which the *preimage* and *image* are *congruent*. *Reflections* (flips), *rotations* (turns), and *translations* (slides) are isometry transformations, while a *size change* (stretch or shrink) is not. Although the size and shape of the figures in an isometry transformation are the same, their orientations may be different. From the Greek *isometros* meaning "of equal measure."

A reflection (flip)   A rotation (turn)   A translation (slide)

isosceles trapezoid A *trapezoid* whose nonparallel sides are the same length. Pairs of base angles have the same measure. See Section 11.4.2: Polygons (*n*-gons).

An isosceles trapezoid

isosceles triangle A *triangle* with at least two sides equal in length. Angles opposite the congruent sides are congruent to each other. See Section 11.4.2: Polygons (*n*-gons).

Isosceles triangles

key sequence The order in which calculator keys are pressed to perform a calculation. See Section 3.1.1: Calculators.

kilo- A prefix meaning 1 thousand.

kilogram A metric unit of *mass* equal to 1,000 grams. The international standard kilogram is a 39 mm diameter, 39 mm high *cylinder* of platinum and iridium kept in the International Bureau of Weights and Measures in Sèvres, France. A kilogram is about 2.2 pounds. See the Tables of Measures and Section 12.6: Weight and Mass.

kilometer A metric unit of *length* equal to 1,000 meters. A kilometer is about 0.62 mile. See the Tables of Measures and Section 12.3: Length.

kite A *quadrilateral* with two distinct pairs of adjacent sides of equal length. In *Everyday Mathematics*, the four sides cannot all have equal length; that is, a *rhombus* is not a kite. The diagonals of a kite are *perpendicular*. See Section 11.4.2: Polygons (*n*-gons).

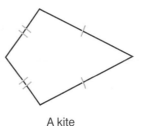

A kite

label A descriptive word or phrase used to put a number or numbers in context. Labels encourage children to associate numbers with real objects. Flags, snowballs, and scary monsters are examples of labels. See Section 9.3: Use Classes and Situation Diagrams.

landmark In *Everyday Mathematics*, a notable feature of a *data* set. Landmarks include the *median, mode, mean, maximum, minimum,* and *range*. See Section 10.2.4: Data Analysis.

leg of a right triangle Either *side* of the *right angle* in a *right triangle;* a side that is not the *hypotenuse*. See Section 11.4.2: Polygons (*n*-gons).

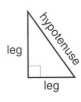

length The distance between two points on a *1-dimensional figure*. For example, the figure might be a line segment, arc, or a curve on a map modeling a hiking path. Length is measured in units such as inches, kilometers, and miles. See Section 12.3: Length.

length of a rectangle Typically, but not necessarily, the longer dimension of a *rectangle*.

line In *Everyday Mathematics*, a 1-dimensional straight path that extends forever in opposite directions. A line is named using two points on it or with a single, italicized lower-case letter such as *l*. In formal Euclidean geometry, line is an undefined geometric term. See Section 11.3: Lines, Segments, and Rays.

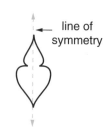

Line *PR* or $\overleftrightarrow{PR}$

line graph A graph in which *data* points are connected by *line segments*. Same as *broken-line graph*. See Section 10.2.3: Organizing and Displaying Data.

line of reflection (mirror line) (1) In *Everyday Mathematics,* a line halfway between a figure and its *reflection* image in a plane. (2) The *perpendicular bisector* of the line segments connecting points on a figure with their corresponding points on its reflection image. Compare to *line of symmetry*.

line of symmetry A line that divides a figure into two parts that are *reflection* images of each other. A figure may have zero, one, or more lines of symmetry. For example, the numeral 2 has no lines of symmetry, a square has four lines of symmetry, and a circle has infinitely many lines of symmetry. Also called a symmetry line. See Section 11.8.1: Line Symmetry.

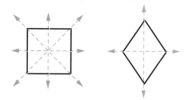

Lines of symmetry are shown in blue.

line plot A sketch of data in which check marks, Xs, or other symbols above a labeled line show the frequency of each value. See Section 10.2.3: Organizing and Displaying Data.

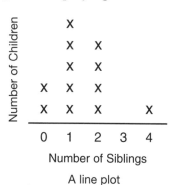

A line plot

line segment A part of a *line* between and including two points called *endpoints* of the segment. Same as *segment*. A line segment is often named by its endpoints. See Section 11.3: Lines, Segments, and Rays.

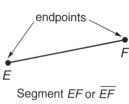

Segment *EF* or $\overline{EF}$

line symmetry A figure has line symmetry if a line can be drawn that divides it into two parts that are *reflection* images of each other. See *line of symmetry* and Section 11.8.1: Line Symmetry.

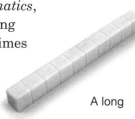

line of symmetry

liter (L) A metric unit of *volume* or *capacity* equal to the volume of a cube with 10-cm-long edges. 1 L = 1,000 mL = 1,000 cm³. A liter is a little larger than a quart. See the Tables of Measures and Section 12.5: Volume (Capacity).

long In *Everyday Mathematics*, the *base-10 block* consisting of ten 1-cm cubes. Sometimes called a rod. See Section 8.6.1: Base-10 Blocks.

A long

long-term memory *Memory in a calculator* used by keys with an M on them, such as [M-] and [M+]. Numbers in long-term memory are not affected by calculations with keys without an M, which use *short-term memory*. See Section 3.1.1: Calculators.

M

magnitude estimate A rough *estimate* of whether a number is in the tens, hundreds, thousands, or other powers of 10. For example, the U.S. national debt per person is in the tens of thousands of dollars. In *Everyday Mathematics,* children give magnitude estimates for problems such as *How many dimes are in $200?* or *How many halves are in 30?* Same as *order-of-magnitude estimate*. See Section 14.1.2: Estimates in Calculations.

mass A measure of the amount of matter in an object. Mass is not affected by gravity, so it is the same on Earth, the moon, or anywhere else in space. Mass is usually measured in grams, kilograms, and other metric units. Compare to *weight*. See Section 12.6: Weight and Mass.

Math Master In *Everyday Mathematics,* a page ready for duplicating. Most masters support children in carrying out suggested activities. Some masters are used more than once during the school year.

maximum The largest amount; the greatest number in a set of data. Compare to *minimum*. See Section 10.2.4: Data Analysis.

mean For a set of numbers, their sum divided by the number of numbers. Often called the *average* value of the set. Compare to other data *landmarks median* and *mode*. See Section 10.2.4: Data Analysis.

measurement division A term for the type of division used to solve an *equal-grouping story* such as *How many tables seating 4 people each are needed for 52 people?* Same as *quotitive division*. Compare to *partitive division*.

measurement unit The reference unit used when measuring. Examples of basic units include inches for *length,* grams for *mass* or *weight,* cubic inches for *volume* or *capacity,* seconds for *elapsed time,* and degrees Celsius for change of *temperature*. Compound units include square centimeters for *area* and miles per hour for *speed*. See Section 12.2: Measurement Systems.

median The middle value in a set of data when the data are listed in order from smallest to largest or vice versa. If there is an even number of data points, the median is the *mean* of the two middle values. Compare to other data *landmarks mean* and *mode*. See Section 10.2.4: Data Analysis.

memory in a calculator Where numbers are stored in a calculator for use in later calculations. Most calculators have both a *short-term memory* and a *long-term memory*. See Section 3.1.1: Calculators.

mental arithmetic Computation done by people "in their heads," either in whole or in part. In *Everyday Mathematics,* students learn a variety of mental-calculation strategies to develop automatic recall of basic facts and *fact power*. See Section 14.3: Mental Arithmetic.

meter (m) The basic metric unit of *length* from which other metric units of length are derived. Originally, the meter was defined as $\frac{1}{10,000,000}$ of the distance from the North Pole to the equator along a meridian passing through Paris. From 1960 to 1983, the meter was redefined as 1,630,763.73 wavelengths of orange-red light from the element krypton. Today, the meter is defined as the distance light travels in a vacuum in $\frac{1}{299,792,458}$ second. One meter is equal to 10 decimeters, 100 centimeters, or 1,000 millimeters. See Section 12.3: Length.

metric system A measurement system based on the *base-ten* (decimal) numeration system and used in most countries and by virtually all scientists around the world. Units for *length* include millimeter, centimeter, meter, and kilometer; units for *mass* and *weight* include gram and kilogram; units for *volume* and *capacity* include milliliter and liter; and the unit for *temperature* change is degrees Celsius. See the Tables of Measures and Section 12.2.2: Metric System.

middle value Same as *median*.

midpoint A point halfway between two other points. The midpoint of a line segment is the point halfway between the endpoints.

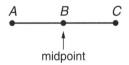

length of $\overline{AB}$ = length of $\overline{BC}$

mile (mi) A U.S. customary unit of *length* equal to 5,280 feet, or 1,760 yards. A mile is about 1,609 meters.

milli- A prefix meaning 1 thousandth.

milliliter (mL) A metric unit of *volume* or *capacity* equal to $\frac{1}{1,000}$ of a liter, or 1 cubic centimeter. See Section 12.5: Volume (Capacity).

millimeter (mm) A metric unit of *length* equal to $\frac{1}{10}$ of a centimeter, or $\frac{1}{1,000}$ of a meter. See Section 12.3: Length.

millisecond (ms or msec) A unit of time equal to $\frac{1}{1,000}$ of a second.

minimum The smallest amount; the smallest number in a set of data. Compare to *maximum*. See Section 10.2.4: Data Analysis.

minuend In subtraction, the number from which another number is subtracted. For example, in $19 - 5 = 14$, the minuend is 19. Compare to *subtrahend*.

mirror image Same as *reflection* image.

mixed number A number that is written using both a *whole number* and a *fraction*. For example, $2\frac{1}{4}$ is a mixed number equal to $2 + \frac{1}{4}$.

modal Of or relating to the *mode*.

mode The value or values that occur most often in a set of data. Compare to other *landmarks median* and *mean*. See Section 10.2.4: Data Analysis.

multiplication/division use class In *Everyday Mathematics,* a situation in which multiplication or division is used. These include *equal grouping/sharing, arrays and area, rates and ratio, scaling,* and Cartesian product situations. See Section 9.3.2: Multiplication and Division Use Classes.

multiplication/division diagram A diagram used in *Everyday Mathematics* to model situations in which a total number is made up of equal-size groups. The diagram contains a number of groups, a number in each group, and a total number. Also called a multiplication diagram for short. See *situation diagram* and Section 9.3.2: Multiplication and Division Use Classes.

rows	chairs per row	total chairs
15	25	?

A multiplication/division diagram

multiplication fact The product of two 1-digit numbers, such as $6 \times 7 = 42$. See *arithmetic facts* and Section 14.3.2: Basic Facts and Fact Power.

multiplication symbols The number a multiplied by the number b is written in a variety of ways. Many mathematics textbooks and *Second* and *Third Grade Everyday Mathematics* use $\times$ as in $a \times b$. Beginning in fourth grade, *Everyday Mathematics* uses $*$ as in $a * b$. Other common symbols are a dot as in $a \bullet b$ and by juxtaposition as in ab, which is common in formulas and in algebra courses. See Section 9.2.1: Arithmetic Symbols.

name-collection box In *Everyday Mathematics,* a diagram that is used for collecting *equivalent names* for a number.

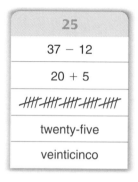

25
37 − 12
20 + 5
~~HHT HHT HHT HHT HHT~~
twenty-five
veinticinco

natural numbers In *Everyday Mathematics,* same as *counting numbers*.

negative numbers Numbers less than 0; the opposites of the *positive numbers,* commonly written as a positive number preceded by a −. Negative numbers are plotted left of 0 on a horizontal number line or below 0 on a vertical number line. See Section 8.4: Positive and Negative Numbers.

negative rational numbers *Rational numbers* less than 0; the opposites of the *positive rational numbers*. For example, -24, $-2.333\ldots$, and $-\frac{5}{8}$ are negative rational numbers. See Section 8.4: Positive and Negative Numbers.

n-gon Same as *polygon*, where n is the number of sides. Polygons that do not have special names like squares and pentagons are usually named using n-gon notation, such as 13-gon or 100-gon.

nona- A prefix meaning nine.

nonagon A 9-sided *polygon*.

nonconvex polygon Same as *concave polygon*.

normal span The distance from the end of the thumb to the end of the index (first) finger of an outstretched hand. For estimating lengths, many people can adjust this distance to approximately 6 inches or 15 centimeters. Same as *span*. Compare to *great span*. See Section 12.1: Personal Measures.

number-and-word notation A notation consisting of the significant digits of a number and words for the place value. For example, 27 billion is number-and-word notation for 27,000,000,000.

number family Same as *fact family.*

number grid In *Everyday Mathematics,* a table in which *consecutive* numbers are arranged in *rows,* usually 10 *columns* per row. A move from one number to the next within a row is a change of 1; a move from one number to the next within a column is a change of 10. See Section 8.6.2: Number Grids, Scrolls, and Lines.

−9	−8	−7	−6	−5	−4	−3	−2	−1	0
1	2	3	4	5	6	7	8	9	10
11	12	13	14	15	16	17	18	19	20
21	22	23	24	25	26	27	28	29	30
31	32	33	34	35	36	37	38	39	40
41	42	43	44	45	46	47	48	49	50
51	52	53	54	55	56	57	58	59	60
61	62	63	64	65	66	67	68	69	70
71	72	73	74	75	76	77	78	79	80
81	82	83	84	85	86	87	88	89	90
91	92	93	94	95	96	97	98	99	100
101	102	103	104	105	106	107	108	109	110

A number grid

number-grid puzzle In *Everyday Mathematics,* a piece of a *number grid* in which some, but not all, of the numbers are missing. Students use number-grid puzzles to practice place-value concepts.

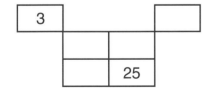

A number-grid puzzle

number line A line on which points are indicated by *tick marks* that are usually at regularly spaced intervals from a starting point called the *origin,* the *zero point,* or simply 0. Numbers are associated with the tick marks on a *scale* defined by the *unit interval* from 0 to 1. See Section 8.6.2: Number Grids, Scrolls, and Lines.

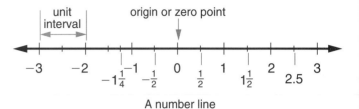

A number line

number model A *number sentence, expression,* or other representation that models a *number story* or situation. For example, the story *Sally had $5, and then she earned $8* can be modeled as the number sentence $5 + 8 = 13$, as the expression $5 + 8$, or by

$$\begin{array}{r} 5 \\ +\ 8 \\ \hline 13 \end{array}$$

See Section 9.2: Number Sentences and Number Models and Section 16.4: Mathematical Modeling.

number scroll In *Everyday Mathematics,* a series of *number grids* taped together. See Section 8.6.2: Number Grids, Scrolls, and Lines.

A number scroll

number sentence Two *expressions* with a *relation symbol.* See Section 9.2: Number Sentences and Number Models.

$$5 + 5 = 10 \qquad 16 \leq a \times b$$
$$2 - ? = 8 \qquad a^2 + b^2 = c^2$$

Number sentences

number sequence A list of numbers, often generated by a rule. In *Everyday Mathematics*, students explore number sequences using *Frames-and-Arrows* diagrams. See Section 15.1.3: Sequences.

$$1, 2, 3, 4, 5, \ldots \qquad 1, 4, 9, 16, 25, \ldots$$
$$1, 2, 1, 2, 1, \ldots \qquad 1, 3, 5, 7, 9, \ldots$$

Number sequences

number story A story that involves numbers and one or more explicit or implicit questions. For example, *I have 7 crayons in my desk. Carrie gave me 8 more crayons. Now I have 15 crayons in all* is a number story. See Sections 9.1 and 16.5.1: Number Stories.

numeral A word, symbol, or figure that represents a number. For example, six, VI, ⱵⱵⱵⱵ /, and 6 are all numerals that represent the same number.

numeration A method of numbering or of reading and writing numbers. In *Everyday Mathematics,* numeration activities include counting, writing numbers, identifying equivalent names for numbers in *name-collection boxes,* exchanging coins such as 5 pennies for 1 nickel, and renaming numbers in computation. See Section 8.2.1: Numeration and Place Value.

numerator The dividend a in a fraction $\frac{a}{b}$ or a/b. In a part-whole *fraction,* in which the *whole* (or *ONE* or *unit whole*) is divided into a number of equal parts, the numerator is the number of equal parts being considered. Compare to *denominator*.

obtuse angle An *angle* with measure between 90° and 180°. See Section 11.4.1: Angles and Rotations.

Obtuse angles

obtuse triangle A *triangle* with an angle measuring more than 90°. See Section 11.4.2: Polygons (*n*-gons).

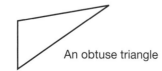

An obtuse triangle

octa- A prefix meaning eight.

octagon An 8-sided *polygon*. See Section 11.4.2: Polygons (*n*-gons).

Octagons

octahedron A *polyhedron* with 8 faces. An octahedron with 8 *equilateral triangle* faces is one of the five *regular polyhedrons*. See Section 11.5.2: Polyhedrons.

odd number A *counting number* that is not divisible by 2. Compare to *even number*. See Section 15.1.2: Odd and Even Number Patterns.

ONE In *Everyday Mathematics,* same as *whole* or *unit whole*.

1-dimensional (1-D) coordinate system A *reference frame* in which any point on a *1-dimensional figure* can be located with one *coordinate* relative to the origin of a number line. Compare to *2-dimensional* and *3-dimensional coordinate systems*.

1-dimensional (1-D) figure A figure such as a line segment, arc, or part of a curve that has length but no width or depth. Compare to *2-* and *3-dimensional figures*. See Section 11.1: Dimension.

open sentence A *number sentence* with one or more *variables*. An open sentence is neither true nor false. For example, $9 + \_\_ = 15$, $? - 24 < 10$, and $7 = x + y$ are open sentences. See Section 15.2.2: Reading and Writing Open Sentences.

operation A rule performed on one or more mathematical objects such as numbers, *variables,* or *expressions* to produce another mathematical object. Addition, subtraction, multiplication, and division are the four basic arithmetic operations. Taking a square root, squaring a number, and multiplying both sides of an *equation* by the same number are also operations. In *Everyday Mathematics,* students learn about many operations along with several procedures, or *algorithms,* for carrying them out. See Chapter 9: Operations and Number Models.

operation symbol A symbol used in *expressions* and *number sentences* to stand for a particular mathematical operation. Symbols for common arithmetic operations are:

addition $+$
subtraction $-$
multiplication $\times$, $*$, $\bullet$
division $\div$, $/$
powering $\wedge$

See Section 9.2: Number Sentences and Number Models.

opposite angle in a triangle The *angle* opposite a *side* of a *triangle* that is not one of the sides of the angle.

Angle C is opposite side AB.

opposite angles in a quadrilateral Two *angles* in a *quadrilateral* that do not share a side.

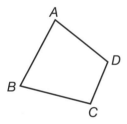

Angles A and C and angles B and D
are pairs of opposite angles.

opposite side in a triangle The *side* opposite an *angle* of a *triangle* that is not a side of the angle.

opposite sides in a quadrilateral Two *sides* in a *quadrilateral* that do not share a *vertex*.

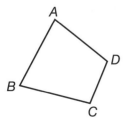

Sides AB and DC and sides BC and AD
are pairs of opposite sides.

order-of-magnitude estimate Same as *magnitude estimate*.

order-of-magnitude increase A 10-times change in a value. Sometimes simply called a magnitude increase. See Section 14.1.2: Estimates in Calculations.

order of operations Rules that tell the order in which operations in an *expression* should be carried out. The conventional order of operations is:

1. Do operations inside *grouping symbols*. Work from the innermost set of grouping symbols outward. Inside grouping symbols, follow Rules 2–4.
2. Calculate all expressions with *exponents*.
3. *Multiply* and *divide* in order from left to right.
4. *Add* and *subtract* in order from left to right.

For example:
$$5^2 + (3 \times 4 - 2) \div 5 = 5^2 + (12 - 2) \div 5$$
$$= 5^2 + 10 \div 5$$
$$= 25 + 10 \div 5$$
$$= 25 + 2$$
$$= 27$$

Same as *algebraic order of operations*.

ordered pair (1) Two numbers, or *coordinates*, used to locate a point on a *rectangular coordinate grid*. The first coordinate x gives the position along the horizontal axis of the grid, and the second coordinate y gives the position along the vertical axis. The pair is written (x, y). (2) Any pair of objects or numbers in a particular order.

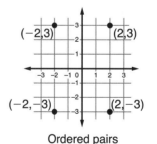

Ordered pairs

orders of magnitude Positive powers of 10 including 10, 100, 1,000, and so on. See *order-of-magnitude increase* and Section 14.1.2: Estimates in Calculations.

ordinal number The position or order of something in a *sequence,* such as first, third, or tenth. Ordinal numbers are commonly used in dates, as in "May fifth" instead of "May five." See Section 8.2.3: Ordinal Numbers.

origin The *zero point* in a *coordinate system*. On a number line, the origin is the point at 0. On a coordinate grid, the origin is the point (0,0) where the two axes intersect.

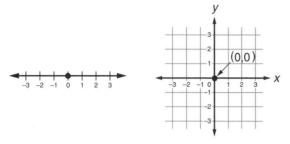

The points at 0 and (0,0) are origins.

ounce (oz) A U.S. customary unit of *weight* equal to $\frac{1}{16}$ of a pound or about 28.35 grams. Compare to *fluid ounce*. See the Tables of Measures and Section 12.6: Weight and Mass.

outcome A possible result of a chance experiment or situation. For example, HEADS and TAILS are the two possible outcomes of flipping a coin. See *event, equally likely outcomes,* and Section 10.1.2: The Language of Chance.

output (1) A number paired to an *input* by an imaginary *function machine* applying a rule. (2) The values for *y* in a *function* consisting of ordered pairs (x, y). See Section 15.1.4: Functions. (3) Numbers or other information displayed by calculator or computer.

pan balance A device used to weigh objects or compare their *weights*. See Section 12.10.3: Scales and Balances.

parallel lines *Lines* in a *plane* that never meet. Two parallel lines are always the same distance apart. *Line segments* or *rays* on parallel lines are parallel to each other. See Section 11.6.1: Perpendicular and Parallel.

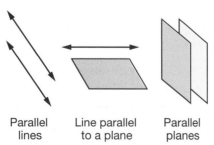

Parallel lines   Line parallel to a plane   Parallel planes

parallel planes *Planes* in space that never meet. Two parallel planes are always the same distance apart. A figure in one plane is parallel to the other plane. Polygons in one plane are said to be parallel to polygons in the other plane. However, 1-dimensional shapes such as lines, segments, and rays in one plane are not necessarily parallel to 1-dimensional shapes in a parallel plane. See Section 11.6.1: Perpendicular and Parallel.

parallelogram A *quadrilateral* with two pairs of parallel sides. *Opposite sides* of a parallelogram have the same length and *opposite angles* have the same measure. All rectangles are parallelograms, but not all parallelograms are rectangles because parallelograms do not necessarily have right angles. See Section 11.4.2: Polygons (*n*-gons).

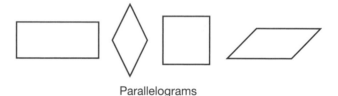

Parallelograms

parentheses See *grouping symbols*.

partitive division A term for the type of division used to solve an *equal-sharing story* such as *If $10 is shared by 4 people, how much does each person get?* Compare to *measurement division*. See Section 9.3.2: Multiplication and Division Use Classes.

parts-and-total diagram In *Everyday Mathematics,* a diagram used to model problems in which two or more quantities (parts) are combined to get a total quantity. See *situation diagram* and Section 9.3.1: Addition and Subtraction Use Classes.

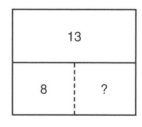

Parts-and-total diagrams for 13 = 8 + ?

parts-and-total story A *number story* in which a whole is made up of distinct parts. For example, *There are 15 girls and 12 boys in Mrs. Dorn's class. How many students are there in all?* is a parts-and-total story. In other stories, the total and one or more parts may be known and the last part unknown. See Section 9.3.1: Addition and Subtraction Use Classes.

pattern A repetitive order or arrangement. In *Everyday Mathematics,* students mainly explore visual and number patterns in which elements are arranged so that what comes next can be predicted. See Section 15.1: Patterns, Sequences, and Functions.

Pattern-Block Template In *Kindergarten* through *Third Grade Everyday Mathematics,* a sheet of plastic with geometric shapes cut out, used to draw patterns and designs. See Section 11.10.1: Pattern-Block Template.

pattern blocks A set of *polygon*-shaped blocks of varying sizes in which smaller blocks can be placed on larger blocks to show fractional parts. The blocks are used for geometric-shape identification and fraction activities. Compare to *attribute blocks*.

penta- A prefix meaning five.

pentagon A 5-sided *polygon*. See Section 11.4.2: Polygons (*n*-gons).

Pentagons

per For each, as in *ten chairs per row* or *six tickets per family*.

percent (%) *Per* hundred, for each hundred, or out of a hundred. $1\% = \frac{1}{100} = 0.01$. For example, *48% of the students in the school are boys* means that, on average, 48 of every 100 children in the school are boys. See Section 8.3: Rational Numbers: Fractions, Decimals, and Percents.

perimeter The distance around the boundary of a *2-dimensional figure*. The perimeter of a *circle* is called its *circumference*. A formula for the perimeter P of a *rectangle* with length l and width w is $P = 2 \times (l + w)$. Perimeter comes from the Greek words for "around measure." See Section 12.3: Length.

perpendicular (⊥) Two *lines* or two *planes* that intersect at *right angles. Line segments* or *rays* that lie on perpendicular lines are perpendicular to each other. The symbol ⊥ means "is perpendicular to." See Section 11.6.1: Perpendicular and Parallel.

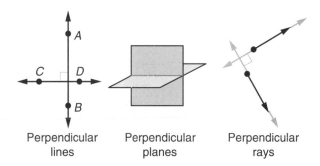

Perpendicular lines | Perpendicular planes | Perpendicular rays

perpendicular bisector A *line, ray,* or *segment* that *bisects* a line segment at a *right angle*.

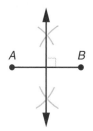

Construction of a perpendicular bisector of $\overline{AB}$

personal-measurement reference A convenient approximation for a standard unit of measurement. For example, many people have thumbs that are approximately one inch wide. See Section 12.1: Personal Measures.

perspective drawing A drawing that realistically represents a 3-dimensional object on a 2-dimensional surface. See Section 11.5.4: Connecting 2-D and 3-D.

pi (π) The ratio of the *circumference* of a circle to its *diameter*. Pi is also the ratio of the area of a circle to the square of its radius. Pi is the same for every circle and is an *irrational number* that is approximately equal to 3.14. The symbol π is the sixteenth letter of the Greek alphabet. See Section 11.4.3: Circles and Pi (π).

Glossary

pictograph A graph constructed with pictures or symbols. See Section 10.2.3: Organizing and Displaying Data.

Trees Planted in Park

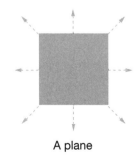

A pictograph

pie graph Same as *circle graph*.

pint (pt) A U.S. customary unit of *volume* or *capacity* equal to 2 cups, or 16 fluid ounces. A handy saying to remember is *A pint's a pound the world around,* meaning that a pint of water weighs about 1 pound. See the Tables of Measures and Section 12.5: Volume (Capacity).

place value A system that gives a *digit* a value according to its position, or place, in a number. In our standard, *base-ten* (decimal) system for writing numbers, each place has a value 10 times that of the place to its right and 1 tenth the value of the place to its left. See Section 8.2.1: Numeration and Place Value.

thousands	hundreds	tens	ones	.	tenths	hundredths

A place-value chart

plane In *Everyday Mathematics*, a *2-dimensional* flat surface that extends forever in all directions. In formal Euclidean geometry, plane is an undefined geometric term. See Section 11.4: Planes and Plane Figures.

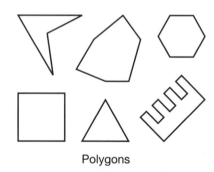

A plane

plane figure A *2-dimensional figure* that is entirely contained in a single *plane*. For example, triangles, squares, pentagons, circles, and parabolas are plane figures; lines, rays, cones, cubes, and prisms are not. See Section 11.4: Planes and Plane Figures.

P.M. The abbreviation for *post meridiem,* meaning "after the middle of the day" in Latin. From noon to midnight.

point In *Everyday Mathematics,* an exact location in space. Points are usually labeled with capital letters. In formal Euclidean geometry, point is an undefined geometric term. See Section 11.2: Points.

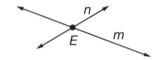

Lines *m* and *n* intersect at point *E*.

poly- A prefix meaning many.

polygon A *2-dimensional figure* formed by three or more line segments (*sides*) that meet only at their endpoints (*vertices*) to make a closed path. The sides may not cross one another. See Section 11.4.2: Polygons (*n*-gons).

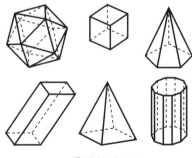

Polygons

polyhedron A *3-dimensional figure* formed by *polygons* with their interiors (*faces*) and having no holes. Plural is polyhedrons or polyhedra. See Section 11.5.2: Polyhedrons.

Polyhedrons

Glossary

population (1) The total number of people living within a defined geographic region. (2) In data collection, the group of people or objects that is the focus of study. Large populations are often studied by picking a representative *random sample* from the population. See Section 10.2.2: Collecting and Recording Data.

positive numbers Numbers greater than 0; the opposites of the *negative numbers*. Positive numbers are plotted to the right of 0 on a horizontal number line or above 0 on a vertical number line. See Section 8.4: Positive and Negative Numbers.

positive rational numbers *Rational numbers* greater than 0; the opposites of the *negative rational numbers*. For example, 7, $\frac{4}{3}$, $\frac{1}{1,000}$, 0.01, 8.125, and $5.111\ldots$ are positive rational numbers. See Section 8.4: Positive and Negative Numbers.

pound (lb) A U.S. customary unit of *weight* equal to 16 ounces and defined as 0.45359237 kilogram. See the Tables of Measures and Section 12.6: Weight and Mass.

power Same as *exponent*.

precipitation Condensed atmospheric moisture that falls to the ground, including rain, snow, and hail. In the United States, rainfall is typically measured in inches. Snow and hail are first melted and then measured like rain.

precise Exact or accurate.

precise calculations The more accurate measures or other data are, the more *precise* any calculations using those numbers can be. See Section 14.2: Approximation and Rounding.

precise measures The smaller the *scale* of a measuring tool, the more *precise* a measurement can be. For example, a measurement to the nearest inch is more precise than a measurement to the nearest foot. A ruler with $\frac{1}{16}$-inch markings can be more precise than a ruler with only $\frac{1}{4}$-inch markings, depending on the skill of the person doing the measuring.

predict In mathematics, to say what will happen in the future based on experimental data or theoretical calculation.

preimage The original figure in a *transformation*. Compare to *image*. See Section 11.7: Transformations.

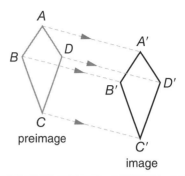

prism A *polyhedron* with two parallel and congruent polygonal regions for *bases* and lateral *faces* formed by all the line segments with endpoints on corresponding edges of the bases. The lateral faces are all parallelograms. Lateral faces intersect at lateral *edges*. In a *right prism*, the lateral faces are rectangular. Prisms get their names from the shape of their bases. See Section 11.5.2: Polyhedrons.

A triangular prism   A rectangular prism   A hexagonal prism

probability A number from 0 through 1 giving the likelihood that an *event* will happen. The closer a probability is to 1, the more likely the event is to happen. The closer a probability is to 0, the less likely the event is to happen. For example, the probability that a fair coin will show HEADS is $\frac{1}{2}$. See Section 10.1: Probability.

product The result of multiplying two numbers, called *factors*. For example, in $4 \times 3 = 12$, the product is 12.

property (1) A generalized statement about a mathematical relationship such as the Distributive Property of Multiplication over Addition. (2) Same as *attribute*.

protractor A tool used for measuring or drawing *angles*. A half-circle protractor can be used to measure and draw angles up to 180°. A full-circle protractor can be used to measure and draw angles up to 360°.

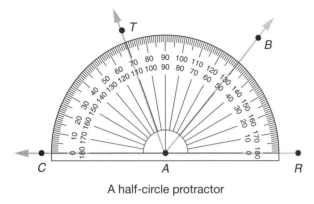

A half-circle protractor

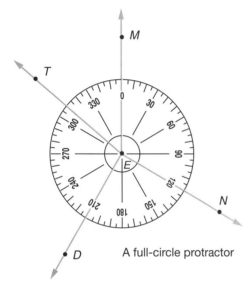

A full-circle protractor

pyramid A *polyhedron* made up of any polygonal region for a *base,* a vertex *(apex)* not in the plane of the base, and all of the line segments with one endpoint at the apex and the other on an edge of the base. All faces except perhaps the base are triangular. Pyramids get their name from the shape of their base. See Section 11.5.2: Polyhedrons.

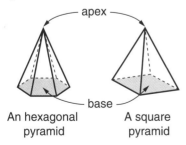

An hexagonal pyramid   A square pyramid

Q

quad- A prefix meaning four.

quadrangle Same as *quadrilateral.*

quadrant One of the four sections into which a *rectangular coordinate grid* is divided by the two axes. The quadrants are typically numbered I, II, III, and IV counterclockwise beginning at the upper right.

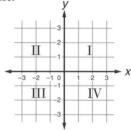

quadrilateral A 4-sided *polygon.* See *square, rectangle, parallelogram, rhombus, kite, trapezoid,* and Section 11.4.2: Polygons (*n*-gons).

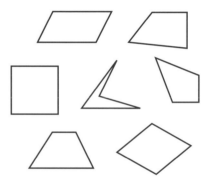

Quadrilaterals

quadruple Four times an amount.

quart A U.S. customary unit of *volume* or *capacity* equal to 32 fluid ounces, 2 pints, or 4 cups. See the Tables of Measures and Section 12.5: Volume (Capacity).

quotient The result of dividing one number by another number. For example, in $10 \div 5 = 2$, the quotient is 2.

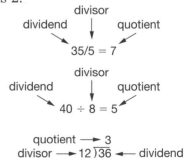

quotitive division Same as *measurement division.*

radius (1) A *line segment* from the center of a circle (or sphere) to any point on the *circle* (or *sphere*). (2) The length of this line segment. The length of a radius is half the length of a *diameter*. Plural is radiuses or radii. See Section 11.4.3: Circles and Pi (π).

random draw Taking an object from a set of objects in which each object has an *equally likely* chance of being chosen. For example, drawing a card from a deck and drawing a domino from a bag of dominoes are random draws. See Section 10.1.2: The Language of Chance.

random experiment An experiment in which all *outcomes* are *equally likely*. No one outcome is more predictable than any other. See Section 10.1.2: The Language of Chance.

random number A number produced by a *random experiment,* such as rolling a die or spinning a spinner. For example, rolling a fair die produces random numbers because each of the six possible numbers 1, 2, 3, 4, 5, and 6 has the same chance of coming up. See Section 10.1.2: The Language of Chance.

random sample A *sample* that gives all members of the *population* the same chance of being selected. See Section 10.2.2: Collecting and Recording Data.

range The *difference* between the *maximum* and the *minimum* in a set of data. Used as a measure of the spread of the data. See Section 10.2.4: Data Analysis.

rate A comparison by division of two quantities with different *units*. For example, traveling 100 miles in 2 hours is an average rate of $\frac{100 \text{ mi}}{2 \text{ hr}}$, or 50 miles per hour. Compare to *ratio*.

rate unit A compound *unit* for a *rate*. For example, *miles per hour, dollars per pound,* and *words per minute* are rate units.

ratio A comparison by division of two quantities with the same *units*. Ratios can be fractions, decimals, percents, or stated in words. Ratios can also be written with a colon between the two numbers being compared. For example, if a team wins 3 games out of 5 games played, the ratio of wins to total games is $\frac{3}{5}$, 3/5, 0.6, 60%, 3 to 5, or 3:5 (read "three to five"). Compare to *rate*.

rational counting Counting using one-to-one matching. For example, counting a number of chairs, people, or crackers. See Section 8.2.2: Plain and Fancy Counting.

rational numbers Numbers that can be written in the form $\frac{a}{b}$, where a and nonzero b are *integers*. The decimal form of a rational number either terminates or repeats. For example, $\frac{2}{3}$, $-\frac{2}{3}$, 0.5, 20.5, and 0.333 . . . are rational numbers. See Section 8.3: Rational Numbers: Fractions, Decimal, and Percents.

ray A part of a *line* starting at the ray's *endpoint* and continuing forever in one direction. A ray is often named by its endpoint and another point on it. See Section 11.3: Lines, Segments, and Rays.

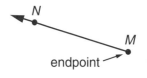

Ray *MN* or $\overrightarrow{MN}$

r-by-c array A rectangular arrangement of elements with r rows and c elements per row. Among other things, an r-by-c array models r sets with c objects per set. Although listing rows before columns is arbitrary, it is in keeping with the order used in matrix notation, which students will study later.

real numbers All *rational* and *irrational numbers;* all numbers that can be written as decimals. For every real number there is a corresponding point on a number line, and for every point on the number line there is a real number.

rectangle A *parallelogram* with all *right angles*. See Section 11.4.2: Polygons (*n*-gons).

rectangular array An arrangement of objects in *rows* and *columns* that form a *rectangle*. All rows have the same number of objects, and all columns have the same number of objects. See r-*by*-c *array* and Section 9.3.2: Multiplication and Division Use Classes.

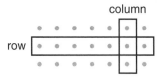

A rectangular array

rectangular coordinate grid (1) In *Everyday Mathematics,* same as *coordinate grid.* (2) A coordinate grid with perpendicular axes.

rectangular prism A *prism* with rectangular *bases.* The four faces that are not bases are either *rectangles* or *parallelograms.* For example, a shoe box models a rectangular prism in which all sides are rectangles. See Section 11.5.2: Polyhedrons.

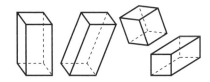

Rectangular prisms

rectangular pyramid A *pyramid* with a rectangular *base.* See Section 11.5.2: Polyhedrons.

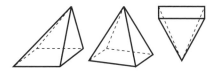

Rectangular pyramids

reduce To decrease the size of an object or figure without changing its shape. Same as *shrink.* See *scale factor.*

reference frame A system for locating numbers within a given context, usually with reference to an *origin* or *zero point.* For example, number lines, clocks, calendars, temperature scales, and maps are reference frames. See Chapter 13: Reference Frames.

reflection A *transformation* in which the *image* of a figure is a mirror image of the figure over a *line of reflection.* Each point A on the figure and its corresponding point A' on the image are the same distance from the line of reflection on a line perpendicular to it. Informally called a *flip.*

A reflection

reflex angle An *angle* with a measure between 180° and 360°. See Section 11.4.1: Angles and Rotations.

A reflex angle

regular polygon A *polygon* in which all *sides* are the same length and all *angles* have the same measure. See Section 11.4.2: Polygons (*n*-gons).

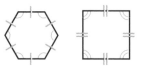

Regular polygons

regular polyhedron A *polyhedron* whose faces are all *congruent regular polygons* and in which the same number of faces meet at each *vertex.* The five regular polyhedrons, known as the Platonic solids, are shown below.

A tetrahedron (4 equilateral triangles) A cube (6 squares) An octahedron (8 equilateral triangles)

A dodecahedron (12 regular pentagons) An icosahedron (20 equilateral triangles)

Glossary

regular tessellation A *tessellation* of one *regular polygon*. The only three regular tessellations are shown below.

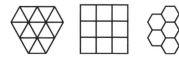

Samples of the three regular tessellations

relation symbol A symbol used to express a relationship between two quantities. See Section 9.2.2: Reading and Writing Number Sentences.

Relation	Meaning
=	is equal to
≠	is not equal to
<	is less than
>	is greater than
≤	is less than or equal to
≥	is greater than or equal to
≈	is approximately equal to

remainder An amount left over when one number is divided by another number. For example, in $16 \div 3 \rightarrow 5$ R1, the *quotient* is 5 and the remainder R is 1. See Section 9.2.1: Arithmetic Symbols.

repeating decimal A *decimal* in which one *digit* or a group of digits is repeated without end. For example, 0.3333. . . and $0.\overline{147}$ are repeating decimals. Compare to *terminating decimal*.

rhombus A *parallelogram* with all sides the same length. All rhombuses are parallelograms. Every square is a rhombus, but not all rhombuses are squares. Also called a diamond. Plural is rhombuses or rhombi. See Section 11.4.2: Polygons (*n*-gons).

Rhombuses

right angle A 90° *angle*. See Section 11.4.1: Angles and Rotations.

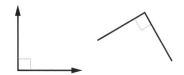

Right angles

right cone or pyramid A *cone* or *pyramid* whose *base* is perpendicular to the line segment joining the *apex* and the center of the base. See Section 11.5.2: Polyhedrons and Section 11.5.3: Solids with Curved Surfaces.

A right circular cone

right cylinder A *cylinder* whose *bases* are perpendicular to the line segment joining the centers of the bases. See Section 11.5.3: Solids with Curved Surfaces.

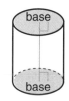

A right circular cylinder

right prism A *prism* whose *bases* are perpendicular to all of the *edges* that connect the two bases. See Section 11.5.2: Polyhedrons.

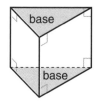

A right triangular prism

right triangle A *triangle* with a *right angle*. See Section 11.4.2: Polygons (*n*-gons).

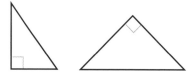

Right triangles

Roman numerals Letters that are used alone and in combination to represent numbers in an ancient Roman system of *numeration*. Roman numerals are found on clocks, building cornerstones, preliminary pages in books, movie copyright dates, and other places.

Roman Numerals		
I = 1	X = 10	C = 100
II = 2	XX = 20 (2 tens)	CC = 200
III = 3	XXX = 30 (3 tens)	CCC = 300
IV = 4	XL = 40 (50 less 10)	CD = 400
V = 5	L = 50	D = 500
VI = 6	LX = 60 (50 plus 10)	CM = 900
VII = 7	LXX = 70 (50 plus 20)	M = 1,000
VIII = 8	LXXX = 80 (50 plus 30)	$\overline{X}$ = 10,000
IX = 9	XC = 90 (100 less 10)	$\overline{C}$ = 100,000
		∞ = 100,000,000 or infinity

rotation (1) A point P' is a rotation *image* of a point P around a center of rotation C if P' is on the *circle* with center C and radius CP. If all the points in one figure are rotation images of all the points in another figure around the same center of rotation and with the same angle of rotation, the figures are rotation images. The center can be inside or outside of the original image. Informally called a *turn*. See Section 11.7: Transformations. (2) If all points on the image of a *3-dimensional figure* are rotation images around a point on a line called the axis of rotation, then the image is a rotation image of the original figure.

A rotation

rotation symmetry A figure has rotation symmetry if it is the *rotation* image of itself after less than a 360° turn around a center or axis of rotation. See Section 11.8.2: Other Symmetries.

rote counting Reciting a string of number words by rote, without understanding their significance. See *skip counting* and Section 8.2.2: Plain and Fancy Counting.

round (1) To approximate a number to make it easier to work with, or to make it better reflect the precision of the data. "Rounding up" means to approximate larger than the actual value. "Rounding down" means to approximate smaller than the actual value. See *round to the nearest* and Section 14.2: Approximation and Rounding. (2) Circular in shape.

round to the nearest To *round* a number up or down in a particular decimal place, depending on which approximation is closer to the actual value. See Section 14.2: Approximation and Rounding.

row A horizontal arrangement of objects or numbers in an *array* or table.

sample A part of a *population* intended to represent the whole population. See *random sample* and Section 10.2.2: Collecting and Recording Data.

scale (1) The relative size of something. (2) Same as *scale factor*. (3) A tool for measuring *weight*. See Section 12.6: Weight and Mass.

scale of a number line The *unit interval* on a number line or measuring device. The scales on this ruler are 1 millimeter on the left side and $\frac{1}{16}$ inch on the right side. See Section 8.6.2: Number Grids, Scrolls, and Lines.

scale drawing A drawing of an object in which all parts are drawn to the same *scale* to the object. For example, architects and builders use scale drawings traditionally called blueprints. A map is a scale drawing of a geographical region. See *scale factor*.

A woodpecker (8 in.) to $\frac{1}{4}$ scale

scale factor (1) The *ratio* of lengths on an *image* and corresponding lengths on a *preimage* in a *size change*. Same as *size-change factor*. (2) The ratio of lengths in a *scale drawing* or *scale model* to the corresponding lengths in the object being drawn or modeled.

scale model A model of an object in which all parts are made to the same *scale* to the object. For example, many model trains or airplanes are scale models of actual vehicles. See *scale factor*.

scalene triangle A *triangle* with sides of three different lengths. The three angles of a scalene triangle have different measures. See Section 11.4.2: Polygons (*n*-gons).

scientific calculator A calculator that can display numbers using *scientific notation*. Scientific calculators follow the *algebraic order of operations* and can calculate a power of a number, a *square root,* and several other functions beyond simple 4-function calculators. Some scientific calculators let you enter and do arithmetic with *fractions*.

scientific notation A way of writing a number as the product of a *power* of 10 and a number that is at least 1 and less than 10. Scientific notation allows you to write large and small numbers with only a few symbols. For example, in scientific notation, 4,300,000 is 4.3×10^6, and 0.00001 is 1×10^{-5}. *Scientific calculators* display numbers in scientific notation. Compare to *standard notation* and *expanded notation*.

second (s or sec) (1) A unit of time defined as $\frac{1}{31,556,925.9747}$ of the tropical year at midnight Eastern Time on New Year's Day, 1900. There are 60 seconds in a minute. (2) An *ordinal number* in the sequence *first, second, third, ...*

sector A region bounded by and including an *arc* and two *radii* of a circle. A sector resembles a slice of pizza. *Circle graphs* are made with sectors corresponding to parts of a data set. Also called a wedge.

sector

segment Same as *line segment*.

semicircle (1) Half of a *circle*. (2) Half of a circle and the *diameter* between the endpoints of the arc. Sometimes the interior of this closed figure is also included. See *circle* and Section 11.4.3: Circles and Pi (π).

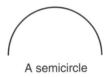
A semicircle

sequence A list of numbers, often with an underlying rule that may be used to generate subsequent numbers in the list. *Frames-and-Arrows* diagrams are used to represent sequences. See Section 15.1.3: Sequences.

set A collection or group of objects, numbers, or other items.

short-term memory *Memory in a calculator* used to store values for immediate calculation. Short-term memory is usually cleared with a $\boxed{C}$, $\boxed{AC}$, $\boxed{Clear}$, or similar key. Compare to *long-term memory*.

shrink Same as *reduce*.

side (1) One of the *line segments* that make up a *polygon*. (2) One of the *rays* or *segments* that form an *angle*. (3) One of the *faces* of a *polyhedron*.

similar figures Figures that have the same shape, but not necessarily the same size. Compare to congruent. See Section 11.6.2: Congruence and Similarity.

Similar polygons

situation diagram A diagram used to organize information in a problem situation in one of the *addition/subtraction* or *multiplication/division use classes*. See Section 9.3: Use Classes and Situation Diagrams.

size change A *transformation* in which the *image* of a figure is an enlargement (*stretch*) or reduction (*shrink*) of the original figure by a given *scale factor*.

size-change factor Same as *scale factor*.

skip counting *Rote counting* by intervals, such as by twos, fives, or tens. See Section 8.2.2: Plain and Fancy Counting.

slanted cylinder, cone, prism, or pyramid A *cylinder, cone, prism,* or *pyramid* that is not a *right cylinder, right cone, right prism,* or *right pyramid*.

A slanted cylinder, cone, prism, and pyramid

slate A lap-size (about 8-inch by 11-inch) chalkboard or whiteboard that children use in *Everyday Mathematics* for recording responses during group exercises and informal group assessments. See Section 3.2.1: Numeration and Computation Tools.

slide An informal name for a *translation*. See Section 11.7: Transformations.

solution of an open sentence A value or values for the *variable(s)* in an *open sentence* that make the sentence true. For example, 7 is a solution of $5 + n = 12$. Although equations are not necessarily open sentences, the solution of an open sentence is commonly referred to as a solution of an equation. See Section 15.2.3: Solving Open Sentences.

solution of a problem (1) The method by which an answer to a problem is obtained. (2) The answer to a problem. See Chapter 16: Problem Solving.

solution set The set of all *solutions of an open sentence*. For example, the solution set of $x^2 = 25$ is {5, −5} because substituting either 5 or −5 for x makes the sentence true.

span Same as *normal span*.

speed A *rate* that compares distance traveled with the time taken to travel that distance. For example, if a car travels 100 miles in 2 hours, then its average speed is $\frac{100 \text{ mi}}{2 \text{ hr}}$, or 50 miles per hour.

sphere The set of all points in space that are an equal distance from a fixed point called the *center of the sphere*. The distance from the center to the sphere is the *radius* of the sphere. The *diameter* of a sphere is twice its radius. Points inside a sphere are not part of the sphere. See Section 11.5.3: Solids with Curved Surfaces.

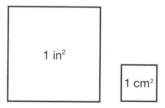
A sphere

square A *rectangle* with all sides of equal length. All angles in a square are *right angles*. See Section 11.4.2: Polygons (*n*-gons).

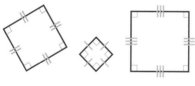
Squares

square array A rectangular *array* with the same number of *rows* as *columns*. For example, 16 objects will form a square array with 4 objects in each row and 4 objects in each column. See Section 9.3.2: Multiplication and Division Use Classes.

A square array

square corner Same as a *right angle*.

square numbers *Figurate numbers* that are the product of a *counting number* and itself. For example, 25 is a square number because $25 = 5 \times 5$. A square number can be represented by a *square array* and as a number squared, such as $25 = 5^2$. See Section 15.1.3: Sequences.

square of a number *n* The product of *n* and itself, commonly written n^2. For example, $81 = 9 \times 9 = 9^2$ and $3.5^2 = 3.5 \times 3.5 = 12.25$.

square pyramid A *pyramid* with a square *base*. See Section 11.5.2: Polyhedrons.

square root of a number *n* A number that multiplied by itself is *n*, commonly written $\sqrt{n}$. For example, 4 is a square root of 16, because $4 \times 4 = 16$. Normally, square root refers to the positive square root, but the *opposite* of a positive square root is also a square root. For example, −4 is also a square root of 16 because $-4 \times -4 = 16$.

square unit A unit to measure *area*. A model of a square unit is a square with each side a related unit of *length*. For example, a square inch is the area of a square with 1-inch sides. Square units are often labeled as the length unit squared. For example, 1 cm^2 is read "1 square centimeter" or "1 centimeter squared." See Section 12.4: Area.

1 in^2
1 cm^2
Square units

standard notation Our most common way of representing *whole numbers, integers,* and *decimals.* Standard notation is *base-ten place-value* numeration. For example, standard notation for three hundred fifty-six is 356. Same as *decimal notation.* See Section 8.2.1: Numeration and Place Value.

Glossary

standard unit A unit of measure that has been defined by a recognized authority, such as a government or a standards organization. For example, *inches, meters, miles, seconds, pounds, grams,* and *acres* are all standard units. See Section 12.2: Measurement Systems.

straight angle A 180° *angle.* See Section 11.4.1: Angles and Rotations.

A straight angle

straightedge A tool used to draw *line segments.* Strictly speaking, a straightedge does not have a measuring *scale* on it, so ignore the marks if you use a ruler as a straightedge.

stretch Same as *enlarge.*

substitute (1) To replace one thing with another. (2) To replace *variables* with numbers in an *expression* or *formula.* For example, substituting $b = 4.5$ and $h = 8.5$ in the formula $A = b \times h$ gives $A = 4.5 \times 8.5 = 38.25$. See Section 15.2.1: Uses of Variables.

subtrahend The number being taken away in a subtraction problem. For example, in $15 - 5 = 10$, the subtrahend is 5.

sum The result of adding two or more numbers. For example, in $5 + 3 = 8$, the sum is 8. Same as *total.*

supplementary angles Two angles whose measures add to 180°. Supplementary angles do not need to be *adjacent.* Compare to *complementary angles.*

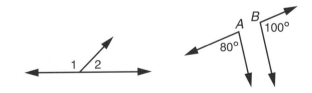
∠1 and ∠2 and ∠A and ∠B
are two pairs of supplementary angles.

surface (1) The boundary of a 3-dimensional object. The part of an object that is next to the air. Common surfaces include the top of a body of water, the outermost part of a ball, and the topmost layer of ground that covers Earth. See Section 11.5: Space and 3-D Figures. (2) Any 2-dimensional layer, such as a *plane* or a face of a *polyhedron.*

surface area The *area* of the *surface* of a *3-dimensional figure.* The surface area of a polyhedron is the sum of the areas of its faces.

survey A study that collects *data.* Surveys are commonly used to study "demographics" such as people's characteristics, behaviors, interests, and opinions. See Section 10.2.2: Collecting and Recording Data.

symmetric figure A figure that exactly matches with its *image* under a *reflection* or *rotation.* See *line symmetry, rotation symmetry,* and Section 11.8: Symmetry.

symmetry The balanced distribution of points over a line or around a point in a *symmetric figure.* See *line symmetry, rotation symmetry,* and Section 11.8: Symmetry.

A figure with line symmetry   A figure with rotation symmetry

 T

tally (1) To keep a record of a count, commonly by making a mark for each item as it is counted. (2) The mark used in a count. Also called "tally mark" and "tick mark." See Section 10.2.2: Collecting and Recording Data.

tally chart A table to keep track of a *tally,* typically showing how many times each value appears in a set of data.

temperature How hot or cold something is relative to another object or as measured on a standardized *scale* such as *degrees Celsius* or *degrees Fahrenheit.* See Section 13.1: Temperature.

template In *Everyday Mathematics,* a sheet of plastic with geometric shapes cut out of it, used to draw patterns and designs. See Section 11.10.1: Pattern-Block Template.

term (1) In an *algebraic expression,* a number or a product of a number and one or more *variables.* For example, in the equation $5y + 3k = 8$, the terms are *5y, 3k,* and 8. The 8 is a constant term, or simply a *constant,* because it has no variable part. See Section 15.2.2: Reading and Writing Open Sentences. (2) An element in a *sequence.* In the sequence of square numbers, the terms are 1, 4, 9, 16, and so on.

terminating decimal A *decimal* that ends. For example, 0.5 and 0.125 are terminating decimals.

tessellate To make a *tessellation;* to tile a surface.

tessellation A pattern of shapes that covers a surface completely without overlaps or gaps. Same as a *tiling.*

A tessellation

tetrahedron A *polyhedron* with 4 faces. A tetrahedron is a *triangular pyramid.* See Section 11.5.2: Polyhedrons.

theorem A mathematical statement that can be proved to be true. For example, the Pythagorean theorem states that if the *legs of a right triangle* have lengths *a* and *b* and the *hypotenuse* has length *c*, then $a^2 + b^2 = c^2$. The Pythagorean theorem has been proven in hundreds of ways over the past 2,500 years.

thermometer A tool used to measure *temperature* in *degrees* according to a fixed scale. The most common scales are *Celsius* and *Fahrenheit.* See Section 13.1.2: Thermometers.

3-dimensional (3-D) coordinate system A *reference frame* in which any point on a *3-dimensional figure* can be located with three *coordinates* relative to the *origin* of three axes intersecting perpendicularly at their origins in space. Compare to *1-* and *2-dimensional coordinate systems.*

3-dimensional (3-D) figure A figure whose points are not all in a single *plane.* Examples include *prisms, pyramids,* and *spheres,* all of which have length, width, and height. See Section 11.1: Dimension.

tick marks (1) Marks showing the *scale* of a number line or ruler. (2) Same as *tally (2).*

tile A shape used in a *tessellation.* A tessellation of only one tile is called a same-tile tessellation.

tiling Same as *tessellation.*

timeline A *number line* showing when events took place. In some timelines the *origin* is based on the context of the events being graphed, such as the birth date of the child's life graphed below. The origin can also come from another reference system, such as the year A.D. in which case the scale below might cover the years 2000 through 2005. See Section 13.2.3: Timelines.

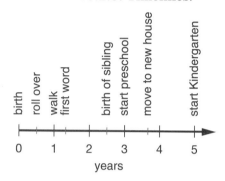

A timeline of a child's milestones

toggle A key on a calculator that changes back and forth between two displays each time it is pressed. For example, on some calculators $\boxed{+/-}$ toggles between a number and its opposite.

total Same as *sum.*

transformation An operation on a geometric figure (the *preimage*) that produces a new figure (the *image*). The study of transformations is called transformation geometry. Transformations are often based on rules for how points behave, as in the translation below. Although the preimage does not actually move under a transformation, it is convenient to think and talk about transformations as moving a figure from one place to another and sometimes changing its size or shape. So *Everyday Mathematics* encourages using informal terms such as *flip, turn,* and *slide.* See *isometry transformation, reflection, rotation, translation, size change* and Section 11.7: Transformations.

A translation

translation A *transformation* in which every point in the *image* of a figure is at the same distance in the same direction from its corresponding point in the figure. Informally called a *slide*. See *transformation* for an example and Section 11.7: Transformations.

trapezoid A *quadrilateral* that has exactly one pair of *parallel* sides. In *Everyday Mathematics,* both pairs of sides cannot be parallel; that is, a parallelogram is not a trapezoid. See Section 11.4.2: Polygons (*n*-gons).

Trapezoids

tri- A prefix meaning three, as in tricycle.

triangle A 3-sided polygon. See *equilateral triangle, isosceles triangle, scalene triangle, acute triangle, right triangle, obtuse triangle,* and Section 11.4.2: Polygons (*n*-gons).

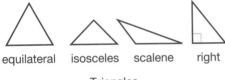

equilateral   isosceles   scalene   right

Triangles

triangular numbers *Figurate numbers* that can be shown by triangular arrangements of dots. The triangular numbers are {1, 3, 6, 10, 15, 21, 28, 36, 45, . . .}. See Section 15.1.3: Sequences.

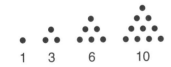

1   3   6   10

Triangular numbers

triangular prism A *prism* whose bases are triangles. See Section 11.5.2: Polyhedrons.

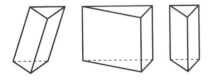

Triangular prisms

triangular pyramid A *pyramid* in which all *faces* are *triangles,* any one of which is the *base.* A regular tetrahedron has four *equilateral triangles* for faces and is one of the five *regular polyhedrons.* See Section 11.5.2: Polyhedrons.

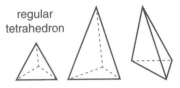

regular tetrahedron

Triangular pyramids

true number sentence A *number sentence* stating a correct fact. For example, $75 = 25 + 50$ is a true number sentence. See Section 9.2.2: Reading and Writing Number Sentences.

truncate (1) In a *decimal,* to cut off all *digits* after the decimal point or after a particular place to the right of the decimal point. For example, 12.345 can be truncated to 12.34, 12.3, or 12. *Integers* cannot be truncated. Same as rounding down in places to the right of the decimal point. See *round* and Section 14.2: Approximation and Rounding. (2) Informally, to cut off a part of a solid figure.

A truncated pyramid

turn An informal name for a *rotation.* See Section 11.7: Transformations.

turn-around facts A pair of multiplication (or addition) facts in which the order of the factors (or addends) is reversed. For example, $3 \times 9 = 27$ and $9 \times 3 = 27$ are turn-around multiplication facts, and $4 + 5 = 9$ and $5 + 4 = 9$ are turn-around addition facts. There are no turn-around facts for subtraction or division. Turn-around facts are instances of the *Commutative Properties of Addition* and Multiplication. See Section 14.3.2: Basic Facts and Fact Power.

turn-around rule A rule for solving addition and multiplication problems based on the *Commutative Properties of Addition* and Multiplication. For example, if you know that $6 \times 8 = 48$, then, by the turn-around rule, you also know that $8 \times 6 = 48$.

2-dimensional (2-D) coordinate system A reference frame in which any point on a *2-dimensional figure* can be located with an *ordered pair* of coordinates relative to the *origin* of two intersecting perpendicular axes in space. Compare to *1-* and *3-dimensional coordinate systems*.

2-dimensional (2-D) figure A figure whose points are all in one *plane* but not all on one *line*. Examples include polygons and circles, all of which have length and width but no height. See Section 11.1: Dimension.

unfair game A game in which every player does not have the same chance of winning. See Section 10.1.2: The Language of Chance.

unit A label used to put a number in context. In measuring *length,* for example, inches and centimeters are units. In a problem about 5 apples, apple is the unit. In *Everyday Mathematics,* students keep track of units in *unit boxes.* See Section 9.3.1: Addition and Subtraction Use Classes.

unit box In *Everyday Mathematics*, a box displaying the *unit* for the numbers in the problems at hand.

A unit box

unit fraction A *fraction* whose *numerator* is 1. For example, $\frac{1}{2}, \frac{1}{3}, \frac{1}{12}, \frac{1}{8}$, and $\frac{1}{20}$ are unit fractions. Unit fractions are especially useful in converting among units within measurement systems. For example, because 1 foot = 12 inches you can multiply a number of inches by $\frac{1}{12}$ to convert to feet.

unit interval The *interval* between 0 and 1 on a *number line.*

unit whole Same as *whole* or *ONE.*

U.S. customary system The measuring system used most often in the United States. Units for *length* include inch, foot, yard, and mile; units for *weight* include ounce and pound; units for *volume* or *capacity* include cup, pint, quart, gallon, and cubic units; and the main unit for *temperature* change is degrees Fahrenheit. See Section 12.2.1: U.S. Customary System.

use class In *Everyday Mathematics,* a problem situation that one of the basic arithmetic operations can be used to solve. Students use *situation diagrams* to help model problems from the different use classes. See *addition/subtraction use classes, multiplication/division use classes,* and Section 9.3: Use Classes and Situation Diagrams.

variable A letter or other symbol that represents a number. A variable can represent a single number, as in $5 + n = 9$, because only $n = 4$ makes the sentence true. A variable can also stand for many different numbers, as in $x + 2 < 10$, because any number x less than 8 makes the sentence true. In *formulas* and *properties,* variables stand for all numbers. For example, $a + 3 = 3 + a$ for all numbers a. See Section 15.2.1: Uses of Variables.

vertex The point at which the *rays* of an angle, the *sides* of a polygon, or the *edges* of a polyhedron meet. Plural is vertexes or vertices. In *Everyday Mathematics,* same as *corner.* See Section 11.4: Planes and Plane Figures and Section 11.5: Space and 3-D Figures.

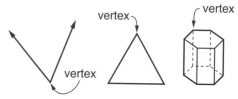

vertical Upright; perpendicular to the horizon. Compare to *horizontal.*

volume (1) The amount of space occupied by a *3-dimensional figure.* Same as *capacity.* (2) Less formally, the amount a container can hold. Volume is often measured in cubic units, such as cm³, cubic inches, or cubic feet. See Section 12.5: Volume (Capacity).

weight A measure of how heavy something is; the force of gravity on an object. An object's *mass* is constant, but it weighs less in weak gravity than in strong gravity. For example, a person who weighs 150 pounds in San Diego weighs about 23 pounds on the moon. See Section 12.6: Weight and Mass.

"What's My Rule?" problem In *Everyday Mathematics,* a problem in which two of the three parts of a *function* (*input, output,* and rule) are known, and the third is to be found out. See Section 15.1.4: Functions.

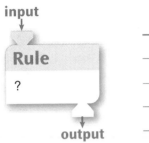

in	out
4	2
7	5
12	10
8	

A "What's My Rule?" problem

whole An entire object, collection of objects, or quantity being considered in a problem situation; 100%. Same as *ONE* and *unit whole.*

whole numbers The *counting numbers* and 0. The set of whole numbers is {0, 1, 2, 3, . . .}.

width of a rectangle The *length* of one side of a *rectangle* or rectangular object, typically the shorter side.

Y

yard (yd) A U.S. customary unit of *length* equal to 3 feet, or 36 inches. To Henry I of England, a yard was the distance from the tip of the nose to the tip of the middle finger. In *Everyday Mathematics,* it is from the center of the chest to the tip of the middle finger. See the Tables of Measures and Section 12.1: Personal Measures.

Z

zero fact In *Everyday Mathematics:* (1) The *sum* of two 1-digit numbers when one of the *addends* is 0, as in $0 + 5 = 5$. If 0 is added to any number, there is no change in the number. Same as the additive identity. (2) The product of two 1-digit numbers when one of the factors is 0, as in $4 \times 0 = 0$. The product of a number and 0 is always 0.

zero point Same as *origin.*

General Reference

Symbols

$+$	plus or positive
$-$	minus or negative
$*, \times$	multiplied by
$\div, /$	divided by
$=$	is equal to
$\neq$	is not equal to
$<$	is less than
$>$	is greater than
$\leq$	is less than or equal to
$\geq$	is greater than or equal to
$\approx$	is approximately equal to
$x^n, x^\wedge n$	nth power of x
$\sqrt{x}$	square root of x
$\%$	percent
$a{:}b,\ a/b,\ \frac{a}{b}$	ratio of a to b or a divided by b or the fraction $\frac{a}{b}$
$a\ [bs]$	a groups, b in each group
$n \div d \to a\ \mathrm{R}b$	n divided by d is a with remainder b
$\{\ \}, (\ ), [\ ]$	grouping symbols
∞	infinity
$n!$	n factorial
$\circ$	degree
(a,b)	ordered pair
$\overleftrightarrow{AS}$	line AS
$\overline{AS}$	line segment AS
$\overrightarrow{AS}$	ray AS
$\llcorner$	right angle
$\perp$	is perpendicular to
$\parallel$	is parallel to
$\triangle ABC$	triangle ABC
$\angle ABC$	angle ABC
$\angle B$	angle B
$\cong$	is congruent to
$\sim$	is similar to
$\equiv$	is equivalent to
$|n|$	absolute value of n

Prefixes

uni-	one	tera-	trillion (10^{12})
bi-	two	giga-	billion (10^{9})
tri-	three	mega-	million (10^{6})
quad-	four	kilo-	thousand (10^{3})
penta-	five	hecto-	hundred (10^{2})
hexa-	six	deca-	ten (10^{1})
hepta-	seven	uni-	one (10^{0})
octa-	eight	deci-	tenth (10^{-1})
nona-	nine	centi-	hundredth (10^{-2})
deca-	ten	milli-	thousandth (10^{-3})
dodeca-	twelve	micro-	millionth (10^{-6})
icosa-	twenty	nano-	billionth (10^{-9})

Constants

Pi (π)	3.14159 26535 89793
Golden Ratio (ϕ)	1.61803 39887 49894
Radius of Earth at equator	6,378.388 kilometers 3,963.34 miles
Circumference of Earth at equator	40,076.59 kilometers 24,902.44 miles
Velocity of sound in dry air at 0°C	331.36 m/sec 1087.1 ft/sec
Velocity of light in a vacuum	2.997925×10^{10} cm/sec

The Order of Operations

1. Do operations inside grouping symbols following Rules 2–4. Work from the innermost set of grouping symbols outward.
2. Calculate all expressions with exponents.
3. Multiply and divide in order from left to right.
4. Add and subtract in order from left to right.

Tables of Measures

Metric System

Units of Length
1 kilometer (km)	= 1,000 meters (m)
1 meter	= 10 decimeters (dm)
	= 100 centimeters (cm)
	= 1,000 millimeters (mm)
1 decimeter	= 10 centimeters
1 centimeter	= 10 millimeters

Units of Area
1 square meter (m²)	= 100 square decimeters (dm²)
	= 10,000 square centimeters (cm²)
1 square decimeter	= 100 square centimeters
1 are (a)	= 100 square meters
1 hectare (ha)	= 100 ares
1 square kilometer (km²)	= 100 hectares

Units of Volume and Capacity
1 cubic meter (m³)	= 1,000 cubic decimeters (dm³)
	= 1,000,000 cubic centimeters (cm³)
1 cubic centimeter	= 1,000 cubic millimeters (mm³)
1 kiloliter (kL)	= 1,000 liters (L)
1 liter	= 1,000 milliliters (mL)

Units of Mass and Weight
1 metric ton (t)	= 1,000 kilograms (kg)
1 kilogram	= 1,000 grams (g)
1 gram	= 1,000 milligrams (mg)

U.S. Customary System

Units of Length
1 mile (mi)	= 1,760 yards (yd)
	= 5,280 feet (ft)
1 yard	= 3 feet
	= 36 inches (in.)
1 foot	= 12 inches

Units of Area
1 square yard (yd²)	= 9 square feet (ft²)
	= 1,296 square inches (in²)
1 square foot	= 144 square inches
1 acre	= 43,560 square feet
1 square mile (mi²)	= 640 acres

Units of Volume and Capacity
1 cubic yard (yd³)	= 27 cubic feet (ft³)
1 cubic foot	= 1,728 cubic inches (in³)
1 gallon (gal)	= 4 quarts (qt)
1 quart	= 2 pints (pt)
1 pint	= 2 cups (c)
1 cup	= 8 fluid ounces (fl oz)
1 fluid ounce	= 2 tablespoons (tbs)
1 tablespoon	= 3 teaspoons (tsp)

Units of Mass and Weight
1 ton (T)	= 2,000 pounds (lb)
1 pound	= 16 ounces (oz)

System Equivalents (Conversion Factors)
1 inch ≈ 2.5 cm (2.54)	1 liter ≈ 1.1 quarts (1.057)
1 kilometer ≈ 0.6 mile (0.621)	1 ounce ≈ 28 grams (28.350)
1 mile ≈ 1.6 kilometers (1.609)	1 kilogram ≈ 2.2 pounds (2.21)
1 meter ≈ 39 inches (39.37)	1 hectare ≈ 2.5 acres (2.47)

Body Measures

1 *digit* is about the width of a finger.

1 *hand* is about the width of the palm and thumb.

1 *span* is about the distance from the tip of the thumb to the tip of the first (index) finger of an outstretched hand.

1 *cubit* is about the length from the elbow to the tip of the extended middle finger.

1 *yard* is about the distance from the center of the chest to the tip of the extended middle finger of an outstretched arm.

1 *fathom* is about the length from fingertip to fingertip of outstretched arms. Also called an arm span.

Units of Time
1 century	= 100 years
1 decade	= 10 years
1 year (yr)	= 12 months
	= 52 weeks (plus one or two days)
	= 365 days (366 days in a leap year)
1 month (mo)	= 28, 29, 30, or 31 days
1 week (wk)	= 7 days
1 day (d)	= 24 hours
1 hour (hr)	= 60 minutes
1 minute (min)	= 60 seconds (s or sec)

Index

Index